RADICAL APPROACHES TO SOCIAL SKILLS TRAINING

Radical Approaches to Social Skills Training

Edited by PETER TROWER

CROOM HELM
London & Sydney

METHUEN
New York

© 1984 Peter Trower
Croom Helm Ltd, Provident House, Burrell Row,
Beckenham, Kent BR3 1AT
Croom Helm Australia Pty Ltd, First Floor, 139 King Street,
Sydney, NSW 2001, Australia

British Library Cataloguing in Publication Data

Radical approaches to social skills training.
  1. Social skills. – Teaching
  I. Trower, Peter
  302'.07   HM132
  ISBN 0-7099-2455-0

Published in the United States of America by
Methuen, Inc., 733 Third Avenue, New York,
NY 10017

Library of Congress Cataloging in Publication Data
Main entry under title:

Radical approaches to social skills training.

  Bibliography: p.
  Includes index.
  1. Social skills – Study and teaching – Therapeutic use.
2. Psychotherapy. I. Trower, Peter, 1938-   .
RC489.S63R33 1984   616.89'1   83-26447
ISBN 0-416-00931-X (Methuen)

Printed and bound in Great Britain

CONTENTS

FOR NIC

CONTRIBUTORS

Mary M. Bandura, Department of Psychology and Social
Relations, Harvard University, William James
Hall, 33 Kirkland Street, Cambridge,
Massachusetts 02138, USA.

Charles S. Carver, Department of Psychology,
University of Miami, P.O. Box 248185, Coral
Gables, Florida 33124, USA.

Benzion Chanowitz, Department of Psychology and
Social Relations, Harvard University,
William James Hall, 33 Kirkland Street,
Cambridge, Massachusetts 02138, USA.

Malcolm Coulthard, English Language Research,
Department of English, University of
Birmingham, P.O. Box 363, Edgbaston,
Birmingham, B15 2TT, England.

W. Edward Craighead, Department of Psychology, The
Pennsylvania State University, University Park,
Pennsylvania 16802, USA.

James P. Curran, Section of Psychiatry and Human
Behavior, Brown University Medical School,
Veterans Administration Medical Center, Davis
Park, Providence, Rhode Island 02912, USA.

Michael G. Dow, Department of Psychology, The
Pennsylvania State University, University Park,
Pennsylvania 16802, USA.

Windy Dryden, Counselling Psychologist, 209 Belchers
    Lane, Little Bromwich, Birmingham B9 5RT,
    England.

Albert D. Farrell, Department of Psychology,
    Virginia Commonwealth University, Richmond,
    Virginia 23284, USA.

Aimee J. Grunberger, Department of Psychology,
    University of Massachusetts, Amherst,
    Massachusetts 01003, USA.

Rom Harre, Sub-Faculty of Philosophy, University
    of Oxford, 10 Merton Street, Oxford, England.

Ellen J. Langer, Department of Psychology and Human
    Relations, Harvard University, William James
    Hall, 33 Kirkland Street, Cambridge,
    Massachusetts 02138, USA.

Michael F. Scheier, Department of Psychology,
    Carnegie-Mellon University, Pittsburgh,
    Pennsylvania 15213, USA.

Geoff Shepherd, Department of Psychology, Fulbourn
    Hospital, Cambridge CB1 5EF, England.

Peter Trower, Department of Psychology, Leicester
    University, University Road, Leicester
    LE1 7RH, England.

Richard Wessler, Department of Psychology, Pace
    University, Bedford Road, Pleasantville, New
    York 10570, USA.

PART I

THEORY AND RESEARCH

INTRODUCTION AND REVIEW

Peter Trower

One of the few facts that emerges clearly in the beleaguered field of mental health is the extent of poor social skills in psychiatric patients. The studies and surveys show skills problems to be a major component in schizophrenia, mental handicap, depression, social anxiety, addiction disorders, psychosexual disorders, psychopathy, childhood and adolescent problems - in fact virtually the whole spectrum of problems categorized as psychiatric. Deficient social skills can be shown to play a major role in these problems, either as a primary cause or secondary effect. There is evidence that maladaptive social behaviour is probably the most common single factor to be found across disorders, either in a primary or secondary form. There is evidence, too, that individuals with the poorest social competence have the worst prognoses and highest relapse rate, and childhood competence level is predictive of severity of adult psychiatric problems.
    The development in the 1970's of social skills training (SST) - espoused as a form of behaviour therapy - excited great interest as offering perhaps the first real option, besides traditional medicine, for tackling this problem on a wide scale. SST was based on the comparatively simple notion that social skills, like any other skills, are learned, and could be taught where lacking, and a wealth of assessment and training methods were then devised and utilized (Goldstein, Sprafkin, & Gershaw, 1976; Liberman, King, deRisi, & McCann, 1975; Trower, Bryant, & Argyle, 1978; Bellack & Hersen, 1979; Curran & Monti, 1982).
    The appeal of SST was not lost on the host of investigators and practitioners who have applied and adapted SST to numerous psychiatric disorders and social problems, as well as to the training of

1

professional helpers themselves. It is commonly used by, and for, counselling, clinical and educational psychologists, psychiatrists, occupational therapists, social workers, psychiatric nurses, volunteer helpers and many others (Argyle, 1981; Ellis & Whittington, 1981).

Few would dispute the need for, and the appeal of, SST. The problem comes with its evaluation. The principal investigators have voiced serious reservations in recent years.

Although now well into its second decade of development, and despite much research effort and popularity, SST has so far proved to be, at best, only modestly successful in mental health. The reviews are in, and few are claiming that SST produces changes that endure and generalize (e.g. Twentyman & Zimering, 1979). Many SST pioneers themselves have written sceptically of research, assessment and training methods (e.g. Bellack, 1979) and there is always a danger that healthy scepticism will give way to terminal pessimism.

THE NEED FOR REFORMULATIONS IN SOCIAL SKILLS TRAINING

How can we make SST more effective? A robust empiricist, or an ideological opponent, might say that SST has had its day, and it is time to turn our attention to other forms of therapy. Fortunately few would maintain this argument, which is the most easily dismissed. SST is modestly successful and would continue to play an invaluable role even without further advances. More importantly, however, one might argue that SST goes on all the time informally. In other words the learning and teaching of social skills is part of the process of normal socialization, so that the real question is, can we augment and learn from this natural process to help those deprived of normal learning opportunities? The answer is yes, but can we do it more effectively?

One approach to this question is to simply carry out more research. The problem here is that a good deal of research has already been done with only modest results, which may mean the research questions may be wrong, because the theories from which they spring are wrong. The time has come, perhaps, for developing new theoretical formulations - a view that a number of SST investigators now clearly share (McFall, 1982).

There are two possible approaches to theoretical reformulation. The first is a conservative one, by way of conceptual clarification, modification and/or enlargement within the set of existing paradigms, and might be termed the evolutionary approach. It is probably fair to say that the conceptual clarification of social skills issues developed by Curran et al. (this volume) represents this conservative position. It is certainly widely advocated, and is well expressed by Schroeder and Rakos (1983) who see the whole of behaviour therapy gradually evolving from an original and simple operant approach to an enlarged approach taking account of cognitions and other variables. (However, it must be stated that they do not make reference to the underlying paradigms except by implication.) The second approach is a radical one, and involves a break with existing paradigms and the construction of new ones. It is the one advocated by myself, and Harre (chapters two and three of this volume) and others, and it is one which might be termed the "revolutionary" approach. It advocates, in effect, a paradigm shift. It embraces much of what has come to be known as the "cognitive revolution" but the term "cognitive" has become somewhat imprecise, some (especially the originators of the cognitive approach) placing it within a radical approach, others within a conservative one, but often the term is used confusedly, as we shall later show.

There are two points that need to be made about paradigms at this stage. Firstly, as any philosopher of science knows, any science begins with a set of presuppositions which guide subsequent theory formation, research and practice and are thus very powerful in formulating the questions we ask and the things we do. However, because the paradigms are assumed, or presupposed, they are not themselves the focus of research inquiry, and therefore invariably operate implicitly, remain unnoticed and tend to be uncritically accepted, as critics like Coyne (1982) have noted. Not surprisingly, researchers and practitioners may be unaware of the very principles which guide their research and practice. This is acceptable so long as the science in question makes good progress, but given the power of such paradigms, they will inevitably create major and persistent problems if they are wrong, and then need to be brought into focus and critically scrutinized. Given the need for reformulation in SST, it is imperative that we also examine the underlying paradigms at this stage, and make a decision on their adequacy. It is my contention that not sufficient attention has been given to this last point, even by those who have recently offered useful reformulations (McFall, 1982).

What are the paradigms underlying SST? A detailed exposition is given in chapter two, but in brief, I am arguing that behaviourism, and particularly methodological behaviourism, provides the paradigms which are most influential in SST. One of the assumptions is that the individual is behaviourally and cognitively under the control of determining forces other than the individual himself - what Bandura calls "uni-directional determinism". This view, in which the individual has a passive role in the push and pull of determining forces, is also common to the psychoanalytic and medical models (though they locate such forces differently), and I have collectively termed them the "organism approach". This approach also contains epistemological and methodological assumptions about behaviour, cognitions and events which gives them the status of independent entities that are causally related, and can be externally varied and manipulated without changing their identities.

If the "organism approach" underlies SST, what is wrong with that? I shall be arguing, along with others, that these powerful guiding paradigms are indeed wrong and likely to produce the very problems that bedevil social skills assessment and training. The solution, it will be proposed, is to change the paradigms, and an alternative set, here termed collectively the "agency approach", should be introduced and used to guide future theory, research and practice. There are a number of complex facets to the "agency approach" (a version of which is particularly well expounded by Harre & Secord, 1972 and subsequently developed by Harre in a series of publications) but for present purposes suffice it to say that it conceptualizes man as a social agent who actively constructs his own experiences and generates his own goal-directed behaviour on the basis of those constructs. It also advocates radically different epistemological and methodological assumptions. The adoption of these assumptions would dissolve several of the present pseudo-issues, and be better fitted to solve others, particularly in assessment and practice. There are obviously objections to these claims and these will be taken up later in this chapter and in chapters two and three.

But at this point it is important to try to state as clearly as possible the implications of these two approaches for the practice of SST, since it is the practice that the whole exercise is about. Such a brief account inevitably is a distortion and is offered at this point purely for explanatory purposes rather than as a critical analysis, which is given in chapter two.

Component Skills Versus Process Skill

I have suggested a distinction elsewhere between social skills per se, i.e., the behavioural components, and social skill i.e., the generative process (Trower, 1982). To some extent, the organism approach is based entirely on social skills training (the acquisition of components) while the agency approach is primarily based on social skill training (the development of the generative process) with skills training playing a secondary role.

In the organism approach, the passive human organism is assumed to be unable to generate his or her own socially skilled behaviour, and is therefore assessed for "deficits" and, as it were, supplied with "skills", through instigative training, and these skills are subsequently reinforced by social stimuli. The commonly voiced problems are, firstly that no one seems to be able to validly identify in a nonsubjective (i.e., "scientific") way either deficits or skills to be taught, so inappropriate ones may be selected, and secondly, the "skills" that are taught often fail to endure or generalize.

In the agency approach the person is assumed to be able to generate his or her own socially skilled behaviour and if failing to do so, is assessed, the source of the breakdown identified, and the individual helped to restore his or her generative capacity. Skills training can then be used within the framework of the individual's own generative activity. As regards the particular problem just mentioned, firstly deficits and skills are readily identifiable, since they are assumed in the agency approach to be a part of common, public (i.e., intersubjective) knowledge and therefore accessible to anyone within the local language community. And, secondly, since the individual can, if therapy is successful, generate his own unique social solutions, he should be able to generalize, maintain and modify his newly developing skills.

However, there are further differences between the two approaches as regards the actual behavioural component skills. It must suffice here to claim that the behavioural skills are misdescribed and misunderstood in terms of the organism approach and quite unlike normal social behaviour. The agency approach claims to correct both of these errors. These points are elaborated in detail in chapter two and in Trower (1983).

PLAN AND PURPOSE OF THE BOOK

Let us now return in the light of the above discussion, to the original question, and the purpose and plan for this volume. The theme of the book addresses the question: how can we improve the effectiveness of SST? A conservative approach is to undertake a critique of the main problems which have impeded progress and develop a conceptual reformulation within the terms of the existing behavioural paradigms.

In chapter one Curran et al. carry out a penetrating analysis on this level, and present a clearer conceptual framework for further research. This goes as far as possible, I believe, within the existing paradigms. However, I have advocated the adoption of a radical approach, involving the critical dismantling of the old system of paradigms, the building of a new one, and the development of theoretical and practical consequences of this change. A first attempt at such a programme is made in the rest of the book.

The radical programme of change proposed involves a series of steps, and the contributions from various authors were invited in order to fulfil these steps. The first five steps are theoretical ones and constitute the first half of the book. The next three are practical and form the second half of the book.

The first step in this enterprize is the largely philosophical one of (a) dismantling the "organism approach" into its constituent parts, critically examining each and attempting to reveal its flaws, and (b) building a new set of paradigms with supporting arguments and developing their implications for SST. This is the aim of chapter two. One of the main implications is that skilled or unskilled behaviour is a product of the cognitions of the agent rather than of eliciting stimuli. In taking this argument further in chapter three, Harre deals with an apparent (and widely assumed) flaw in the argument by revealing the essentially public, rather than the inner nature of these cognitions and indeed most psychological properties attributed to the individual. It is the group as a whole and not just the individual which creates, sustains or abandons such attributed qualities, as cold, unassertive etc., by means of "symbiotic" interaction. Therefore, we should attend to the group (family, etc.) when assessing or training in social skills, and not the individual separately from his symbiotic group.

   *Whereas chapter two reviews well known concepts,
much influenced by Harre and Secord (1972), and which
have been partially assimilated into social psychology (e.g., Ginsburg, 1979), in chapter three Harre is
pursuing a quite new development in his ethogenic
theory which stands to influence a new generation of
research.*
   *The second main step in the programme is to
review cognitive social psychological theories which
can be said to exemplify various facets of the agency
approach, and to see what they can offer the development of SST. Some of the theories - reviewed by
Wessler in chapter four, are well known but have had
a very limited impact on SST, and as far as I know,
have not been considered as even germane to the area
except by a few. It is no accident, of course, that
these theories have been neglected - after all they
have been available for many years. The neglect is
the result of exclusion by the tenets of positivism
and other "organism" approaches. However, within the
agency approach these theories are seen as not only
relevant but essential to an understanding of social
skills.   In his review, Wessler shows that the
theories give a central role to conscious monitoring,
both in structuring experience and in generating and
modifying social action. He shows how they highlight
the roles of cognition, emotion and behaviour in a
continuous two-way system of interaction with the
social environment.*
   *The third step is to develop a new and spec-
ific social skill model. Such a model needs to take
account of the central concepts of agency such as
self and self-monitoring, choice, evaluation,
expectancy and emotion, as well as the purely
cybernetic functions of feedback and adjustment which
are contained in the social skill model of Argyle and
Kendon (1967), but which falls short of the agency
principles. In my opinion the best developed model
so far of the appropriate kind is that described by
Carver and Scheier in chapter five. Such a model is
essential if we are to translate the abstract principles of the agency approach into practical procedures for training, since it will enable us to
identify how normal people learn skills.*
   *However, we also require, as the fourth step in
our programme, a precise understanding of how some
people fail to learn skills, even when they have
normal environmental opportunities or even traditional SST. In Carver and Scheier's model, a central role is given to a conscious monitoring process,
in goal selection, action, judgement and so on. This*

cognitive activity is the generative source of social action in an agency approach, and failure can occur at this source, i.e., a failure in this conscious, constructive process. Precisely how this may occur is explored in chapter six (this volume) by Bandura, Langer and Chanowitz. They argue that an individual may not be controlling his behaviour "mindfully", i.e., consciously, but operating automatically or "mindlessly", guided not by relevant feedback but by ingrained, automatic and often irrational beliefs. This penetrating and data-based account gives a valuable lead to changes in the practice of SST, where clients are failing in their generative cognitive activity.

In addition to the cognitive processes so far dealt with, the agency approach also advocates a radically different view of the nature of social behaviour, and this has implications for assessment and the content of training. This brings us to the fifth step: what can be offered in the "structural" tradition that has the acceptable scientific precision of measurable behavioural elements? In chapter seven, Coulthard gives an account in some depth of a particular structural analysis of conversation and its verbal and paralinguistic elements, which has precision and predictive power. Much further work is needed before this approach can be incorporated into SST, but Coulthard points the way with a viable framework.

Thus far we have a somewhat skeletal theoretical basis in part I for an agency approach to SST. We next turn in part II to an equally schematic outline for practice. In a book of this type, which aims to break new ground and spur future developments, there is bound to be a lag between theory and practice. The next section of practice therefore inevitably fails to incorporate in detail the preceding theoretical ideas, though it does incorporate the philosophy. To expect a thorough integration at this stage is premature - that will hopefully be the next stage of development. However, considerable progress can be made at this stage, utilizing new and recent work, especially cognitive therapy.

I made a distinction earlier between social skills (the actual behavioural components) and social skill (the generative process). Part II is devoted entirely to the latter. This decision was made for two reasons. Firstly, advances in cognitive therapy, but not in applied linguistics, enable its adoption by and application to SST to be made at this stage (it has already been made by others). The need for *this arises because the agency switches emphasis from simply teaching clients component behavioural skills to teaching clients how to generate their own social skills and use them appropriately. Since this "mindful" process (Bandura et al., this volume) depends upon continuous, conscious monitoring and productive cognitions, it is obvious that "cognitive" therapy has a role to play here.*

The second reason for focussing on the generative process, or social skill, is that this has been most neglected in the literature on traditional SST (including research by the present author).

The chapters in this section proceed in three steps. Firstly, given the central role of cognitions in the structuring of experience and generation of skills, we need to assess the type and extent of faulty cognitions and thinking patterns in unskilled clients. In chapter eight, Dow and Craighead carry out a comprehensive and clear review of cognitive deficits in relevant client populations. Needless to say they find substantial evidence of such problems.

The next step focusses on the assessment of the individual client, using procedures based on the assumptions of the agency, or at least a cognitive approach. One aspect of this large task inevitably focusses on how the individual systematically construes the environment and himself, evaluates his actions and the responses of others. In chapter nine, Shepherd gives us both a critical review of cognitive-based instruments and detailed guidance on the use of one of these.

The third step moves on to therapy. The aim here is to help the client become a self-directed, skill-generating agent, to be able to learn skills where previously he was blocked. Of the various cognitive therapies which may facilitate this development, rational-emotive therapy is, in my opinion, conceptually the closest to the agency approach, with its emphasis on investigating the client's personal philosophy and moral evaluations. In the next two chapters, chapters ten and eleven, Dryden gives clear and comprehensive advice on the use of RET in skills training and learning.

ANTICIPATED CRITICISMS

This completes the account of the book's theme and content. There are of course many potential criticisms and counter claims. The main one is that the agency approach is invalid, and that the organism approach is not only correct but the only approach which is valid scientifically. This is discussed fully in chapter two. Another potential counter claim which we need to discuss now is simply that no-one seriously holds the position attacked - i.e. the "organism approach" is a straw man. There is good evidence however, that the approach is widely held and influential, and this is now briefly reviewed.

Firstly, operant formulations, which have long had a major influence on SST (Schroeder & Rakos, 1983) explicitly embrace an organism approach, particularly in the concept of stimulus control. In a latest "policy" statement on applied behaviour analysis, Baer states that "private events" (i.e., thoughts) are "behaviors", subject to environmental control and "in no sense are autonomous causes of observable behavior...." (Baer, 1982, p.278). Secondly, many of those in the mainstream classical conditioning tradition equally adhere to the passive organism model. Wolpe, one of the initiators of assertiveness training, has often repeated his belief that all human behaviour is conditioned or determined. "We always do what we must do. Our thinking is behavior and as unfree as any other behavior." (Wolpe, 1980, p.198). Thirdly, psychiatry embraces the organism approach, both in its medical tradition - locating control in physiological malfunction - and in its psychoanalytic tradition - placing the source in unconscious psychic mechanisms.

My characterization of these and other schools as clear-cut organism approaches is nothing new. Many writers have previously done so. For example Beck says that the major schools - neuropsychiatry, psychoanalysis and behaviour therapy - share the basic assumption that "the emotionally disturbed person is victimized by concealed forces over which he has no control". (Beck, 1976, p.2).

It might be argued, however, that the majority view, now being "eclectic", cannot be dichotomized in this way into organism v agency approaches. It is often argued that the "cognitive revolution" has helped to produce such an eclecticism in a broadened model of behaviour therapy which encompasses cognitions as well as behaviours (Franks et al., 1982). However, this may simply mean that cognitions have been incorporated into the organism paradigms and that no change in underlying paradigms has been made at all. There is plenty of evidence that the transition has not in fact been widely made. Schwartz (1982) notes that most of the research in the "cognitive" area is more of a mediational behaviouristic than truly cognitive type, and Coyne (1982)

*makes a similar point. Cognitive and social learning
theorists like Beck and Bandura have placed their
theories in direct <u>opposition</u> to organism approaches,
and incorporating <u>cognitions</u> into an organism approach is not cognitive theory nor therapy (see
Arnkoff, 1980). Liotti and Reda (1981) point out
that the two approaches (in their terms associa-
tionism v rationalism) are of incompatible philosophical natures, and an eclectic mix of the two simply
produces conceptual confusion (as a reading of
Schwartz's 1982 review clearly shows).*

*In summary, my argument is that the organism
approach is indeed widely held and influential, and
given its long tradition in behaviour therapy and
particularly SST, is bound to influence practitioners
implicitly, if not explicitly, in their practice.*

*Another type of claim concerns the basis of
evidence, namely that there is no "evidence" for the
agency approach. If this type of statement is legitimate at all, it should clearly be stated of the
"organism" approach, which by virtue of the unprom-
ising results in SST to date, cannot claim favourable
evidence. As regards evidence in psychology in
general, it is ironic that in the same year that
Wolpe (1978) proclaims that it is an illusion that
human animals are free rather than under the
"domination of causal sequences", a leading animal
psychologist, drawing unsuspected functional parallels between people and rats on the basis of extensive animal experiments states "non-human animals may
possess capacities far beyond those we have
been willing to ascribe to them in the past...."
(Hulse, 1978, p.336).*

*However, this is not the place to review the
empirical evidence for the two approaches, for this
is not an empirical argument. Empirical discovery
can only be applied within the framework of a set of
assumptions about what are to count as facts and
evidence (see chapter two), and it is the assumptions
that we are here disputing. This stage of inquiry is
philosophical rather than empirical, designed to
reveal logical coherence and incoherence rather than
facts. Alternative theories and postulates can be
subsequently generated (and are discussed in this
book) and these, in turn put to the test.*

*With regard to the practical implications of the
organism v agency approach, these are given in detail
in chapter two and the reader is referred to that
section.*

*In the light of the above discussion, the book
offers the SST researcher and practitioner both*

conservative and radical critiques and a theoretical re-orientation to what I have termed the agency aproach, and guidance on some applications of this approach in practice. I use the terms "agency" and "organism" to represent the two opposing approaches, but these are my adopted terms and their use does not imply their acceptance and endorsement by other authors. Indeed authors were not so much invited to contribute to the basic argument (with the exception of Harre, chapter three), but rather to present their own and other people's work because it exemplified various facets of the approaches. I believe it is fair to say that all contributors thoroughly fulfilled their briefs.

REFERENCES

Argyle, M. (Ed.). *Social skills and health.* London: Methuen, 1981

Argyle, M., & Kendon, A. The experimental analysis of social performance. In L. Berkowitz (Ed.), *Advances in experimental social psychology,* (Vol.3). New York: Academic Press, 1967

Arnkoff, D.B. Psychotherapy from the perspective of cognitive theory. In M.S. Mahoney (Ed.), *Psychotherapy process.* New York: Plenum Press, 1980

Baer, D.M. Applied behavior analysis. In G.T. Wilson & C.M. Franks (Eds.), *Contemporary behavior therapy.* New York: Guilford Press, 1982

Beck, A.T. *Cognitive therapy and the emotional disorders.* New York: International Universities Press, 1976

Bellack, A.S., & Hersen, M. (Eds.). *Research and practice in social skills training.* New York: Plenum Press, 1979

Coyne, J.C. A critique of cognitions as causal entities with particular reference to depression. *Cognitive Therapy and Research,* 1982, 6, 3-14

Curran, J.P., & Monti, P.M. *Social skills training: A practical handbook for assessment and therapy.* New York: Guilford Press, 1982

Ellis, R., & Whittington, D. *A guide to social skill training.* London: Croom Helm, 1981

Franks, C.M., Wilson, G.T., Kendall, P.C., & Brownell K.D. *Annual review of behavior therapy* (Vol. 8). New York: Guilford, 1982

Ginsburg, G.P. *Emerging strategies in social psychological research.* Chichester: Wiley, 1979

Goldstein, A.P., Sprafkin, R.P., & Gershaw, N.J.

Skill training for community living. New York: Pergamon Press, 1976

Harre, R., & Secord, P.F. *The explanation of social behaviour*. Oxford: Blackwell, 1972

Hulse, S.H. Cognitive structure and serial pattern learning by animals. In S.H. Hulse, H. Fowler, & W.K. Honig (Eds.), *Cognitive processes in animal behavior*. Hillsdale, N.J.: Erlbaum, 1978

Liberman, R.P., King, L.W., deRisi, W., & McCann, M. *Personal effectiveness*. Chicago: Research Press, 1975

Liotti, G., & Reda, M. Some epistemological remarks on behavior therapy, cognitive therapy and psychoanalysis. *Cognitive Therapy and Research*, 1981, 5, 231-236

McFall, R.M. A review and reformulation of the concept of social skills. *Behavioral Assessment*, 1982, 4, 1-34

Schroeder, H.E., & Rakos, R.F. The identification and assessment of social skills. In R. Ellis & D. Whittington (Eds.), *New directions in social skill training*. London: Croom Helm, 1983

Schwartz, R.M. Cognitive behavior modification: A conceptual review. *Clinical Psychology Review*, 1982, 2, 267-294

Trower, P. Towards a generative model of social skills: A critique and synthesis. In. J. Curran & P. Monti (Eds.), *Social skills training: A practical handbook for assessment and treatment*. New York: Guilford Press, 1982

Trower, P. Social skills and applied linguistics. In R. Ellis and D. Whittington (Eds.), *New directions in social skill training*. London: Croom Helm, 1983

Trower, P., Bryant, B.M., & Argyle, M. *Social skills and mental health*. London: Methuen, 1978

Twentyman, C.T., & Zimering, R.T. Behavioral training of social skills: A critical review. In M. Hersen, R.M. Eisler, & P.M. Miller (Eds.), *Progress in behavior modification* (Vol.7). New York: Academic Press, 1979

Wolpe, J. Cognition and causation in human behavior and its therapy. *American Psychologist*, 1978, 33, 437-446

Wolpe, J. Cognitive behavior and its role in psychotherapy. In M.J. Mahoney (Ed.), *Psychotherapy process: Current issues and future directions*. New York: Plenum Press, 1980

Editorial Introduction, Chapter One

SOCIAL SKILLS: A CRITIQUE AND A RAPPROCHEMENT

James P. Curran, Albert D. Farrell and Aimee J. Grunberger

What is wrong with social skills training? How can we make it more effective? What issues are impeding progress in its development? These are the kinds of questions addressed in chapters one and two. Curran, Farrell and Grunberger (all clinical psychologists) call the opening shots in reviewing what is wrong and what should be done. From a conservative critical stance within the traditional behavioural paradigms, they undertake a conceptual analysis of issues which have been the focus of considerable polemics recently. They discover a confused and misleading polarization of attitudes within key concepts. They focus on three issues which have been treated mistakenly as dichotomous, either/or issues, as a result of which false arguments have been generated and progress impeded (a similar point is made by Kendler (1981) about psychology in general). The three issues can be couched as questions: what should we be trying to measure and change - molar or molecular units? What should we be focussing on - the person or the situation? What are the causes of social inadequacy - skill deficiency or something else, such as anxiety? Once these issues are thus polarized, then investigators look for solutions at one or the other pole - focus on the molar, not the molecular, the person not the situation, skill deficiency, not other causes, or vice versa. In dismissing the other pole they leave themselves open to objections, for example of subjectivity in molar measurement and related objections to the fallacious invoking of internal mental causes such as traits, in focussing on the person. Conversely, at the other extreme, measuring only molecular behaviours and situation elements faces the objection of reductionism and hence the loss of psychological meaning. Curran et al. give a critical discussion of the two sets of arguments - the dispositional objections to molar recording and person focus, and the reductionist objection to molecular recording and situation focus, and believe the arguments are not valid. They also suggest that the model is wrong - these are not dichotomous poles, but points on a continuum, and this allows a much more fruitful discussion of relatedness and interaction between molar and molecular, person and situation. This point is particularly important in considering skill deficit v other explanations of inadequacy - the connection between deficits and other variables, such as cognitions, is what is at issue.

Chapter One

SOCIAL SKILLS: A CRITIQUE AND A RAPPROCHEMENT

James P. Curran, Albert D. Farrell and Aimee J. Grunberger

INTRODUCTION

There appear to us to be three pivotal issues which, because they have often been characterized as either/or issues, have hampered investigation in the area of social skills. The alleged dichotomous nature of these issues appears to us to be more illusory than real and the polemics surrounding them have, in our opinion, impeded progress in the investigation of social skills. These three issues are: (1) the proper unit of recording (molar vs. molecular); (2) the proper focus of observation (person vs. situation); and (3) the origin of inadequate social performance (skills deficit vs. other explanations for inadequate performance).

It is our contention that these issues are not dichotomous but are better perceived as gradients. In our opinion, there is no right or wrong side to these issues, but rather each should be regarded as a differential emphasis or different observational point which may or may not possess utility for any particular prediction task at hand. That is, differential emphasis on any of these issues may be appropriate depending upon the questions asked.

In writing this chapter, we frankly found difficulty addressing these issues for several reasons. First of all, each of these issues is interrelated with each of the others in a complex fashion. Secondly, each issue appears to subsume to some extent other issues in social skills research and, consequently, we had some difficulty in specifically labeling what we thought were essential issues. For example, the second issue which we have labeled as a person vs. situation focus appears to us to subsume issues such as a behavioral component vs. task analyses approach (McFall, 1982) to social skills assessment. Thirdly, in discussing each of these issues, we quickly found ourselves mired in the controversy revolving around the "trait attribution" and the "reductionistic behavioral" approaches to conceptualization and assessment.

Let us clarify our last statement. It appears to us that the end points of each of these issues have been associated with either a trait attribution approach or a reductionistic behavioral approach to social skills assessment. For example, both Trower (1982) and McFall (1982) in recent papers have equated molar and molecular social skills recording with trait attribution and reductionistic behavioral models of assessment, respectively. We feel that the equation is not accurate. That is, while we readily concede that at either end point on the continuum of these issues, it is easy to slip into either a trait attribution or a reductionistic behavioral stance, we feel that this need not necessarily be the case. In fact, it is our contention that the end points as well as intermediate points along the continuum possess some utility for social skills assessment and treatment. While we feel that many of the arguments leveled against trait attribution and reductionistic behavioral approaches to assessment in general (Mischel, 1968) and against their use in social skills assessment in particular (Curran, 1979; McFall, 1982; Trower, 1982) are valid, they should not blind us to the utility, and in fact the necessity, of assessment at the end points of these continua.

In support of our argument, we would like to review the objections to the trait attribution and the reductionistic behavioral models of assessment. We will begin by first examining the objections to trait approaches and the relationship of these objections to our three issues, and then we will examine the objections to the reductionistic behavioral approach within the context of these issues.

OBJECTIONS TO THE TRAIT ATTRIBUTION MODEL

A familiar objection to the trait approach to personality assessment is that it tells us more about the attributes of the observer than the observed. In the case of global ratings of social skills, however, we are interested in the judgments of observers. Presumably these observers are representative of observers in the natural environment who will be making similar judgments resulting in consequences to the subjects. In fact it can be argued that we need to

study the processess involved in making these judgments if we are to make progress with respect to
isolating social norms and evolving a definition of
social skills.

Another argument against the trait approach is
that it predicts consistency of behavior across
situations and across time. This argument is often
made against the use of molar ratings and a focus on
person variables in social skills research. However,
there is nothing inherent about a molar judgment or a
focus on person variables that necessitates such an
inference. Consistency of social competency ratings
across time and occasions is an empirical question
and one that needs to be answered. The use of molar
ratings does not necessarily mean that they will be
used in a dispositional sense nor does a focus on
person variables necessarily mean that environmental
parameters will be ignored.

When we are making global judgments of social
skills, we are determining an individual's capability
with respect to performing the response rather than
trying to estimate the typical or characteristic
level at which he responds. In fact it can be argued
that molar ratings are more apt to take into account
situational factors and variations in response
classes than are molecular ratings.

There are times when molar social competency
ratings possess utility when used in a summary fashion across situations.

As scientists, we need to generalize; that is,
we cannot treat each event as completely unique. If
it is possible to adequately sample situations which
are representative of a universe of situations which
we wish to generalize to, then social competency
ratings based on these situations may be compiled in
a summary fashion and provide useful information
(Wessberg, Curran, Monti, Corriveau, Coyne & Dziadosz
1981). This summary index would provide useful information of a problemistic nature regarding expectations of competent performance. For example, if an
individual has been observed in ten dating-like
situations and has been given on the average a rating
of 8 on a 10-point scale for his performance in these
situations, one would expect this individual to do
better, in general, in dating situations than another
individual who receives an average score of 2.

As Wessberg et al. (1981) noted, the summary
index is much like batting average statistics compiled on baseball players. It does not tell you how
the person bats or under what circumstances he or she
bats best. However, we do know that a .400 hitter

is, in general, a more competent hitter than a .200 hitter.

There is no question that when one uses molar units of recording or focuses on person variables there is a tendency to slip into a trait way of thinking (dispositional, across situations, etc.) and we must guard against it (Curran, 1979). The consistency of social skills across situations and across time should be answered empirically. More efforts need to be exerted in examining environmental parameters which are maintaining and controlling behavior in various situations.

OBJECTIONS TO THE REDUCTIONISTIC BEHAVIORAL MODEL

The reductionistic behavioral approach to assessment has been identified closely with molecular recording and to some extent with situational analyses and an emphasis on behavioral components to the neglect of cognitive factors. We feel that a number of the criticisms leveled at the reductionistic behavioral approach to assessment are justified. However, this does not mean that we should abandon molecular recordings, discontinue our attempts to measure situational factors, or stop training patients to master certain behavioral components. It is true as we said earlier that we are a long way from identifying important behavioral components, nor do we know how to weigh them or integrate them (Curran, 1979). However, this does not mean that we should stop pursuing this line of investigation.

Trower (1982) has criticized the practice wherein molecular recordings are disembedded from naturally occurring sequences of elements. Trower argues that we cannot judge the skill of the subject from an isolated segment without knowledge of higher order categories and personal cultural background information. He states that situations provide a context of the rules of the road and the goals in which episodes and elements are identified, defined, and understood. It is true that, in the past, an emphasis on behavioral units has led to ignoring essential patternings or relationships and events, but this does not mean that such relationships have to be ignored (Fischetti, Curran, & Wessberg, 1977).

McFall (1982) feels that a reductionistic behavioral model with its emphasis on specificity and its avoidance of general classification is an extreme and indefensible position. Specificity can only be carried so far and classification cannot be avoided. Each event cannot be treated as unique. An undue emphasis on specificity would necessarily lead to an idiographic approach to assessment. If all situations are unique, then we cannot have prediction from one situation to another. We agree with McFall that situational specificity can be carried to an extreme and meaningless limit; however, situational analyses need not reach this limit. We feel that we can neither ignore situations in our predictions nor treat each situation as unique but need to instead find means by which to classify situations which can assist us in our predictions. We will address this issue in greater detail in the section of our chapter on situations and persons.

McFall (1982) argues that the reductionistic behavioral approach to assessment produces definitional problems because no particular behavior can be considered intrinsically skillful, independent of situational context, its effects and objectives. A relativistic approach to the definition of social skills is further complicated, McFall feels, by the principle of equifinality. Stated most simply, the principle of equifinality suggests "that there is usually more than one way to skin a cat" or accomplish a task. This principle means that the definition of social skills should be open-ended, allowing other as yet unspecified behaviors to be added to the list of effective ways to achieve a specific objective in a particular situation. Interestingly, McFall's principle of equifinality is similar to the arguments given by trait theorists against strictly behavioral approaches to measurement. Trait theorists have argued that a physical description of an environmental circumstance and response characteristics are not sufficient to indicate the relationship and all manifestations of that trait because behavioral attributes are so topographically dissimilar. While we agree with McFall that "there is usually more than one way to skin a cat", this should not preclude us from attempting to define what component behaviors lead to a socially skillful or unskillful response.

Trower (1982) cogently argues that the teaching of specific molecular behaviors in social skills training packages in all probability will not lead to a clinically significant change in the adequacy level of these patients. We believe that Trower is quite correct in saying that, and we agree with his argument that we need to teach our patients generative skills, that is, the ability to generate skillful behavior. We will address this issue at length in the section of this chapter on skills deficits vs. other explanations for inadequate social performance. It will suffice to say here that teaching patients generative skills is not incompatible with teaching them specific behavioral components.

Our point is that while we agree with many of the arguments made against both a trait attribution approach and a reductionistic behavioral approach to social skills assessment and treatment, we feel that such arguments should not lead to a de-emphasis of any of the end points on the three continua which we have specified: molar/molecular, person/situation, and skill deficit/other explanations for inadequate social performance. We readily concede that it is easy to slip into either of these orientations, and one must be cautious not to do so.

We hope, in the remainder of this chapter, to demonstrate the utility of each end point of the three continua proposed as well as intermediate points along the continuum. In this we adhere to the principle that the molar/molecular issue cannot be separated; the latter depends on the former for measuring, the former on the latter for substance.

Before proceeding to the rest of the chapter, we would also like to reinforce a distinction McFall (1982) makes between social competency and social skills. McFall proposes that the word competent be used as a general evaluative term referring to the quality or adequacy of a person's overall performance in a particular task. Social skills, on the other hand, are the specific abilities required to perform competently at the task. McFall's definition implies that it is possible for a person to have some, but not all, of the skills required for performing competently at a given task. On the other hand, the definition also implies that a person who performs competently at a task necessarily has the required skills to do so. We regard McFall's distinction between competency and social skills as useful because it underscores the high level inference required in making a molar judgment regarding overall social competency. In the past, the term social skills has been used to connote both highly complex inferential molar judgments and less inferential molecular judgments.

MOLAR VERSUS MOLECULAR UNIT RECORDING

Within the social skills literature, investigators have employed both molar-level (e.g., ratings of overall skill, assertiveness, interpersonal effectiveness) and molecular-level (e.g., frequency

21

of duration measures of eye contact, speed latency, number of smiles) approaches to assessment. As previously discussed in this chapter, there is a tendency to represent these two approaches as a dichotomy and to characterize this choice regarding the unit of recording as a choice between a trait-attribution model and a reductionistic behavioral model of social skills. In this section, we will argue that while there is a strong tendency to associate molar-level recordings with a trait-attribution model and molecular-level recordings with a reductionistic behavioral model, this is mainly due to our narrow view of these assessment approaches. We intend to demonstrate that it is appropriate to view molar and molecular recordings as end points on a continuum, rather than as a dichotomy; and, while both approaches have shortcomings for the unwary there is much utility in each, as well as in inter-mediate-level recordings along the continuum.

Molar-level Recording

To many the use of molar recordings to assess social skills implies a trait conceptualization of social skills. This implication is most likely related to the long history of ratings in personality research. Thus, when investigators employ molar recordings such as global ratings of a subject's social skills, it is sometimes assumed that they are interested in the degree to which an individual possesses a greater or lesser amount of social skill across situations. Trower (1982, p.401) for example, states: "Assertive-ness, social skill, self-expression or social anxiety scores presumably imply cross-situational consistency of behaviour, e.g., overall skill, and it is an easy step then to evoking dispositional entities that cause this." In the light of well known shortcomings of the trait approach (e.g., Mischel, 1968; Peterson, 1968) it is not surprising that investigators who associate molar-level assessment with a trait approach are less than enthusiastic about its utility. However, as we have noted in the previous section, a molar recording approach does not necessarily assume a trait-attribution model.

In addition to their association with the trait model, molar recordings can be criticized on two additional grounds - subjectivity, and the amount of information provided (or not provided). The sub-jectivity of molar recordings is very evident in instances where untrained judges are used to rate the social skills of a subject on a Likert-type scale. In this approach the judges' ratings are based on their impressions and the behavioral basis of these impressions is unknown.

Even when trained judges are used, the behavioral basis of their ratings is not clear. Judges may be trained to attend to specific behaviors but the basis for selecting these behaviors is rarely clearly specified. In most cases, it is evident that investigators let their own judgment serve as the "criterion". It remains to be seen whether the judgment of these investigators is any better than that of our untrained judges, and whether trained judges actually pay any attention to these behaviors when they rate.

Molar ratings can also be criticized for the paucity of information they provide. A rating of "2" on a 9-point scale suggests that a subject does not appear very skillful, but does not tell us why. It is obvious that any two subjects whose social skills level in a given situation was rated a "2" may have received this rating for very different reasons. It is exactly this question of why they received a "2" that is of primary importance in designing a treatment program. Molar ratings do not provide us with the level of information that is frequently needed. They may at best tell us how skillful a subject performs in a particular situation; they cannot tell us why he or she appears that way. The finding of significant level differences between raters (Farrell, Mariotto, Conger, Curran, & Wallander, 1979) creates further problems for molar recordings. We cannot even be sure if a subject whose performance is rated a "2" by one judge is perceived as more or less skillful than a subject whose performance is rated a "4" by a different judge.

In spite of our uncertainty about what judges attend to when they rate, it is clear that molar-level recordings of social skills provide us with very important information. When we initiate social skills training with clients it is certainly our hope that they will change their impact on others, that is, that those individuals they interact with will see these clients' behavior as more skillful in situations where they were previously seen as unskillful. Presumably our observers are representative of observers in the natural environment who are making these judgments concerning our clients. That these judgments are not completely idiosyncratic can be seen from the studies where untrained judges demonstrate moderate agreement among themselves (Conger, Wallander, Mariotto, & Ward, 1980; Millbrook Farrell, & Curran, unpublished manuscript), and

23

different judges across different laboratories have demonstrated good agreement (Curran, Wessberg, Farrell, Monti, Corriveau & Coyne, 1982). Results have demonstrated that with training judges can come to excellent agreement both with respect to the rank-ordering and mean level performance of subjects in certain situations (Farrell, Curran, Zwick, & Monti, 1984).

Because they provide a measure of social validity (Wolf, 1978), molar ratings will continue to be of importance in social skills research. If this is the case, does this mean we are forced to employ a trait model of social skills? As mentioned previously, it is our contention that the use of molar-level recordings does not force us to adopt a trait approach to social skills. It is our conceptualization of social skills which dictates how we interpret our data and what operations we perform on them, not vice versa. After obtaining ratings of a subject's behavior across a variety of social situations, we have several options for how we can treat these data. We can look at each score individually, or we can combine scores across situations. In looking at individual scores we can construct a "profile" of ratings for that subject and use this profile to pinpoint relative strengths and weaknesses in how that subject is able to handle various situations. The importance of such individual profiles was demonstrated in a study by Farrell et al. (in press) who investigated the consistency of subjects' rated social skills and anxiety across eight different simulated scenes on the Simulated Social Interaction Test (SSIT - Curran, 1982). This study found that while there were no group differences in skill ratings across different SSIT items (i.e., no main effect for different items), there were substantial differences in how individual subjects performed across these different situational items (i.e., a large person x situational item interaction).

Instead of looking at individual ratings, we could sum or average an individual subject's rating across situations. While this appears to assume a trait approach, again, this depends on our interpretation of the resulting scores. In trait terms we may regard this score as the individual's level of "social skills". On the other hand, we might regard this as a test of the generalization of social skills across situations, or where similar situations are involved, as a measure of the subject's performance in that particular type of situation. In either case, the consistency of social skills across situations is an empirical question. It is not appropriate to assume either consistency or lack of consistency for behavior within different types of social situations.

In summary, there is a tendency to associate molar-level recordings with a trait-attributional model of social skills. It is our contention that this need not be the case and depends upon how the data are interpreted. Molar-level recordings have weaknesses in that they are relatively subjective and do not provide us with a very important source of data which is necessary to evaluate the social validity of our skills training program.

Molecular-Level Recording

Due to its reliance on strict operationalism and focus on discrete behavior, the molecular approach to assessing social skills has been associated with a strict behavioral model of social skills. As mentioned previously, critics of the molecular approach have argued that molecular-level recordings are too simplistic, fail to account for the complex interactions among behaviors, and suggest that certain behaviors are intrinsically skillful (McFall, 1982; Trower, 1982).

In addition to the problem of how to link up discrete molecular behaviors, there is the problem of identifying them in the first place. How can we specify the domain of all behaviors that should be considered skillful? Does it make sense to discuss behaviors independent of their situational context? A high rate of a particular behavior may be regarded as skillful in one situation (e.g., talking while at a social event such as a party). Also as McFall (1982) points out in his principle of equifinality there may be many ways to perform skillfully in a particular situation.

Molecular recordings do have a number of advantages. In contrast to molar-level recordings, these observations are generally more objective and as a result very high inter-observer agreement can be obtained (e.g., Conger & Farrell, 1981). In terms of specificity, molecular-level recordings are very precise in identifying particular deficits. It is our contention that molecular-level recordings offer great promise, but that little of this promise has been realized because they have not received sufficient attention. Relative to other assessment approaches, molecular-level recordings require a great deal of resources. Initial attempts to employ

25

molecular-level recordings in the social skills area did not meet with much success (e.g., Glasgow & Arkowitz, 1975; Twentyman & McFall, 1975). For these reasons, investigators in the social skills area may have prematurely abandoned molecular-level recordings (Conger & Farrell, 1981).

At the present time our molecular-level instruments are at a fairly crude stage of development. We have primarily focused on rates of individual behaviors (e.g., Conger & Farrell, 1981) and have not yet tried to link behaviors together into patterns. The fact that our current molecular-level recording systems are simplistic is not a sufficient basis for arguing that molecular-level recordings are too simplistic. Molecular-level units of recording can be employed to study very complex interactions among behaviors. An example of this is the work of Duncan and Fiske (1977) in which they use a molecular-level approach to study complex variables such as turn-taking behaviors in social interactions. The problem of identifying appropriate behaviors can also be solved. Conger and his colleagues (Conger, Wallander, Mariotto, & Ward, 1980; Conger, Wallander, Conger, & Ward, 1980) provide a good example in a series of studies where they employed peers to generate behavioral cues for evaluating the social skills of college males. Results of these studies indicated that peers generated behavioral cues which coincided with major variables investigated in the social skills area, that these peers were in fact sensitive to differences in these behaviors in video-taped interactions they observed, and that they were able to relate these cues to global judgments. Another promising approach to investigating molecular-level recordings is the study of their relationship to molar-level recordings. Conger and Farrell (1981), for example, found that simple frequency measures of subject talk, gaze and confederate talk were strongly related to trained judges' ratings of anxiety and social skills for a college subject population. In a subsequent study, Millbrook, Farrell and Curran (unpublished manuscript) replicated these results using a different simulated situation, untrained judges and separate samples of psychiatric patients and control subjects.

In conclusion, molecular-level recordings have been criticized as too simplistic, and unable to account for complex interactions among behaviors. While our current molecular-level instruments are justifiably criticized on this basis this does not imply that the molecular approach is useless. We are in a very early stage of using molecular-level recordings. A model which employs molecular-level recordings and relates specific components into more complex processes may be within our reach. Such a model would provide us with needed information about the complex behaviors under study by social skills researchers.

The Molecular-molar Continuum

It was stated earlier that molar and molecular recordings should be viewed as endpoints on a continuum rather than as a dichotomy. One of the problems in viewing these two approaches as a dichotomy has been the association of these assessment approaches with different theoretical formulations of social skills. In the previous sections we have attempted to demonstrate that this association is unnecessary, that the use of molar recordings does not bind us to a trait conceptualization of social skills, and that a molecular approach to assessment does not necessitate a rigid behavioral approach. There are limitations with both approaches, but each also has considerable strengths. In particular, the strengths of one approach seem to complement the weaknesses of the other. The molar approach allows judges to consider complex interactions among behavioral and situational characteristics and lends social validity to the assessment, but is relatively subjective and provides little specific information about the subject; the molecular approach on the other hand is extremely objective and specific in the information it provides, but does not easily incorporate complex interactions among behaviors nor does it readily consider situational characteristics. For this reason it seems unproductive to argue against one approach in favor of the other. The more reasonable approach is that we need to study both for the different types of data they provide us, and we stand to gain much from studying the relationships between these two types of recordings. For example, we know little about the behaviors that judges pay attention to in evaluating social skills. Perhaps it is possible to build a model of a judge's decision-making process in arriving at these ratings. Such a model would provide information of great importance for both assessment and designing treatment programs.

Finally, conceptualizing molar and molecular recordings as a continuum allows us to consider a variety of assessment approaches in between. These "intermediate-level" recordings may be able to capitalize on some of the advantages of both molar

27

and molecular-level approaches. The utility of an intermediate-level approach has been suggested in two preliminary studies of the Behaviorally Referenced Rating System for Social Skills (BRRSSS) developed by Wallander (1981). This instrument employs five separate non-verbal (e.g., use of facial expression, use of eyes) and six verbal (e.g., language, speech delivery, conversation content) rating dimensions with empirically-derived anchor points. In the first of these studies (Wallander, 1981) the BRRSSS was found to have good reliability, satisfactory concurrent validity with both molar and molecular recording approaches, and was able to differentiate subjects who were a priori considered likely to display different levels of social skills. In a second study, Farrell, Rabinowitz, Wallander and Curran (1981) investigated the reliability and validity of a modified version of the BRRSSS in a psychiatric inpatient sample and a control sample. As in the orginal study by Wallander, very good reliability was found and the BRRSSS showed an intuitively acceptable pattern of relationships to molar ratings of social skills and individual molecular recordings of component behaviors. Parenthetically, it is interesting to note that the validation of the BRRSSS has proceeded by relating scores on this instrument to molar recordings to assess social validity and to molecular recordings to assess accuracy of the ratings. While we encourage the development of intermediate level recordings, they are not likely to reduce the need for either molar or molecular assessment approaches.

FOCUS OF OBSERVATION: PERSON/SITUATION

As we mentioned in the introduction, an emphasis on person variables has been more closely associated with the trait approach to assessment while an emphasis on situational variables has been more closely identified with the behavioral approach to assessment. We have already made the point that person/situation emphasis need not be equated with trait vs. behavioral approach to assessment. It is rather our contention that we need to assess both person variables and environmental variables, and most importantly, the interaction between person and environmental variables if we are to make progress in both social skills treatment and assessment. Depending upon the assessment task at hand, a differential emphasis on either person variables or situational variables may be appropriate.

The question of where to focus the attention of our assessment, situations or persons, can be illustrated by the following example. If we were requested to select the best athlete out of a population of individuals, we could adopt at least two different types of assessment strategies. Keep in mind that in both types of strategies, we would more likely sample rather than exhaustively observe the whole universe. One strategy would be to observe individuals in a sample of games which had been selected on some basis as being representative of the population of games. For example, we may wish to choose games which would emphasize different types of athletic ability; hence, our sample may include such diverse games as boxing and fencing, horseback riding and skeet shooting, basketball and swimming, etc. Another strategy would be to again sample, on some basis, a number of personal attributes of all the individuals in the population. For example, we may wish to sample response capabilities which would generalize over many different games such as speed, endurance, strength, visual acuity, etc. Parenthetically, we would also probably want to assess other person variables in addition to muscular-skeletal skills such as the ability to withstand pressure (anxiety proneness), athletic competitiveness (motivation to compete), etc. Likewise, in attempting to predict whether an individual's social performance will be regarded as competent, not only is it necessary to measure muscular-skeletal response capabilities but other person and situational variables also need to be assessed.

Sampling at the Interface of the Person vs. Situation Interaction

As we mentioned previously, whether the focus of our observation is on the person or the situation, we need to sample these dimensions on some systematic basis. It is our contention that such sampling be done at the interface of the person vs. situation interaction no matter what type of sampling strategy is employed (e.g., rational, empirical, etc.). That is, sampling at the interface should take into account both person and situation factors.

A concept that McFall (1982) proposed as a bridge between competency and skill appears to us to be at the interface of the person vs. situation interaction. That concept is the "task" which McFall regarded as an organizing and directing force on behavior. McFall noted that tasks could be hierarchically organized; for example:

>At a global level, one task might be find-
>ing a spouse. Nested within that global
>task would be various smaller tasks, like
>meeting potential spouses, dating and devel-
>oping an intimate relationship. Dating, in
>turn, might be broken into sub-tasks such as
>initiating, conversing, parting, etc. Each
>of these could be sub-divided further into
>component tasks; for example, initiating a
>date might be segmented into smaller units
>such as selecting a person to approach, po-
>sing the date, etc. Conceivably, each of
>these might be decomposed into even smaller
>units. (McFall, 1982, p.28)

As an example of a previous task approach to
assessment, we offer intellectual assessment.
Intelligence tests are more or less organized around
tasks such as Coding, Block Design, Comprehension,
Vocabulary, Similarity, etc. These tasks require
different types of skills and in different combinations. They are situations which require different
response capabilities (e.g., social judgment, short
or long-term memory, hand-motor coordination) if an
individual is to successfully manage them. In the
case of intelligence, tests were chosen on a rational
basis, namely it was thought that these tests best
tapped those abilities which represented intellectual
functions. Empirical procedures were used to valid-
ate the tasks chosen on a rational basis.

In the social skills literature, examples can be
found of task-oriented assessment items which appear
to be neither exclusively person-or-situation-
oriented but rather appear at the interface of the
person by situation interaction. For example,
Goldsmith and McFall (1975) attempted to develop a
simulation measure of social skills for psychiatric
patients by utilizing Goldfried and D'Zurilla's
(1969) behavior-analytic procedures. They interviewed sixteen psychiatric patients who had self-
reported that they were interpersonally anxious and
asked each of them to give specific examples of difficult interpersonal situations that they had experienced. Situational contexts which were generated
were making friends, having job interviews, relating
to authority, etc., and critical moments within these
interactions were initiating or terminating the
interactions, making personal disclosures, handling
conversational silences etc. It appears to us that
the items generated were neither exclusively person-
or situationally-oriented but rather task oriented

such as making friends and relating to authorities.

In our own work (Curran, 1982) when we attempted to develop a measure of overall social competency, we chose tasks wherein situations are described which required different types of social skills response capabilities in order to successfully cope. We attempted to choose different types of problematic situations which were relatively independent of each other and were representative of the universe of problematic social situations. We constructed social simulation scenarios based on the situational factors isolated by Richardson and Tasto (1976) as representative of situations which elicit social anxieties. Each of the eight simulations comprising our Social Simulation Interaction Test (Curran, 1982) may be viewed as a different task requiring subjects to utilize different social skills response capabilities such as delivering criticism, receiving compliments, demonstrating empathy, etc. We feel that each of these tasks requires a good number of social skills components and that such task-relevant behaviors cut across many different types of social situations. In a sense, what we are attempting to assess is whether an individual can integrate a number of behavioral, cognitive, motivational and emotional components necessary to perform competently on a given task. Our Simulated Social Interaction Test scenes, then, are basically an intersect between skills we thought were important and those situations which seem to call for those types of skills. As mentioned previously, it is our contention that the focus of observation should not be either on situations or on the person but on both the situation and the person and the intersection between the person and the situation.

To return to our analogy regarding the selection of the best athletes from a population of individuals, what we need to do is to sample tasks which adequately represent the universe of athletic activities. In fact, this goal has already been achieved with the ten tasks representing the decathlon. The decathlon is regarded as the ultimate test to select the world's best athletes. The reason the decathlon is regarded as the ultimate test of athletic ability is that its different tasks require vastly different response capabilities (e.g., speed, strength, endurance, etc.). It is certainly possible to argue for the inclusion or exclusion of particular tasks within the decathlon and the manner in which performances on each of the tasks are weighed to come up with a composite score can be questioned.

However, there is a fair amount of consensus that the decathlon is a good measure of overall athletic ability.

Cross-situational Generalizability

We would like to make one more point before moving on to the next section of our chapter. The point is, given that social skills are regarded as response capabilities, then some degree of stability, consistency and generalizability, may be expected, at least for the more intermediate level skills. That is, if one has the ability to deliver criticism in the most socially appropriate way, then it may be reasonable to expect that this ability should be consistent, stable over time, and generalizable over many different situations. At the most molar-level (i.e., general social competency), it would be reasonable to expect that since some individuals possess most of the intermediate level skills capabilities they should be judged as socially competent in most social situations. In fact, it might be reasonable to expect that the ability to be perceived as socially competent might be normally distributed. That is, some individuals may be perceived as competent in most situations while other individuals are perceived as incompetent in most situations with the majority of people falling some place in between (i.e., competent in some situations, incompetent in others). There is little evidence for cross-situational consistency of molecular social behaviors (Bellack, Hersen, & Lamparski, 1979; Bellack, Hersen, & Turner, 1978). However, there is no reason to expect cross-situational consistency for many of these molecular behaviors mainly because of the irrelevancy of these behaviors with respect to judged competency in these different situations and because of McFall's principle of equifinality. On a more molar level, there is evidence (Wessberg et al., 1981) that judges perceive some consistency in the social competency level of subjects across quite different settings. It is our guess that this consistency in perceived social competency in subjects across settings is probably due to the fact that some individuals are consistently perceived as competent while others are consistently perceived as incompetent. With respect to stability, we do know that hospital staff members (Curran, Miller, Zwick, Monti, & Stout, 1980) perceived some patients to have long standing generalized difficulties interacting with people. Trower, Bryant, and Argyle (1978) reported that inadequate patients were likely to have had histories of poor mixing with others and a failure in dating situations, and to report considerable difficulty in a wide range of social situations, in particular those involving actively seeking contact with relative strangers, especially those of the opposite sex. Children who have peer relationship difficulties appear to have numerous later adjustment difficulties of both a social and non-social nature (French & Tyne 1982).

Again, to pursue an analogy from the athletic domain, some athletes are known as "natural athletes". This term connotes that no matter what the sport, certain individuals have the capability to master the activity quickly and become good at it. These individuals seem to possess the intermediate levels of skill such as speed, strength, dexterity, competitiveness, ability to withstand pressure, etc., which makes them capable of mastering most sporting activities. Even if they have never played the game before, they are able to master it in a very short period of time. It is as if once they learn the rules and have a few practice runs, they are playing the game as if they had been playing it all their lives.

Trower (1982) provides a description of what we would call a "natural socially skilled athlete" would look like by describing their intermediate level capabilities:

> The skilled person, being an external
> monitor, will be a relatively accurate
> perceiver of those situations and person
> cues which will guide him in appropriate
> rule-following behavior. They will pos-
> sess situation and person schemata that
> are intersubjectively valid, i.e., shared
> by the community, so that his inferences
> from social cues will be valid and his
> subsequent behavior will be intelligible
> and warrantable (Harre, 1977). His
> outcome expectancies (inferences) will
> be empirically based and have reason-
> able predictive validity, namely he will
> have reasonable factual knowledge of his
> capabilities, and the difficulties pre-
> sented by the situation. His self-evaluation
> of competence (self-efficacy evaluation)
> will also be empirically based, reflecting
> past successes and failures, in predicting
> future successes and failures (self-efficacy
> expectations). (Trower, 1982, p.421-422)

33

As can be seen, most of the intermediate level capabilities in Trower's description are of a cognitive nature and are consistent with his generative model of social skills. We will be discussing some of these person variables in the next section.

We would like to conclude this section by reiterating our position that we must examine both situation and person variables and the interaction between situation and person variables in our conceptualization of social skills. Given that social skills are regarded as response capabilities, then some degree of stability, consistency, and generalizability may be expected for molar level skills, although the degree of generalizability is an empirical question.

SKILL DEFICITS VERSUS OTHER EXPLANATIONS

Again this issue has been often posed as an either/or issue. Inadequate social performance is attributed to either an inadequate behavioral repertoire or to some other factors which are interfering with what would be adequate performance if these other interfering mechanisms were not present. In other words, an apparent deficit (sub-standard behavior) may exist either because the skill is lacking or because of some other interfering factor. It should be obvious that we cannot measure a deficit. What we can observe is an individual's performance and from it we can determine whether an individual has certain response capabilities. We cannot determine whether an individual is incapable of a response because other person variables or situation variables may be interfering with the response. That is, we can determine whether certain responses or behavioral tendencies exist within the person's repertoire but we cannot determine with any degree of certitude which responses do not exist.

This is probably more apparent when we are recording molecular units of behavior than when we are making more molar judgments. For example, it is rather silly to speak of an individual as having a deficit (in the absolute sense) with respect to eye contact. Certainly, individuals who are not visually impaired and who can move their head can make eye contact. However, this is also true on a more molar level. For example, we may observe an individual over a lengthy period of time in a wide variety of circumstances and may incorrectly come to the conclusion that he is incapable of displaying affection for other human beings. He is cold and indifferent to his children, is rude and standoffish with his co-workers, and never compliments his wife or tells her that he loves her. However, does this mean that the individual is incapable of demonstrating affectionate behaviors? If we offered this man a million dollars to display affectionate behaviors towards his wife or threatened to shoot him if he did not, would the individual be able to perform in an affectionate manner? Even under these circumstances, our hypothetical individual may not perform in an affectionate manner even though he is capable because he prefers to be dead rather than continue on in a miserable marriage.

Perhaps contributing to the either/or skill deficit controversy is the dual manner in which the word deficit is used. The word "deficit" is actually defined in two subtly different ways, one of which connotes an absolutist position and one of which connotes a relativistic position. For example, Webster (1976, p.297) defines deficit as a wanting but also defines it in terms of amount or quality. Deficient is defined as lacking in some necessary quality or element and also defined as not up to a normal standard or complement. Since it is impossible to determine whether an individual has a deficit in the absolute sense, it appears to us to be most useful to speak of a deficit in a relativistic manner.

What we are saying then is that performance in a social situation is multiply determined by numerous person and situational factors. We should not assume, as often is the case for those who follow a naive medical model, that there is one underlying etiological factor responsible for inadequate social performance. When studying person variables, we must examine, to use terminology proposed by Wallace (1982), receiving, processing and sending functions which are inherent in the performance of social behaviors. We must focus on expectations and motivational states preceding the actions, the emotional state during the interaction and the perceived and actual outcomes. It should be apparent to anyone doing social skills training that it is often not enough merely to teach a skilled response to a subject for that subject to apply this new skill in the natural environment. Given the importance of these other variables, the question then becomes how can we best assess these variables and teach them? We will limit our discussion to what has become known as cognitive variables because of space limitations and in keeping within the theme of this book.

Social Skills: A Critique

Assessment of Cognitive Variables

Given the difficulties encountered in the behavioral assessment of social skills when we are dealing with observable and quantifiable performance components (Curran & Mariotto, 1980), the assessment of cognitive variables appears to be a Herculean task. Not only are cognitive deficits (meaning anything from self-damning cognitions to faulty problem-solving to irrational beliefs) not observable, but they are extremely difficult to elicit in a direct and spontaneous fashion.

Glass and Merluzzi (1981) have addressed the difficulty in measuring cognitive variables more exhaustively than space allows us here but a few points can be highlighted. Self-report measures of cognitive variables at best can do nothing but "lead the witness". For example, if we attempt to measure self-statements and maladaptive cognitions in a self-report questionnaire, we can never be sure whether we are addressing pertinent questions and problem areas from basically an infinite universe of all possible self-statements and cognitions. Self-report questionnaires attempting to measure cognitive factors also appear to be susceptible to response set bias. The subject may wish for various reasons to give an unfavorable portrayal of his or her state, or conversely may withhold negative thoughts in order to appear more rational. Who but the most clinically depressed or anxious subject would admit to believing "it is catastrophic if I do not succeed at everything"?

Procedures other than questionnaires have been developed in order to assess self-reports of cognitions. In some laboratories, subjects have been asked to recall and list everything that went through their minds before, during and after a behavioral assessment, or to "think aloud" (Genest & Turk, 1980) while performing a motor test. The former method suffers from a variety of possible distortions, omissions and errors in retrieval, not to mention self-consciousness elicited by the recording equipment. The latter method precludes adaptation to social interaction; the subject may focus on the verbal interactions of a social skills role play or on verbalizing self-talk, but not on both.

While it is certainly fashionable to talk about cognitive variables, very little progress has been made in the assessment of such variables. It appears that cognitive therapy has far outdistanced in sophistication and theoretical groundings the methodologies available for its measurement.

Cognitive Variables in Treatment

We feel that it is about time that social skills investigators confessed that they do more than just teach skeletal-muscular responses. Subjects in their training groups indeed do think and their conceptual-izations may be altered by the training procedures. Even in the most rigidly structured molecular response acquisition training programs more is taught than merely new muscular-skeletal responses. In social skills training programs, goals are discussed, various response acquisition strategies are explored, and possible outcomes to these various strategies are debated. General strategies and rules for employing certain behavioral strategies are given by the therapist. Therapists discuss with subjects primary and secondary goals of interaction. Therapists and group members try to delineate the difference between assertive, aggressive and non-assertive behaviors. Various social norms are discussed. In fact during social skills groups it is not uncommon for subjects to discuss their negative self-statements, ir-rational beliefs, etc. Clearly more cognitive therapies may possess some utility in handling these issues rather than a strictly behavioral approach. Unfortunately, it is true that many of these com-ponents have not been highlighted when social skills training programs have been discussed in the past but rather the focus has been mainly on the response acquisition of muscular-skeletal behavior. We say that this is unfortunate because it has contributed to the rigid drawing of boundaries between social skills and cognitive approaches to treatment. It has led each side to engage in polemics in attempting to defend their treatments rather than attempting to dissect and analyze the utilities of each treatment strategy vis-a-vis our patient populations. As Barlow has recently said:

> We are not asking the most pertinent
> questions. With whom will these pro-
> cedures work and with whom will they
> fail? What are the most efficient
> and effective methods for delivering
> these procedures? How can we facilitate
> generalization and maintenance of treat-
> ment effects? (Barlow, 1981, p.147)

Our treatment strategies and procedures while differing in emphasis generally result in influencing all three spheres: behavioral, cognitive and emotional. Bandura (1977), in his paper on self-efficacy theory, enumerates the ways in which self-perceptions, instructions and expectancies interface with social interactions. For example, individuals who come to believe they are more skillful in certain social situations are less likely to generate anxiety-provoking thoughts when the situations arise. On the other hand, a successful performance can provide data (i.e., more adaptive reality testing, fewer expectations of negative outcome, less severe physiological arousal) with which the individual can temper irrational cognitions. In our own social skills training program, we have witnessed marked increases in verbalized positive self-statements and a decrease in expectations of negative consequences resulting from social performances, or what Bandura termed "efficacy expectancies" and "outcome expectancies", respectively. We have noticed, for example, that if a subject is able to assertively deliver an appropriate criticism as part of an in vivo homework assignment, he may come back into the group the next day and say, "I can do it", or "this is better than the way I've been doing it in the past". These positive self-statements are then reinforced by other group members and the therapist.

There is evidence that social skills response acquisition groups are effective in changing cognitions. The results from treatment-outcome studies, while by no means conclusive, indicate that social skills training alone, or combined in a cognitive-behavioral package is not only effective in increasing social performance on behavioral measures, but in increasing positive self-statements and other cognitions as well. In fact, in some studies, social skills groups have done as well as cognitive orientated groups in changing cognition. Linehan, Goldfried, and Goldfried (1979) found no differences at follow-up on any measures between a behavioral, rational restructuring and combined group. Hammen, Jacobs, Mayol, and Cochran (1980) found that no cognitive or cognitive-behavioral therapies were clearly superior to behavioral interventions alone. The Hammen et al. (1980) study included in its assessment battery measures of both cognition and social skills.

The findings that social skills training groups affect cognition is not too surprising when one actually examines what occurs in a skills training group (establishing goals, generating response options, exploring probable outcomes, etc.). Furthermore, the response acquisition and role-playing aspects of social skills training groups may be particularly helpful in facilitating the acquisition of new cognitions. As Bandura noted when discussing the apparent discrepancy between the use of cognitive processes to explain change in the face of evidence that response acquisition treatments are most effective in promoting change:

> The apparent divergence of theory
> and practice can be reconciled by
> postulating that cognitive processes
> medicate change but that cognitive
> events are induced and altered most
> readily by experience of mastery
> arising from effective performance.
> (Bandura, 1977, p.191)

In effect, cognitive orientated therapy may be too cognitive for many of our patients. In doing cognitive therapy with some of our patients, we may be asking them to "buy into an idea" which they do not fully comprehend. Frisch (1977) reported that psychiatric inpatients stated that they had difficulty understanding and applying the rational-emotive aspects of a combined treatment group (cognitive-behavioral) focusing instead on the more concrete social skills.

Our point is that often our treatment approach to a particular patient must be multi-modal because we are interested in effecting changes in behavior, cognitions and emotions. Our various treatment programs may emphasize one of these objectives but in all probability affect all three spheres. We would like to address one more point before concluding this section of the chapter and that is the recent attempts by some researchers to incorporate all person variables into an all inclusive social skills model.

Social Skills Model and its Limitations
Investigators have begun to incorporate many person variables into a social skills model (Hersen, 1979; McFall, 1982; Phillips, 1978; Wallace, 1982). Phillips' model of social skills is so inclusive that he posits the lack of social skills as the essential behavioral deficit. For Phillips, psychopathology results from an organism's lack of skills and negative emotional states and maladaptive cognitions occur in lieu of social solutions to problems. The incorporation of cognitive and physiological person variables into a social skills model has the distinct advantage of eliminating the deficit vs. other factors dichotomy by blurring the distinction between

these other factors and muscular-skeletal skill deficits. However, as we noted earlier:

> If we do not restrain ourselves and put some limits on the construct of social skills, it will expand to include all human behavior and social skills training will soon come to mean any process which is capable of producing changes in human behavior. If such an expansion does occur, it would obviously render these terms meaningless. (Curran, 1979, p.323)

An all inclusive social skills model may create in us a tendency to view all problems as deficit problems and to see all treatment as response acquisition training. While there is some utility in viewing problems as deficit problems and treatment as a response learning experience, it may also stifle our conceptualizations and restrict our treatment options. For example, an individual may experience anxiety associated with dating situations due to a classically conditioned emotional response. If that is the case, then the treatment of choice would be CS exposure in a non-threatening atmosphere rather than the acquisition of a new skeletal-muscular response. Parenthetically, this example also illustrates how the three issues which we have highlighted in this chapter (molar-molecular, situation-person, deficit-other explanations) are intricately related. For example, a male may possess all the molecular behaviors that are required to be judged socially competent in introducing himself and initiating conversation (as witnessed by his socially competent performance with a same sex group of peers). However, although the component behaviors still are available within his behavioral repertoire, this same individual in a different situation (e.g., introducing himself to an opposite sex group of peers) may be conditionally anxious, and, therefore, unable to perform in a manner which would be regarded as socially competent.

SUMMARY AND CONCLUSION

It is our contention that social skills research and practice has been hampered by regarding three issues inappropriately as dichotomies. These issues are: (1) The proper unit of recording (molar vs.

molecular), (2) the focal point of observation (situation vs. person) and (3) skill deficit vs. other interpretations of inadequate social performance. It is our belief that each of these issues, rather than being dichotomous, are really end points of a continuum and that we may sample any point on the continuum and find useful data depending upon specific purposes of an assessment. These issues interweave with each other and often seem to blur with one another.

Situations cannot be separated from persons and vice versa. When a question is asked about the social competency of an individual, it is usually asked with respect to a class of situations. These situations may be broadly based such as all social situations or be made increasingly specific by various parameters, such as social situations with peers, social situations with opposite sex peers, or even more scientifically, social situations with opposite sex peers which could be construed as dating situations. Regardless of how broad or specific the situational context is, it can always be broken down into more circumscribed situations. Any class of situations can be viewed as infinite by varying different parameters. For assessment purposes, we have to sample within the infinite domain of situations and generalize across the universe with respect to an individual's social competency. In order to adequately sample within a class of situations, categories of significant events must be noted, which returns us to personal competency attributes. For example, in dating situations important events might be initiating conversations with strangers, requesting a date from a stranger, making small talk when on dates, planning a successful date, etc. The social rules of each of these situations and the criteria for distinguishing between adequate and inadequate performance in each of these situations need to be determined. One should note that as one starts specifying subclasses within situations, they appear to give direction to the types of behaviors that should be sampled within each of these subclasses of situations. That is, certain behaviors appear to be more important or salient in certain situations than others.

It is our opinion that we will continue to rely on both molar and molecular units of recording. Molar units will continue to be used because they allow us to consider complex interactions and lend social validity to the assessment. Molecular recordings will continue to be used because they indicate those components which need to be trained. In speaking about these molecular components, we are not talking just about skeletal-muscular components like eye contact but components of other person variables such as the ability to remember what precisely was said in a situation. We also anticipate more frequent use of intermediate levels of recording. It is our hypothesis that certain intermediate level routines of behavior may demonstrate a good deal of generalizability across many different situations. We are talking about such intermediate levels of recording as the ability to criticize others, ability to anticipate consequences, etc.

The third issue, skill deficit vs. other explanations for poor social performance, can never be resolved with certitude. We observe social performance and hence can only assess response capabilities, not deficits. Performance is due to situational variables, person variables and inter-actions between situation and person variables. Situational and task analysis need to be undertaken. Social rules and mores need to be studied, etc. Unfortunately, social skills researchers have focused on skeletal-muscular responses to the neglect of other person variables such as emotional states, motivational factors and cognitive processes. In this volume, numerous cognitive variables important to competent social performance will be reviewed including cognitive strategies and constructs, subjective values, negative self-statements, irrational beliefs, person and situation schemes, cognitive and behavioral construction competencies, self-efficacy, etc. While we have reservations about labeling these cognitive processes as social skills, these variables must be accounted for if we are to understand, assess and predict social competencies and if we are to train our patients to perform in a more socially competent manner.

REFERENCES

Bandura, A. Self-efficacy: Toward a unifying theory of behavioral change. Psychological Review, 1977, 84, 191-215

Barlow, D.H. On the relation of clinical research to clinical practice: Current issues, new directions. Journal of Consulting and Clinical Psychology, 1981, 49, 147-155

Bellack, A.S., Hersen, M., & Lamparski, D. Role-play tests for assessing social skills: Are they valid? Are they useful? Journal of

Consulting and Clinical Psychology, 1979, 47, 335-342

Bellack, A.S., Hersen, M., & Turner, S.M. Role-play tests for assessing social skills: Are they valid? Behavior Therapy, 1978, 9, 448-461

Conger, A.J., Wallander, J.L., Mariotto, M.J., & Ward, D. Peer judgements of heterosocial anxiety and skill: What do they pay attention to anyhow? Behavioral Assessment, 1980, 2, 243-259

Conger, A.J., Wallander, J.L., Conger, J.C., & Ward, D. Peers as judges of social competence: They do pay attention. Paper presented at the annual convention of the Association for the Advancement of Behavior Therapy, 1980

Conger, J.C., & Farrell, A.D. Behavioral components of heterosocial skills. Behavior Therapy, 1981, 12, 41-55

Curran, J.P., Wessberg, H.W., Farrell, A.D., Monti, P.M., Corriveau, D.P., & Coyne, N. Social skills and social anxiety: Are different laboratories measuring the same constructs? Journal of Consulting and Clinical Psychology, 1982, 50, 396-406

Curran, J.P. Pandora's box reopened? The assessment of social skills. Journal of Behavioral Assessment, 1979, 1, 55-71

Curran, J.P. The simulated social interaction test: A measure of social skills. In J.P. Curran & P.M. Monti (Eds.), Social skills training: A practical handbook for assessment and training. New York: Guilford Press, 1982

Curran, J.P., Miller, I.W., Zwick, W.R., Monti, P.M., & Stout, R.L. The socially inadequate patient: Incidence rate, demographical and clinical features, hospital and post-hospital functioning. Journal of Consulting and Clinical Psychology, 1980, 48, 375-382

Curran, J.P., & Mariotto, M.J. A conceptual structure for the assessment of social skills. In M. Hersen, D. Eisler, and P. Miller (Eds.), Progress in Behavior Modification, 1980

Curran, J.P. Social skills: Methodological issues and future directions. In A.S. Bellack & M. Hersen (Eds.), Research and practice in social skills training. New York: Plenum Press, 1979

Duncan, S., & Fiske, D.W. Face-to-face interaction: Research, methods and theory. Hillsdale, N.J.: Lawrence Erlbaum Associates, 1977

Farrell, A.D., Curran, J.P., Zwick, W.R., & Monti, P.

M. Generalizability and discriminant validity of anxiety and social skills ratings in two populations. Behavioral Assessment, 1984

Farrell, A.D., Rabinowitz, J., Wallander, J.L., & Curran, J.P. Behaviorally referenced rating system for social skills: Reliability and validity with psychiatric patients. Paper presented at Association for the Advancement of Behavior Therapy, Toronto, 1981

Farrell, A.D., Mariotto, M.J., Conger, A.J., Curran, J.P., & Wallander, J.L. Self-ratings and judges' ratings of heterosexual-social anxiety and skill: A generalizability study. Journal of Consulting and Clinical Psychology, 1979, 47, 164-175

Fischetti, M., Curran, J.P., & Wessberg, H.W. Sense of timing: A skill deficit in heterosexual-socially anxious males. Behavior Modification, 1977, 1, 179-194

French, D.C., & Tyne, T.J. The identification and treatment of children with peer relationship difficulties. In J.P. Curran & P.M. Monti (Eds.), Social skills training: A practical handbook for assessment and treatment. New York: Guilford Press, 1982

Frisch, M.B. Social skills and stress management training to enhance interpersonal competencies. Unpublished doctoral dissertation. University of Kansas, 1977

Genest, M. & Turk, D.C. Thinking aloud approaches to cognitive assessment. In T.V. Merluzzi, C.R. Glass & M. Genest (Eds.), Cognitive Assessment. New York: Guilford Press, 1980

Glasgow, R., & Arkowitz, H. The behavioral assessment of male and female social competence in dyadic heterosexual interactions. Behavior Therapy, 1975, 6, 488-498

Glass, C.R., & Merluzzi, T.V. Cognitive assessment of social-evaluative anxiety. In T.V. Merluzzi, C.R. Glass & M. Genest (Eds.), Cognitive Assessment. New York: Guilford Press, 1981

Goldfried, M.R., & D'Zurilla, T.J. A behavioral-analytic model for assessing competence. In C.D. Spielberger (Ed.), Current topics in clinical and community psychology (Vol. 1). New York: Academic Press, 1969

Goldsmith, J.B. & McFall, R.M. Development and evaluation of an interpersonal skill-training program for psychiatric patients. Journal of Abnormal Psychology, 1975, 84, 51-58

Hammen, C.L., Jacobs, M., Mayol, A., & Cochran, S.

D. Dysfunctional cognitions and the effectiveness of skills and cognitive-behavioral assertion training. Journal of Consulting and Clinical Psychology, 1980, 48, 685-695

Hersen, M. Modification of skill deficits in psychiatric patients. In A.S. Bellack & M. Hersen (Eds.), Research and practice in social skills training. New York: Plenum Press, 1979

Kendler, H.H. Psychology: A science in conflict. New York: Oxford University Press, 1981

Linehan, M.M., Goldfried, M.R., & Goldfried, A.P. Assertive therapy: Skill training or cognitive restructuring? Behavior Therapy, 1979, 10, 372-388

McFall, R.M. A review and reformulation of the concept of social skills. Behavioral Assessment, 1982, 4, 1-33

Millbrook, J.M., Farrell, A.D., & Curran, J.P. Behavioral components of social skills: A look at subject and confederate behaviors. Unpublished manuscript, 1983

Mischel, W. Personality and assessment. New York: Wiley, 1968

Peterson, D.R. The clinical study of social behavior, New York: Appleton-Century-Crofts, 1968

Phillips, E.L. The social skills basis of psychopathology: Alternatives to abnormal psychology and psychiatry. New York: Grune and Stratton, 1978

Rathjen, D.P., Rathjen, E.D., & Heniker, A. A cognitive analysis of social performance. In J.P. Foreyt & D.P. Rathjen (Eds.), Cognitive behavior therapy: Research and applications. New York: Plenum Press, 1978

Richardson, F.C., & Tasto, D.L. Development and factor analysis of a social anxiety inventory. Behavior Therapy, 1976, 7, 453-462

Trower, P. Toward a generative model of social skills: A critique and synthesis. In J. P. Curran & P.M. Monti (Eds.), Social skills training: A practical handbook for assessment and treatment. New York: Guilford Press, 1982

Trower, P., Bryant, B., & Argyle, M. Social skills and mental health. Pittsburgh, Pennsylvania: University of Pittsburgh Press, 1978 (Also London: Methuen)

Twentyman, C., & McFall, R.M. Behavioral training of social skills in shy males. Journal of Consulting and Clinical Psychology, 1975, 43, 384-395

Wallace, C.J. The social skills training project

of the mental health clinical research center for the study of schizophrenia. In J.P. Curran & P.M. Monti (Eds.), Social skills training:A practical handbook for assessment and treatment. New York: Guilford Press, 1982

Wallander, J.L. Development and evaluation of a behaviorally referenced rating system for het- erosocial skills. Unpublished doctoral dis- sertation, Purdue University, 1981

Webster's New Collegiate Dictionary. Springfield, Massachusetts: G. & C. Merriam Co., 1976

Wessberg, H.W., Curran, J.P., Monti, P., Corriveau, D.P., Coyne, N.A., & Dziadosz, T.P. Evidence for the external validity of a social simulation measure of social skills. Journal of Be- havioral Assessment, 1981, 3, 209-220

Wolf, M.M. Social validity: The case for subjective measurement or how applied behavior analysis is finding its heart. Journal of Applied Be- havior Analysis, 1978, 11, 203-214

A RADICAL CRITIQUE AND REFORMULATION: FROM ORGANISM TO AGENT

Peter Trower

In this chapter I have addressed some of the same fundamental problems as Curran et al., but have adopted a radical position and argued for a paradigm shift as a first step in solving the problems. The first part of the chapter reviews the problems in social skills training (SST), describes the "organism" and "agency" approaches and how these are relevant to the conduct (and problems) of SST, and argues for the abandonment of the former and the adoption of the latter. The chapter then explores the implications of the agency approach. The first of these is the emphasis on the agent's ability to generate appropriate skills, rather than on the behavioural skills per se. The second is on the person's monitoring tendencies - his interpretation of his own and other people's behaviour, and the third is on his moral evaluation of these meanings and the emotional consequences that flow from this. All three levels need to be worked on in an agency approach.

Finally the chapter suggests how the agency approach may solve or dissolve some of the fundamental problems, how it may develop a new role for SST, and offers some conclusions about how these theoretical suggestions might be translated into practice.

Chapter Two

A RADICAL CRITIQUE AND REFORMULATION: FROM
ORGANISM TO AGENT

Peter Trower

An interested layman would surely find it strange to
learn that social skills training (SST) is based on
the assumption by psychologists that peope are
helpless behaving organisms rather than - as any layman might think - acting agents, choosing and
pursuing their own goals. He/she would surely be
puzzled, at the very least, to be told that this is
the only possible assumption to make, and that
treating people as choosing agents is unscientific
and unsound. He/she might not be so surprised,
however, to learn that SST is afflicted with a number
of critical problems - one being that at best, it is
only modestly effective. One would hardly expect it
to work particularly well when based on such a
counter-intuitive idea.
    The thesis in this chapter is that this (imagin-
ary) layman's incredulity is at least partly right.
It will be asserted that SST is indeed largely based
on this "organism" approach, that the approach is
wrong and has produced a number of serious problems,
that the more intuitive "agency" approach is the
valid one for a number of logical, philosophical,
moral and empirical reasons, and that a paradigm
shift from the former to the latter is required if we
are to avoid a crisis of confidence in this promising
therapy. The chapter elaborates these issues, and
draws implications for SST in the future.
    However, I shall also suggest that the layman is
wrong in one important respect. Socially unskilled
people, including a wide range of psychiatric
patients, appear to believe they are passive organisms, and behave accordingly. However, the solution
is not to accept this as an unavoidable fact around
which SST must be based, but to treat it as the
problem. In other words, an effective SST had best
be based on helping the client restore or recover his

48

agency - not to reinforce his passivity.

THE PROBLEMS

There has recently been a spate of critical studies and reviews on SST which have ranged widely in their level of scepticism (Bellack, 1979a,b, 1983; Curran, 1979a,b; McFall, 1982; Marzillier, 1978; Trower, 1980, 1982; Twentyman & Zimering, 1979). Curran et al. (this volume) have outlined some of these problems, and the following list also covers some of the current concerns:

1. There is no agreed definition of social skills, even though we all seem to "know what social skills are intuitively" (Curran, 1979b; McFall, 1982). This makes it difficult to carry out research, assessment or training in any systematic way.

2. A related point, that there is no consensus or standard by which to define skill deficits. This makes it difficult to know what to measure and what to change.

3. Another related point, that there is no standard objective source for guiding the selection of any skills. This creates problems for selecting clear training targets.

4. Assessment instruments and procedures are of doubtful validity and reliability (Bellack, 1979a, 1983; McFall, 1982). Role play tests may be too artificial (low ecological validity) for either assessment or training. Global measures are unreliable and subjective. Quantitative measures are of questionable validity in terms of social psychological criteria (Curran et al., this volume).

5. Trained behaviours do not maintain well in time (Twentyman & Zimering, 1979; Marzillier, 1978).

6. Trained behaviours do not transfer well to situations outside the training setting (Twentyman & Zimering, 1979; Shepherd, 1978).

7. Attempts are rarely made to measure or change the patient's negative cognitions which may block successful SST (Trower, O'Mahony & Dryden, 1982).

Most of the critics see the main way forward as more empirical research, and it would be churlish to deny that further, imaginative research is sorely needed. However, the way forward is not simply or even mainly, more research, but a change in the underlying paradigms upon which research - and practice - is based. I shall argue that the problems outlined above are products more of faulty paradigms than lack of knowledge.

The main argument is for a change from an "organism" to an "agency" approach in SST, from the paradigm of people totally determined by forces outside their control, rendering them in effect passive organisms, to the paradigm of people as active agents, who are partially self-determined and who can influence their environments. This recommended change draws upon schools within the so-called "cognitive revolution" exemplified by cognitive behaviour therapy and social learning theory, and upon the "ethogenic" approach (Harre & Secord, 1972; Harre, 1977). The "organism" approach explicitly or implicitly underlies most SST research and practice with some notable exceptions. Its main tenet* is that "behaviour" is under the control of external and/or internal forces, behaviourists holding the former, psychiatrists the latter, view of the location of control. Behaviour is usually taken to include what others would normally call voluntary actions (such as social skills), and even thoughts, both of which are construed as overt and covert responses respectively, to emphasize their control by other variables.

What this means is that people cannot control their thoughts, let alone their social actions or influence the actions of others.

The external controlling variables advocated by behaviourism include almost any identifiable event or stimulus in the environment which can be shown to be correlated with a behavioural response; the internal controlling variables advocated by psychiatry include mental entities or events such as an "illness" like schizophrenia or a sympton like anxiety, and also include brain events like lesions or changes in electrochemistry. Either way the human organism is totally controlled and therefore helpless, and beliefs to the contrary are irrelevant "epiphenomena" or further symptoms of the underlying cause. Another feature of the organism approach (behavioural version) is to analyze the behaviour of the organism

---

* This characterization of the organism approach is made by many others, e.g., Smail, 1978; Ingleby, 1981.

down into basic, elementary parts, in the belief that the complex whole is the sum of its simple constituent parts, each of which can then be separated, identified, measured and modified if found to be "deficient".

The organism approach (behavioural version) influences and often dictates the "proper" scientific practice of SST, despite the apparent influence of cognitive models. The trainer is recommended to view the patient "objectively" (i.e., externally) as a behaviourally deficient organism (problem) which needs to be modified (treatment goal) then to proceed to examine the patient for these deficiencies (behavioural assessment), apply a treatment (behavioural SST) which is designed to instigate the missing or deficient "response component skills". This type of description and choice of words will be found in many standard texts and research papers on SST. Much research has now been done to isolate the verbal and the nonverbal components of social skills so that trainers are led to believe a deficient component can be replaced by a new one, much as it can in a faulty machine. The now modified and good-as-new patient should "work". Training invariably therefore stops at this point.

In this enterprise the investigator/trainer may not consider it a proper pursuit, by the tenets of the paradigm, to ask his patient to express his view of his problem, his desires and intentions, his self-concept, his expectations and so on, since these subjective variables are not only "unscientific" (being allegedly unobservable) but have no direct utility because the "organism's" behaviour is externally determined.

In the event of the intervention failing, the trainer is traditionally led to seek for a solution in further behavioural instigation rather than, for example, assessing and trying to help the client overcome his own distorted assessment, negative inferences and allied helplessness beliefs. Official doctrine does not view these attitudes as blocks to change. In an extreme case, the trainer may not see a difficulty if the patient's view of the problem and the treatment goals conflicted with his own, since these beliefs of the patient would be non-functional in the passive organism paradigm, and he (the trainer) might construe his own view as hard data and not cognitive.

To clarify the argument further it may help to consider an imaginary case in which the therapist is attempting to conduct training in strict accordance with the official "scientific" doctrine. In this example, we have a female trainee therapist and a 20-year-old male patient who is lonely, depressed, has difficulty making friends and is referred "for social skills training". The therapist's first job is to assess the patient. To get a sample of his socially deficient behaviour, she intoduces a "volunteer" stranger and instructs the pair to have a two minute conversation, which is videotaped. This simulated sample is (unwisely) taken as a valid representation of the getting-to-know people problem. The therapist then analyses the patient's behaviour into simple elements, such as gaze, facial expression, posture movement, tone of voice, talk time, latency etc., and obtains the durations and frequencies of these. She also rates more psychological dimensions like warmth, assertiveness and general social skills.

The purpose now is to increase the patient's current low output of glances and so on. After training, our patient may be performing at much higher frequencies and durations in terms of elements, but regrettably, the global impressions may not have changed. As any lay person could tell us, getting a shy and gauche person to perform more does not make him more skilled, but potentially more embarrassing.

The puzzled therapist now asks the question: "what are social skills?" She consults the literature - common practice in any scientific enterprize - but the definitions offered (and they are hard to come by) are shot through with vagueness, and give her little practical help. However, she finds more precise instructions in further articles, suggesting that skilful assertiveness consists of a mean of n seconds of smiling, talking loudly etc., in a given time period.

> Is this what she needs? A sort of cook-
> book of social skills in which she looks
> up the recipe, say, for assertiveness or
> warmth, and it gives the behavioural in-
> gredients - a quantity of eye contact, a
> measure of smiling, an amount of talk, a
> pinch of this and a dash of that.
> (Trower, 1983, p.32)

The upshot is that our therapist has failed to find out what is a social skill, and by implication what is a social deficit, and if she proceeds as she started, may end up trying to train her client to do things which are bizarre rather than simply gauche, and encouraging the idea that faking "warmth" etc. is right and proper.

The closer this procedure is followed,* the more counter-productive it will surely be. Firstly, the patient, unconvinced by the procedure may quit altogether. Secondly, he may continue but fail to carry out his unnatural homework assignments. Thirdly, he may attempt the assignments, but report them to be "failures", that the treatment is not "working" and he feels worse. Fourthly, he may concede he has learned new "skills" but they are not appropriate in the situations that matter. The patient feels helpless and hopeless. The therapist will agree with the first point but may be inadvertently contributing to the second. There must be a better way.

One better way would be put forward by more sophisticated behaviourists. They would argue, with some justification, that simply training component skills is unlikely to succeed because it neglects the variables that actually produce behaviour, namely the reinforcing contingencies. The essence of social skills training, in common with any operant programme, should be to shape up new behaviours and then ensure that these are linked to and thereby elicited by reinforcing stimuli in variable situations at variable times in order to be "generalized" and "maintained". But so long as the passive organism assumption is maintained, most of the problems already alluded to will remain unresolved or ignored – the patient's cognitive blocks to change, failure to attend to the patient's intentions etc. In addition, since the patient is helpless, the trainer and others have total responsibility for organizing subtle gradients of reinforcing stimuli in the patient's social environment - a practically

* Fortunately many SST practitioners probably do not follow this "official" doctrine, but instead draw upon their own "subjective" and intuitive understandings and tacit knowledge of social behaviour, but do so unofficially, probably realizing that their particular "scientific community" would disapprove of such deviations. To what extent therapists follow such principles is hard to gauge but probably depends on how they are trained, and on how "scientific" they are trying to be, and whether, for example, they are conducting research rather than simply carrying out clinical practice. My point is simply that following such guidelines is likely to detract from rather than add to successful outcome.

impossible task for anyone, least of all a busy therapist. If the intervention still failed, the trainer would presumably have to undertake even further arduous, unguided trial and error explorations for combinations and occurrences of stimuli until the focal responses are elicited. As before, he may not consider utilizing, or modifying, the patient's own behaviour-outcome expectancies – which may be at variance with the true contingencies – since such "invalid" expectancies (cognitions) would not be considered instrumental in the patient's failure to perform or adapt to contingencies. The behavioural trainer has no recourse to the patient's own desires, plans and efficacy expectations, and would not attempt to influence them, since these cognitions are deemed non-functional in an externally determined organism. The trainer can see no purpose in instructing the patient about beneficial behaviour-outcome connections, either verbally or by modelling displays, or by any form of feedback, since an externally determined organism can make no use of such information in directing his own behaviour. If the trainer used such procedures, they would be construed as stimuli for reinforcing behavioural operants.

The reader may have a difficulty at this point, since, even if sympathetic to the argument, he may want to say that it is an unavoidable _fact_ that people are externally controlled, and we must work with those limitations. Alternatively, the reader may assert that the behavioural or organism paradigm is the only _scientific_ paradigm, and for _that_ reason dictates how we conduct our SST research and practice.

In order to refute both points, and to prepare the ground for our alternative agency approach, we need to look critically at the underlying philosophical assumptions, some of which are explicitly endorsed by radical behaviourists, and most of which are implicitly endorsed by clinical and other psychologists and psychiatrists (see introduction this volume). The latter is an important point, since professionals are often unaware – and even deny – that they hold assumptions, because the assumptions are not themselves the objects of perception but rather provide the conceptual framework which _guides_ our perceptions, categories and hypotheses. Indeed the radical behaviourist would by definition disavow the role of any cognitive assumptions, and assert that its position was not a paradigm but _the_ science of behaviour dealing directly with _the_ facts.

What then are the underlying alleged assumptions, and what is the case for their scientific status?

THE ORGANISM APPROACH

The organism approach is essentially based on "empiricism", which amounts to the theory that a basis in fact rather than ideas is the only possible science, especially for psychology. This distinction (between facts and ideas) depends upon an acceptance of Cartesian dualism, after the seventeenth-century philosopher Rene Descartes, namely that there are two quite independent types of phenomena, the mental and the physical/behavioural. Having accepted this as a premise, the empiricist concludes that since only physical/behavioural phenomena are observable (mental phenomena being unobservable by definition), then only physical/behavioural phenomena can legitimately be of interest to science.*

There are three main principles of empiricism which are derived from, or at least depend upon, the above assumption. To quote from Harre and Secord they are:

> A mechanistic model of man, a Humean conception of cause that places stress on external stimuli and a related methodology based upon the logical and epistemological theories of logical positivism (Harre & Secord, 1972, p.29).

The mechanistic model has already been partly discussed. In the behaviourist version, better known as the classic S-R conditioning theory, the organism is subjected to a certain stimulus, and responds in a predictable manner, or in the S-O-R version, conditioned changes inside the organism lead to changes in the responses not directly predictable from the immediate stimulus alone. The nature of the connection between S and R is explained by the second paradigm, the billiard ball model of causality, developed by the empiricist philosopher David Hume. In this view causation is nothing more than the regular sequence of one kind of event and another of the kind which usually follows. The prototype event is the

---

* In another version there are such things as "private behaviours" but this certainly does not acknowledge them as "mental".

occasion of one billiard ball striking another - the impact is followed by the movement of the second ball, but does not produce it. One important feature of the theory is that any causal connection assumed to exist between the two events is to be treated as a psychological phenomenon produced in the observer by the repetition of the sequence, and of no interest to science. Another important feature of the theory is that the things in which the cause-effect relation occurs play the part only of bearers and not producers of this externally applied impetus. "We have the picture of the human actor as a helpless spectator carried along on the flood tide of physical causes." (Harre & Secord, 1972, p.32)

The third and related assumption is that of logical positivist methodology. This doctrine stressed operationism as a theory of definition and the principle of verification as a theory of meaning. Propositional assertions were to be reduced to their elementary constituents or logical atoms, which were thought to correspond to absolutely simple observational facts. From these could be built more complex propositions.

These paradigms underlie most psychological research, in which logically independent entities or variables are varied and examined for their Humean causal relations. Elements of behaviour and stimuli are "torn" from their contexts to prevent contamination from these other "variables", and manipulated on the assumption that they retain their identities and meaning and of course subjects supposedly remain totally compliant on the assumption that there are no internal, generative sources of control.

Does this form of empiricism constitute the only true science (i.e., do we have to carry out SST in this way)? The argument in support of this position would claim (1) it is the only science based upon a solid foundation of immutable facts (simple, observable behaviours and stimuli) and (2) postulated theories which can be tested (by the hypothetico-deductive method) by means of this factual evidence. The (cognitive) agency approach is rejected as unscientific because it invokes essentially unobservable mental events and entities which cannot qualify as proper facts, and theories which are untestable. The rejection of all mental phenomena (on which the agency approach is said to depend) means that psychologists have to operate within the three paradigms.

We cannot consider all the rejoinders in detail but will list some of the main ones.

1. There are no such "things" as immutable <u>or</u> simple facts. This is the doctrine of naive realism which is more or less completely abandoned by philosophers and indeed by most physicists - we can get no closer to reality than our own sense experience and we have no sure way of evaluating its correspondence with the real world (see Mahoney, 1976, for this and other objections). Most now concede "factual relativity" - that facts are necessarily conceptualized, which means they are embedded in inferences, assumptions and theories at source. The same phenomena can be described in many different ways. For example human behaviour can be described in terms of physical movements <u>or</u> intentional actions, depending on one's point of view - organismic in the first case, agentive in the second. Behaviours can be seen as independent variables which can be isolated and manipulated without changing their meanings, or they can be seen as elements in a larger structure such that their meanings will change if removed from their position in the structure. The description and meaning of the phenomena will be different depending on these different views, which will lead us to select, organize, categorize and analyze differently. However, as Brenner (1982) and Collett (1980) point out, even if we analyze in purely behavioural terms, without any ascribed social meaning, the analysis would not be observer-independent - we still have to decide on the units of segmentation (see also McFall, 1982). A number of different structures can be assigned to the same movement when observers find reason to do so. This is even more so when we assign social meaning interpretations. We have to <u>interpret</u> the behaviour stream before we can even describe it.

2. The scientific method (hypothetico-deductive reasoning, hypothesis testing, theory evaluation) is fraught with logical problems, some authors even claiming that traditional psychological research practice is largely illogical (Mahoney, 1976). For example, the practice of stating a hypothesis, predicting a result, obtaining the predicted result and claiming confirmation of the hypothesis is an invalid use of confirmatory reasoning. It is further weakened because of the imprecision of Humean conceptions of cause.

3. No scientific propositions can be justified on purely rational grounds. This discovery was made by Bartley (1962) and argued in his book "Retreat to

Commitment". In brief, he states that everyone must
sooner or later fall back on a dogmatic commitment
which cannot itself be justified. One implication
of this is that no one approach can claim exclusive
scientific status - a point made by Campbell (1975)
who observes that all knowledge claims go beyond the
evidence and are highly presumptive and corrigible.
Campbell states that this is agreed by such major
philosophers as Quine, Popper, Hanson, Toulmin, and
Polanyi as well as Bartley.

4.   There is no factual evidence - and no factual
evidence is possible - for proving that the cause of
behaviour lies in the environment rather than the organism, as the behaviourist might demand. No amount
of experimenting will show more than a correlation
between events and behaviour, i.e., it will not
reveal a cause, let alone a direction of cause.

5.   We cannot "see" causal laws themselves as we see
objects and movements but only infer them from such
objects and movements. Hence causes are ideas, not
facts - a point made by Hume. Since there can be no
direct "empirical" proof of causal laws of the kind
which underlie the organism model, namely the theory
of external causation, the model is based upon a
principle which it expressly disavows, which is contradictory, and the model fails by its own criteria.
Even a weak version of the theory, namely that the
probability of a response is increased following a
reinforcer (which strictly must give up the idea of
an external direction of control) is still based upon
a non-empirical assumption about the future resemb-
ling the past - an inference that goes beyond the
evidence. A strict Humean regularity account of
cause - i.e., a pure empirical account - admits of no
accumulation of probabilities whatever, so that on
this account, the organism theory is no theory at all
(see Harre & Madden, 1975). Any use of causal concepts supports a cognitive view, since causality is a
cognition.
       So far, we have hopefully weakened the case for
"empiricism" and demolished the case for its being
the only true science. What about the objections to
the (cognitive) agency approach (described in detail
below)? We shall consider two of these.

6.   The argument that cognitions are unobservable is
the converse twin of the claim to empiricism's pure
facts, and both arguments depend upon an acceptance
of Cartesian dualism which, as we have seen, is that

there are two quite independent types of phenomena, the mental and the physical/behavioural. We are here disputing not only the behaviourist conclusion - that physical phenomena are observable and real (scientific) and mental phenomena unobservable (unscientific) but the premise that gives rise to this fallacious dichotomy - that the mental and physical are logically independent phenomena. This proposition has long been abandoned by most philosophers but still explicitly or implicitly accepted by many psychologists, even those "cognitive" psychologists who appear to accept cognitions as legitimate "data".

Philosophers would nowadays assert that concepts (cognitions) and objects (facts), or more broadly mind and matter, are not independent but are connected by logical necessity. They also assert that thought has necessary reference to publicly verifiable objects and products, or put another way, thought is embedded in a public communication system, namely language (Coulter, 1981). These are arguments we shall deploy later.

7. The agency approach, is more, not less, scientific than the organism approach. One argument of this type is made by Harre and Secord (1972) who state that the agency approach offers a true causal (explanatory) theory of behaviour compared to the organism model's correlational (probabilistic) theory which is effectively only descriptive. The former can aspire to discovering a proper law regarding precise, rule-following behaviour while the latter simply notes regularities in past behaviour.

THE AGENCY APPROACH

The most basic distinguishing characteristic of the agency approach is the central generative role of cognition in the form of perception, conception, belief, aim, desire, intention, etc. The organism model, as we have seen, presupposes the correctness of dualism, namely the logical independence of the mental and the physical, leading behaviourists to abandon the "mental" and to build their theories entirely in physical terms, namely observable behaviour and stimuli and their associations, or to give the "mental" some pseudo-physical status such that they can be treated theoretically like any other behaviour or stimuli.

In order to give cognition its proper status, the agency approach has to start by showing that dualism is a fatal first step and proving that it is an entirely false doctrine, and that the mental and the physical cannot be separated. Once the dualist step is taken, then one is forced either to become a "physicalist" e.g., a behaviourist and reject mental phenomena because they cannot by definition have external identifiable criteria, or a "mentalist" who advocates the autonomous and mysterious influence of invisible inner events. Both lead to the organism approach and the allied problems criticized earlier.

The fatal flaw can be avoided by abandoning dualism entirely. One argument (there are others e.g., Hampshire, 1982) that aims, on purely logical grounds, to show the inseparability of the mental and physical is that of the philosopher Strawson (1959). As I understand it, he demonstrates, by a purely logical form of argument, that the concept of a "person" is logically primitive, that it cannot be further reduced to simpler and separable mental and physical components. In other words a person cannot be either a mindless body or a bodiless mind, and this implies that if psychology is a science of persons it has to take account of the two properties and their necessary connection.

Very briefly, part of Strawson's argument maintains that the very possibility of attributing mental properties to an individual necessarily (by the force of logic) involves attributing tangible properties too, namely bodies and behaviour. The argument proceeds in stages. First, I have experiences, states of consciousness etc. The force of "have" here means they are my experiences as opposed to yours or simply "there" and not anybody's. Second, to be able to ascribe experiences to myself, I must be able to ascribe them to others i.e., for a psychological predicate to have meaning it must be applicable to different subjects. What this amounts to is that I could not even think of myself as a psychological individual, as an "I" at all unless I had criteria for distinguishing myself from others, i.e., I could not say "I am a conscious, experiencing person" unless I distinguish other persons who aren't me. Third, if there are other conscious, experiencing persons I must be able to recognize them as such, i.e., have public criteria for ascribing experiences and states of consciousness.

This necessary criterion is met by the fact that others have bodies, i.e., bodies and behaviour are the criteria for ascribing states of consciousness. So Strawson concludes there are two logically adequate criteria for ascribing states of consciousness (i.e., psychological predicates) - subjective experience <u>and</u> behaviour. He further concludes that psychological predicates have the <u>same</u> <u>meaning</u> whether other-ascribed or self-ascribed, e.g., "we were both angry (terrified, puzzled, etc.)".

Despite minor quibbles, Strawson's argument is established as logically coherent and compelling by philosophers, and provides a coherent basis for the agency approach. We shall show later that the essential logical connection between the mental and the physical which this argument establishes, produces totally different consequences from that of dualism – consequences which are fully exploited in the agency approach.

The agency approach is based on three principles which stand in opposition to the three principles of the organism approach discussed earlier.

Firstly, it adopts a model of man as an agent who can initiate and direct his actions towards a goal and who can <u>also monitor</u> this activity such that he can evaluate, plan and comment on it as well as actually perform it. Secondly, it espouses a causal theory radically different from either the mentalists' or behaviourists', in which actions are necessarily related to their productive cognitions and vice versa. Thirdly, it advances a scientific methodology which is structural rather than parametric, and is closer to linguistics than social sciences which use statistics, manipulation of dependent and independent variables and so on.

The Concept of Agency

I shall first describe the model as developed by Harre and Secord (1972) and then discuss its status. Harre and Secord view man as a rational agent, who chooses means (behavioural skills, etc.) that will attempt to satisfy his ends (desired rewards). Ends or goals are one of the main priciples around which behaviour is organized. In this model the agent is active rather than passive – he seeks out and processes information and generates monitors and controls his actions (rather than being impinged upon by stimuli and responding reflexively) in order to achieve goals. The concept of agent (Harre, 1979) entails that a person can represent to himself a wider range of possible actions than can be realized, can realize from these possibilities a course of action, and can abort any particular course of action for another. The actions are generated according to, and constrained by, rules – both discourse rules and situational rules – which make the actions both intelligible (comprehensive to others) and

warrantable (permissible and proper). However, man
not only monitors his performance but monitors his
monitoring (and is capable of self-intervention).
This second order monitoring allows for a continuity
of conscious self-awareness and hence awareness of
self.

The model can be put more simply as follows: as
agents we have the power of action. We monitor our
actions, but because we also are aware of our monitoring and have "the power of speech" we can provide
commentaries upon and accounts of our performances,
and plan ahead of them as well. The "power" to plan
and give accounts and commentaries is the feature
around which the science of psychology must turn. In
this anthropomorphic model of man we not only have
the person as agent but the person as watcher, com-
mentator and critic as well. It follows from this
that the most characteristic form of human behaviour
is the conscious following of rules and the intentional carrying out of plans.

One of the immediate objections to this model is
that there is no direct evidence for it, and any number of other theories could be offered. For example,
suppose a subject stated that he intended to carry
out some action and then carried it out. This does
not prove he is an agent controlling his behaviour
because he could still be being controlled externally, being "caused" to state his intention and
behave in a certain way. Could we prove the latter
then? No, because there is nothing in any stimulus
or event that can be objectively seen to be controlling - only an event, then another event following in
succession. The causal connection is contributed by
the subject, not the environment, and therefore is
not a piece of evidence, but purely psychological,
merely a hypothesis, belief, etc. about empirical
events. Such assumptions as causality cannot
themselves be tested, but precede and shape all such
investigations and are the means by which we make
sense of phenomena. However, this is not a weakness
but a strength for the agency model because it proves
that the individual hypothesizes about and thereby
actively constructs the very phenomena to which he
responds, and is therfore the source and not the
terminus in the causal chain.

This point was better put by Kant, the eight-
eenth-century philosopher, who is probably the
originator and main influence in the agency approach.
Kant had the, to some extraordinary, notion that the
"phenomenal" world is not independently existent, but
has its being in essential relation to consciousness.

A Radical Critique

Since man can only have sense impressions and no possible access to a "real" world, how does he turn these impressions into an objective spatio-temporal world of causally related substances? The answer is, by projecting a structure of rules upon them, including spatio-temporal rules and rules of substance and causality. For example we could make no sense at all of events without projecting on to them (among other principles) the causal principle: "every alteration has a cause".

This is not an idiosyncratic view of Kant's but is widely shared by eminent philosophers and scientists today. Wittgenstein pointed out that there are necessarily certain assumptions which determine the nature of "reality", and it is against the background of these that we <u>then</u> make testable assertions. Quine points out that our judgments about what there is are always embedded in some theory. Quine is worth quoting at length. In discussing the nature of physical objects, he says:

> As an empiricist I continue to think of
> the conceptual scheme of science as a
> tool ultimately for predicting future
> experience in the light of past experi-
> ence. Physical objects are conceptually
> imported into the situation as convenient
> intermediaries - not by definition in
> terms of experience, but simply as irred-
> ucible posits comparable, epistemologic-
> ally, to the gods of Homer. For my part
> I do qua lay physicist, believe in physical
> objects and not in Homer's gods; and I
> consider it a scientific error to believe
> otherwise. But in point of epistemological
> footing the physical objects and the gods
> differ only in degree and not in kind. Both
> sorts of entities enter our conception only
> as cultural posits. The myth of physical
> objects is epistemologically superior to
> most in that it has proved more efficacious
> than other myths as a device for working
> a manageable structure into the flux of
> experience. (Quine, 1969, p.44)

The status of causality is similar to that of objects. Even the most stripped down behaviourist statement about probabilities of response depends upon a prior <u>belief</u>, that the future will resemble the past, in order to have "probabilities", for without the prior belief, how could we speak of probabilities?

Causality, then, is a cognitive principle - and one of the conditions of the possibility of knowledge. This realization has led to a number of recent psychological theories and studies about how people explain events. Studies show, for example, that it is not the <u>actual</u> reinforcing contingencies that affect behavioural approaches, but what the subject believes or expects the contingencies to be (W. Mischel, 1973). In other words, their behaviour depends on their causal hypotheses, and Ross (1977) and others have observed that people generally are susceptible to making systematic errors in their causal hypotheses, and we shall return to examine these later when we discuss applications of the agency approach to SST.

The Intentional Account of Cause

The Humean account of cause insists that cause and effect must be independently identifiable, for if not, we have a degenerate causal statement of the form "E was caused by the cause of E" which supposedly tells us nothing at all (though this claim itself is not necessarily true). Within dualism this creates problems of the form "Mental event A caused physical event B" e.g., an act of Will caused a certain behaviour. We seem again forced either to reify mysterious mental entities if we are to have a causal theory, or to abandon the idea that mental phenomena have any causal role. However, the problem is created by the paradigms, namely dualism coupled with Hume's account of cause. We have abandoned dualism, which leaves the way open for another causal account.

This account is that, in brief, the mental and behavioural are linked by logical necessity rather than contingently and identifiable only by virtue of this bond. Since psychologists tend to see the problem in terms of private (inaccessible) versus public (accessible), the argument about the status of cognitions can be made roughly as follows: cognitions are necessarily both public and private. In seeing you wave, smile, look, etc., my seeing is private, your actions are public. But, my private seeing necessarily has a public referent, your action. For how could I "see" if there were no action to be observed (and never had been one to be imagined and remembered)? Conversely how could your action "be" (an observable) without me or someone seeing it? The very empiricist notion of an observable, and indeed all "phenomena" entail both concept and object and their logical connection. This applies not only to propositional assertions (about facts) but speech acts (about doing things) and emotions which are equally about things and events.

Cognitive contents, then, are publicly verifiable, and it is in this sense only that we should talk of cognitions, since private awareness (e.g., the act of seeing) without referents is literally senseless, for it contains nothing beyond its intentional object. This also entails that cognitions are not private events or entities at all — they do not have but rather confer ontological status (thinghood).

This account taken from Brentano and developed by T. Mischel (1975) and others (Natsoulas, 1981) states that mental phenomena are distinguished from physical phenomena by the essential characteristic of the former to be acts directed towards some content, and therefore inherently relational. This is the relation of being "intended" or meant, by someone about something. The only way that mental phenomena can be individuated is by the reference to the intentional object of the thought, and the only way that bodily movements can be individuated as an action is by reference to the agent's intention. This means that mental and physical phenomena are logically, not contingently, related. To quote T. Mischel:

> It is only in virtue of these noncontingent links that desire, intentions, etc., can be individuated as the desire for X, the intention to Y, etc. Similarly behaviors that are characterized in psychological rather than physical terms are indentified in relation to what the agent intends, aims at, wants (T.Mischel, 1975, p.188-189).

(This does not mean as Shaffer (1969) maintains, that, for instance, an intention to act necessarily produces the intended action; rather, it is necessary that it could produce that, and only that, type of action.)

To clarify the idea of intentional cause, consider the role of personality in the traditional sense of "causing" outgoing behaviour. In this dualist account, an inner personality or homunculus called "extraversion" (construed as a mental billiard ball) causes a person to go to lots of parties, talk a lot, etc. The rejected account is replaced by the

65

following: "extraversion" is not a mental event but simply a rule, rule-structure or schema (which Cantor and Mischel, 1979, have investigated in its role as a personality prototype), which specifies certain types of behaviours, their sequences and social goals. The schema has two functions: to recognize (or construe) extravert individuals, and to guide the "construction" of an extravert. The latter simply means that the agent can generate extravert behaviour (as in self-presentation) by use of the guiding rule (or at least learn to do so). The mental (extravert rule) and the physical (extravert behaviour individuated by the rule) are thus necessarily related, provide an explanation of how the former may produce the latter, and invoke no mysterious mental events. An intention, want or desire can be identified in terms of this same external referent - the desire to be extravert.

McFall (1982), is implicitly using an intentional account in his concept of a "task". As a background to this, he notes the poor consensus on what behavioural units are to be assessed in SST and that the "molecular" model does not tell us how to chunk a stream of activity into meaningful units of behaviour. He asks, would a Martian counting molecular units of behaviour, like players touching the bills of their caps, lead them to understand baseball? This echoes the point made earlier, that individuation of the appropriate behavioural sequence is only possible by reference to the agent's intention. McFall then offers an analysis of a task in just these terms - "A task corresponds to a person's answer to the question, 'what are you doing?'" These "behavioural programmes" organize and direct performance, have a logic and structure and so on.

There is no real alternative to this and the structural type of analysis (next section). Social skill trainers, in conforming to the positivist doctrine, try to analyze patients' behaviour"s" into non-intentional, purely physical, elements of gaze, gesture and posture - the simple "facts" - but find the meaning has mysteriously vaporized, as we saw in the introduction. Unwittingly, they have broken the necessary conceptual links between the psychological and the behavioural (Coulter, 1979). What trainers do, of course, is to reintroduce intentional, psychological concepts, not from the literature, but from their own tacit knowledge about human beings, social interaction, social rules and norms. However, they do it "unofficially" and implicitly (Trower, 1982).

Structural Methodology

In opposition to positivism, which advocates breaking complex phenomena down into simple, verifiable facts, structuralism advocates that the meaning lies _in_ the complex structure and not the elements, which derive their significance from their place in the structure. This view reflects ideas from the psychology of perception, such as the concept of "pregnanz" and figure-ground in the Gestalt tradition, and in the notions of perceptual rules of constancy, invariance and completion. It is also related to the developmental theories of Piaget, and the "schemata" (Neisser, 1976) and "script" (Schank & Abelson, 1977) theories of cognitive psychologists. It owes an inheritance both to Kant, in the notion that "reality" is constructed by cognitive rules applied to sense data, and to the later Wittgenstein, in the notion that the ultimate meaning of a word (and presumably any socialy meaningful element of behaviour) lies in its use or function within a "language game" (presumably any social episode, be it a situation or social routine) and not outside language in some ostensive real world. Wittgenstein highlighted the central importance of language as _the_ structure of ordinary human knowledge, providing both the framework for and limits of this knowledge. This idea is developed further by Berger and Luckmann in "The Social Construction of Reality" (1966) (although making no reference to Wittgenstein) who say that language is the vehicle for the social construction of reality, and serves this role in the form of discourse or conversation by making objective ("real" and behavioural) the so-called subjective (experiences, thoughts, feelings, ideas, plans, etc.).

Harre gives one of the clearest expositions of the difference between the structural and positivist approaches, as follows:

> The gas law PV=RT, relating pressure, volume and temperature, is a relation between parameters such that one can hold constant any one parameter and vary the others, and the property represented by that parameter will remain unaffected by the abstraction. As far as pressure, volume and temperature are concerned, a gas is not a structure of internally related properties. On the other hand an element of an internally related structure ceases to be that element if detached from the structure.

> In a parametric process the elements
> interact causally but retain their
> identity and do not change in type if
> detached from the structure....in a
> structured entity the component parts
> derive their meanings from the other
> details to which they are internally
> related. A handshake is not the same
> action when embedded in a betting rou-
> tine as when part of a greeting....
> (Harre, 1977, p.286-287)

Obvious examples of social structures at a
molecular level are common social routines such as
greetings, introductions, apologies, partings
(Goffman, 1971), all of which have strictly ordered
behavioural sequences and specified moves. Ventola
(1979), Kendon and Ferber (1973) and others have
empirically established the structures of greetings
and conversation openings. At a more molar level
situations are also structured by rules which both
constitute the situation and the meaning of elements,
and regulate behaviour within it. Argyle (1976) has
used the analogy of games, comparing bargaining,
cocktail parties and so on with cricket or football,
where the rules specify roles, sequences of moves,
goals, pieces, etc. Bower, Black and Turner (1979)
obtained the structures of situations like eating
out, Sinclair and Coulthard (1975) have identified
some of the hierarchical rule structures of normal
discourse while Brazil et al. (1980) have revealed
the intonation patterns by which such structuring is
achieved by conversational partners. It is "structures" too, that McFall (1982) and Carver and Scheier
(this volume) are advocating in their suggested
hierarchies.
Structural methodology is implied in the logical
connection between cognition and action. Since persons construct social phenomena - events, situations,
settings, institutions, personalities, subcultures
and cultures etc. which go to make up the totality of
social reality - and since they construct them by the
application of rules, the way is clear to examine
such phenomena by means of human explanations (including accounts and demonstrations), i.e., via the
agent's point of view, rather than some mythical
"objective" physicalist point of view which attempts
to bypass the human perspective. We now need a
structural methodology for studying and assessing
social skills. Fortunately, we do not have to begin
anew this development, since Harre and his colleagues

have already begun to make progress in this enterprise over the last ten years (Harre & Secord, 1972;
Harre, 1979; von Cranach & Harre, 1982; Brenner,
1978).

IMPLICATIONS OF THE AGENCY APPROACH FOR SST

Having briefly surveyed some of the foundations of
the agency approach, we can now explore its implications for understanding social skill and developing
SST.   Three key concepts will be discussed: the
performance, the monitoring and the evaluation of
skills.

The Performance of Skills

The agency approach asserts that SST should give
precedence not to behavioural skills per se but to
the generative process that governs the production of
behaviour in social interaction.   To do so we must
consider the goal that the individual wants or intends, the cognitive schemata which specify the
reality of the situation, beliefs about action
choices, their expected outcomes and self-efficacy,
the rules for appropriate conduct, and the interpretation of feedback resulting from any change in
the situation as a result of action.

Some of these functions, couched in less cognitive terms, are contained in the social skill model
of Argyle and Kendon (1967), which has been closely
associated with British SST research. Similar models
have been put forward recently by McFall (1982) and
Wallace (1982), and most comprehensively, from an
agency perspective, by Carver and Scheier (this
volume).

The model may be termed a processing or performance model of social skill, to distinguish it from a
components or competence model of social skills (competence here not used in the sense used by McFall, as
a judgment of performance, but the ability to carry
out a performance). Both are required for socially
skilled behaviour to occur. In other words, a person
needs knowledge of how to act, i.e., a repertoire of
skills (competence) and to decide to carry out the
act (performance), the latter depending upon wanting
a goal, selecting the appropriate situation, having
positive expectancies, belief in self-efficacy, etc.
Performance without competence results initially in
unskilled behaviour, but competence without performance produces no behavioural outcome at all, resulting in the eventual deterioration of competence
through lack of practice. Performance therefore, is

primary, in that an action is produced which can be changed and improved by feedback. It seems clear that the Argyle and Kendon social skill model, and part of the agency approach, is about this performance process. However, most SST research did not and does not generally utilize a model of performance processes, but adheres to a competence model, which fits more comfortably in with the organism approach. Competence-focussed research has as its aim the instigation of skilled components in individuals judged to be deficient in such skills (described earlier). This has generally been the meaning of social skills training, where the word skills has referred to such deficient but trainable skill components as eye gaze, facial expression or single utterances or larger components like assertiveness.

Such studies have had a mediocre track record in terms of generalization and maintenance, as well as the problems mentioned above. A major contribution to this may well be the neglect of performance processes.

This brings us to one implication of the agency approach - to develop a form of skill performance training, designed not to teach the client what to do but how to <u>learn</u> what to do.

The burden of competence training, to comprehensively teach all the necessary skills of normal social behaviour in individuals judged as deficient is an impossible and misguided goal (though this is not to deny that competence training does have a valuable role). Performance training, on the other hand, has the more rational goal of helping individuals become more efficient problem solvers, or behaviour generators, able to develop their own skills, to set up and aim for personal goals, and to cope with changing circumstances. Utilizing the agent's point of view and power to set goals, perceive, act and learn, is central to this idea.

<u>The Monitoring and Interpretation of Skills</u>
Notwithstanding the necessity of social skills models, they are not sufficient within an agency approach. The limitation of the models is that they deal mainly with the first level of monitoring, or pure unreflective performance, and not with the second level of monitoring, or reflecting upon performance and skill processes (a distinction that Carver and Scheier [this volume] <u>do</u> make and build into their model). Certainly they are goal-directed models in which constant behavioural adjustments are made in the light of perceived feedback, to obtain

closer approximations to a goal or standard. However, this does not necessarily involve the notion of
a conscious choosing, judging agent, and can equally
apply to a cybernetic machine or computer, which does
not choose or evaluate its own goals. If we accept
that, as agents, we have the power to reflect upon
our performance processes (as well as perform them),
we discover a whole new dimension of possibilites
(Bhaskar, 1979).

As reflective agents we can give rational and
persuasive explanations for past, present or intended
actions, in the form of commentaries, accounts,
excuses, and so on; we can formulate, evaluate and
abandon goals; we can invent rules for recognizing,
explaining or actually constructing (guiding)
actions, and can accept or refuse existing rules for
these purposes; we can continue or interpret ongoing
actions in the feedback loop cycle, abandon one
course of action, select from a choice of others and
pursue a chosen course; we can plan possible future
actions. These are all activities which distinguish
the agent from cybernetic machines which can only
pursue supplied goals. Indeed a number of authors
believe the true meaning of agency comes from this
second level of reflective ability (e.g., Hampshire,
1982; Harre & Secord, 1972). The loss or dysfunction
of this ability, as occurs in many psychiatric
disorders, is a more profound problem than simple
lack of skills and requires a more rad-ical solution,
as I later hope to show. Just how profound can be
gauged by considering a further implication of the
agency approach. This is that the above listed
generative cognitive "powers" of agents (see Harre &
Madden, 1976, for an analysis of "powers" as a
scientific concept) enable them to make, i.e.,
create, influence and maintain, supportive social
realities including desired social selves which take
on a physical world objectivity (though they can also
change and abandon them). Conversely the loss of
this ability leads to failure to create, influence
and maintain a positive reality or a positive social
self.

We need to clarify here what is meant by social
reality and social self. One form of explanation is
as follows. The organism model advocates one type of
reality, namely the natural order of material things,
causally determined, and the organism approach is an
attempt to reduce the person to this physical realm
(Wolpe, 1978). The agency approach advocates that
persons, through their power of reflection and action
bring about a second type of reality, namely a man-

made reality, constructed by man for man, and recognizable in such forms as situations and settings, institutions, cultures and sub-cultures and indeed all socially organized groups of people. This subject has been most developed as the sociology of knowledge and the seminal work is that of Berger and Luckmann (1966). They point out that groups of persons invent rule-prescribing and role-conferring structures which take on the appearance of objective realities. More generally, social order is a purely human product, yet it is experienced as the reality of everyday life on a par with the natural order, and people soon forget its human origins. This objective reality then impinges on the individual, in that he internalizes or privatizes the rules, norms, roles and behaviour patterns of the "objective" reality. Berger and Luckmann describe the process as an ongoing dialectic that has three "moments": society is a human product. Society is an objective reality. Man is a social product. Another aspect of this dialectic is that society exists only as individuals are conscious of it, but also that individual consciousness is socially determined. This echoes the earlier point about the necessary relation between cognition and the physically real, and shows the true meaning of the interdependence.

Society construed as "objective reality" is known as the process of reification, namely the

> apprehension of the products of human activity as if they were something other than human products - such as facts of nature.... Through reification the world of institutions appears to merge with the world of nature. It becomes necessity and fate....
> (Berger & Luckmann, 1966, p.107-108)

One of the social objects produced in this reification process is the self - a person's social/psychological as opposed to physical identity depends upon his or her various roles, which in turn depend upon human-made institutions, and these in their turn on larger cultural collectives.

The overiding goal of the agent is the production of objects, and events which will become "real" through the process of reification and take their place in real society, and one of the most important of these projects is the production of the social self. Since Goffman's "Presentation of Self in Everyday Life" (1971), this topic has become a major concern of social psychologists and has many complex ramifications (see Baumeister, 1982, for a review). However, we can briefly say that the presentation of a desired and appropriate social self is the agent's most important production, is capable of reification like other products, and that the process of production (as with all social products) is by way of rule following action (as in roles) and by conversational and other forms of accounting. The production of the self by rule following social interaction and conversational accounting is mediated by social skills, so that the successful presentation of a self, and indeed the construction and maintenance of all social objects and events, is partially dependent upon social skills (though other factors are important, such as status). It is to be expected that poor social skills may result in an inferior self-presentation and an inferior role in terms of social influence. Indeed if self-presentation is equated with self-identity, and is in turn a reified social product, then it is possible for such an identity to be changed, lost or destroyed as we shall consider later. The value of social skills to an agent, then, is no less that the means to create, defend and maintain his social self and his social products.

The implications here for our unskilled clients are obvious. It might seem obvious, too, that unskilled clients simply need to be taught the social skills that they lack. But this assumes that the client is in every other way functioning as a rational agent, and only lacks the skills. This is rarely, if ever, the case. The client is deficient not only in his social skills, but in his powers of reflective agency - a fact overlooked in "organism" SST. How we go about helping the client in this larger task is the subject of the last section of this chapter and the second half of the book. However, let us begin here with a number of pointers.

To tackle the problem of dysfunctional agency we need to assess the client's construing and action-generating cognitions, for this is where the creative ability of the agent lies (Harre, 1979). But which cognitions should we be looking for? A large part of any person's cognitive operations is concerned with identifying entities (the tendency to reify, seen above) and then placing them in an explanatory causal network. The reader will see the link here with earlier discussion of the Kantian cognitive principles of substance and causality. Cognitive psychology is concerned with these processes of human judgment, and progress made in identifying systematic errors ordinary people make in arriving at what they believe to be are the facts (Nisbett & Ross, 1980; Wessler, this volume). Beck (1976) has mapped those inferential cognitions that are functionally related to emotional disorders. Clearly a distorted inferential knowledge base is of great relevance to SST since it leads clients to make false judgments about self and others and deployment of the wrong (e.g., defensive) behavioural strategies, to generalize and misattribute mistakes, to reify failures and so on. Dryden (this volume) deals comprehensively with the assessment of these cognitions, and Dow and Craighead (this volume) review client types who suffer such deficits.

Of course, clients not only misperceive events, but dysfunctional inferential cognitions enter into the construction of the client's very reality. Because of the close reciprocal relationship between construing and action, clients become caught in self-fulfilling prophecies, whereby they bring about the very consequencs they predict by virtue of the prediction (Trower, 1980; Wessler, this volume).

The Evaluation of Social Skills

We have discussed how people make inferential constructions of self and society, and the distortions which unskilled and other clients are prone to make. We have also discussed how these processes occur at a secondary, reflective level rather than the primary level. However, there is one further step in the judgmental process which is of yet greater importance - that of evaluation. This can be described as follows.

It is at the reflective level that people are aware of their agency, i.e., that they have the power to initiate social actions, and thereby aware of the responsibility for those actions (or lack of them).

As agents reflecting on their own actions (or non actions) they can evaluate those actions as good or bad, worthy or unworthy, and attribute to themselves, as agents, responsibility for those good, bad or indifferent acts. From this follow various moral, emotional and behavioural consequences.

How does a reflective agent come to evaluate his actions as good or bad, effective or useless? To understand this, we must consider the distinction between rules and laws - a distinction which underlies the difference between the intentional and Humean accounts of cause. Rules and laws both refer to regularities of events but whereas natural bodies are said to be bound by, or determined by laws, agents can actively follow or conform to rules. Toulmin (1969) states that the behaviour of agents often is "rule-conforming" while that of natural phenomena is "law-governed". With the notion of rule-following, we can specify whether a person performed correctly or not, or deviated from a norm or standard and so on. The failure to conform to, or follow, a rule which specifies a normal or standard social practice may be classified as abnormal, substandard, deviant or simply a failure (Douglas, 1970).

Social behaviour and social situations are based upon rules as we have seen, and it is socially desirable, even imperative, in some instances, that people conform to them. Failure to conform, to break the rules, involves social censure (which in itself is governed by meta-rules - Scheflen & Scheflen, 1972) i.e., moral judgment. Such judgment necessarily involves the second level monitoring or reflecting upon actions. So in social skills terms, we can say that an agent can not only behave skilfully or unskilfully in following or deviating from a normative rule (as in a social routine like a greeting), but he and others can reflect upon his skill or lack of skill and judge it to be a success or failure, normal or deviant, i.e., a moral judgment. In the agency approach, unlike the organism approach, we are made aware that the unskilled client is reflecting upon his rule-following and certain, therefore, to be making moral judgments about his role-deviant, unskilled, behaviour, and attributing responsibility to himself.

As suggested earlier, the presentation of an appropriate social self is one of the important products of the self-monitoring of social performance. This means that self-presentation is a goal in itself and hence skilful social performances become goals in themselves. This goal is quite unlike extrinsic, material goals involved in such activities as buying and selling or striking a bargain. The salesman's extrinsic goal may be his sales target, but he may have a self-presentation goal of delivering his sales patter elegantly and with panache. Social anxiety - strongly correlated with skill difficulties - differs from other anxieties in that the agent's concern is not a physical but a psychological danger. His/her concern is the elegance, rationality, appropriateness, reasonableness and so on of his/her own social acts - greetings, conversations, partings etc. Such

clients voice concern about "not knowing what to talk
about", "drying up", "stuttering", "saying the wrong
thing" etc. All such concerns centre on the motive
to present the social self as a rule-following, normal, non-deviant, i.e., a proper "moral" person
(Harre, 1979 and this volume; Wegner & Vallacher,
1980). As Harre points out later in this volume,
part of this self-presentation enterprize involves
explaining or accounting for one's own behaviour - a
process whereby the meanings of actions are constructed or reconstructed. Accounting occurs in daily
life in the form of normal discourse or "gossip", is
used to support and justify the self or others and
has as its aim the evaluation or re-evaluation of the
actions in question - the apportionment of blame,
guilt, praise and so on. The moral meanings of such
actions are thus negotiated, and those that are persuasive are accepted as the "reality". Such negotiated realities or "facts" are psychologically
powerful, since if people can thereby construct
social realities they can construct or destroy moral
selves. The writings of R.D. Laing can be construed
as a description of the destruction of selves in
schizophrenic families (Laing & Esterson, 1964), and
the research which shows a strong relation between
schizophrenic relapse and hostile families can be
construed (though not by the investigators) as supporting this idea (Brown, Birley & Wing, 1972;
Vaughn & Leff, 1976).
    The presentation and insinuation of positive and
negative selves requires skills of persuasion, dom-
inance, assertiveness, etc., in other words, as
already noted, social skills. Those who have such
skills are likely to exercise greatest power in the
moral evaluation of self and others, since their
accounts are most likely to be taken as realistic and
valid. Conversely, those who have poor social skills
will be least likely to be able to present themselves positively or to defend themselves against
negative evaluation of powerful others. Schizophrenics and other poorly skilled psychiatric patients fit
this picture, partly for the reason just described,
and partly because they are seen as ineffective,
cold, unassertive, withdrawn and generally difficult
to get on with - i.e., have poor self-presentation.
As we commented earlier, it follows from the agency
model that these individuals will reflect upon and
evaluate their social behaviour and through that,
themselves. They will also assimilate the evaluations of significant others. The final global
evaluation is likely to be, and often is, one of

total worthlessness, uselessness, and as in schizophrenia, potentially the complete loss of the sense
of self.

The problems discussed in this section are all
problems that the therapist must face in addition to
the straightforward teaching of skills. I shall make
some suggestions how this may be done in the last
section.

THE PROBLEMS OF SOCIAL SKILLS TRAINING REVISITED

At the beginning of the chapter, six problems in SST
were listed and a number of others referred to. It
is time to look at these problems again from the
agency perspective. I will deal with them one at a
time but they do inter-relate and each has relevance
for the others.

Firstly, problems with the definition of SST. I
have elsewhere suggested (Trower, 1980, 1982) a two-
fold distinction between social skills which are
identifiable elements and sequences of rule-governed
behaviour like social routines, and social skill
which is the process of generating behaviour designed
to achieve a goal. Most investigators have not been
very successful in the identification of social
skills, mainly because they have been caught on the
horns of the dualist dilemma, such that they sought
either to give a purely behavioural (i.e., totally
non-cognitive) operational definition in terms of
observed movements like amount of speaking and looking etc., which by definition must be stripped of any
social meaning, or they sought to define it in men-
talistic terms, without reference to behaviour, with
subsequent loss of reliability and valid criteria.
Investigators should not be surprised that they
cannot find what is meant by social skills because
they have separated the source of (cognitive) meaning
from the behaviour. There are no purely physical
criteria for appropriate social behaviour, because
people supply the criteria cognitively - by creating
social realities out of rules, and through them,
norms. People's constructs enter the definition of
the phenomena - that is the difference between psychological and physical descriptions of behaviours.
Such information can only be gained by tapping agreed
social meanings.

Even when we have agreed definitions of social
skills we cannot judge whether an individual is
socially skilled until we know what his intention is.
The organism approach also creates the problem here
by directing the investigator away from asking the

patient, i.e., not to treat him as an agent as this is "unscientific". The point is related to the last one. A definition in external terms fails because social skill is <u>intentional</u>, that is directed by an agent to a goal. Skilled or unskilled behavioural sequences can only be individuated as skilled or unskilled by reference to the individual's goal, desire, want or need, e.g., if he spills soup on his host, this may be intentional and not simply unskilled in the sense of clumsy, gauche, etc. What the behaviour is evidence for can only be established by reference to the intention. We can <u>then</u> judge whether it was <u>also</u> socially appropriate. Often a patient's behaviour may be skilled by others' point of view but not his own, and we can only discover this through the client's intention.

Secondly, and another related problem. It is true that there is no pure behavioural standard for social skill deficits, if this means in terms of pure physical observables like movements, and there could be none, because there is no such thing as a social skill deficit outside human interpretations – no such thing resides in the "empirical" data. The problem again disappears in an agency approach.

Thirdly, it is equally true that there is no "objective" criterion for good skills, but only an inter-subjective, or social criterion. The confusion arises because the question implies an agency concept can be used in an organism approach – the same confusion, incidentally, which led Tolman and many followers to invent intervening variables (T. Mischel, 1969, p.155-156).

Fourthly, with regard to assessment devices, a whole range of problems arise for the foregoing reasons, in that assessors are unwittingly measuring either <u>pure</u> behaviour, totally debugged of its cognitively structured sequences, or <u>pure</u> trait or other mental variables, totally debugged of their intentional, referential nature. Fewer "agency" measures exist, but these would seek intentional cognitions and social knowledge schemata, tap selective perception, inferences, evaluations, standards and outcome expectations. Many other problems with measuring devices arise from adopting an exclusively parametric rather than structural methodology, leading investigators to believe they can take elements of skill out of their contexts without destroying their meanings – as exemplified in the Behavioural Assertiveness Test – Revised (BAT-R) (Eisler, Hersen, Miller, & Blanchard, 1975). Even factors as obvious as role-playing versus real enactment, which change meanings by providing a different frame (see Goffman's "Frame Analysis", 1974) are overlooked, even in studies where comparisons are made between the two.

Fifthly, and sixthly, it would be predicted within an agency approach (but obscured in an organism approach) that people will behave similarly in situations that they perceive as similar, and this was found by Magnusson and Ekehammer (1978). To neglect the individual's point of view implicitly credits situations with the notion that all given stimuli of class X have the same stimulus value for all organisms of class Y. A similar point can be made for neglecting the client's own goals and intentions and expectations since if these were at variance with those being provided, or if the client had zero expectations of achieving goals, one would predict poor maintenance and generalization. The agency approach not only deals with these problems, but treats the client as a (potential) goal-seeking, problem solving agent who will generate unique solutions for new problems, and thus be able to generalize and maintain his own skills.

The last, seventh, question is of course, not a question that arises out of the organism approach, but is addressed to the organism approach.

A NEW ROLE FOR SOCIAL SKILLS TRAINING:
FROM ORGANISM TO AGENT

The gist of my argument is that only an agency approach can provide a coherent explanantion of the social behaviour of persons and should be adopted as a basis for SST. However, it must be admitted that many psychiatric patients, particularly those lacking in social skills, appear to conform more to the organism rather than the agency paradigms, and the organism approach may well appear to explain and predict the behaviour of such individuals.

To take one group of patients, a number of studies show depression to be related to social inadequacy and poor skills (Coyne, 1976; Libet & Lewinsohn, 1973; Weissman & Paykel, 1974; Bothwell & Weissman, 1977; Howes & Hokanson, 1979). It has been shown by a number of authors that depressives perceive themselves as helpless and their situations as hopeless. They see themselves as unable to produce changes in their situations, and systematically attribute the cause of such failures to external sources or internal dispositions like stupidity. As a result, they view themselves as powerless victims or worthless individuals and therefore give up all attempts at problem-solving action. Depressive behaviour characteristically conforms to this picture. This picture closely resembles the organism approach, which depicts the organism as entirely under the control of environmental or psychic forces and thus helpless. Many other types of patient can be seen in this light, particularly institutionalized schizophrenics. Patients are encouraged and indeed taught to view this aproach as the correct one, particularly in terms of the medical model of mental illness.

However, the fact that patients often conform to the organism model does not support that approach, for the alternative view is that these patients fully <u>believe</u> they are passive organisms, that this is a dysfunctional belief like any other, leading to passive behaviour and emotional problems, i.e., to function <u>in fact</u> like organisms.

It is difficult to imagine (outside an organism approach) how SST can be very successful if the individual has "lost" his power of agency, yet it is precisely this that has been forgotten in behavioural SST (Trower, O'Mahony & Dryden, 1982). The task of the SST therapist must therefore be not only to teach skills, but to facilitate the client's recovery of his power of agency, i.e., to change his view of himself as a passive organism. How can we best conceptualize the idea of loss of and restoration of agency, preparatory to such a therapeutic enterprise? One way is again in terms of Harre and Secord's (1972) two levels of monitoring. At the first level an agent behaves as described earlier, somewhat like a cybernetic machine, as in the social skills model and in a number of other models of this feedback-loop, problem-solving type (D'Zurilla & Nezu, 1982; Kanfer & Busemeyer, 1982; Kirschenbaum & Tomarken, 1982; McFall, 1982; Spivack, Platt & Shure, 1976; Wallace, 1982), and failure can be specified at various points, such as faulty encoding, etc. But before considering these we must also look at the second reflective level of monitoring, since the two are in (or should be in) continuous mutual interaction - a fact overlooked by many feedback-loop theories, with notable exceptions (Carver & Scheier, this volume).

As argued earlier, a system operating only at the first level is not operating necessarily as an agent. I would assert that depressed and other patients are failing to be full agents because the second level of monitoring is dysfunctional in various ways. One way is due to patients not fully and consciously monitoring their ongoing actions and the situation at hand, but mainly operating on auto-pilot - via automatic thoughts and behaviour - such that there is created the illusion, to the reflective self, that there is no cognitive mediation or choice operating, as it were, between stimulus and response. Deliberate, agent-like, intentional choices are not being made regarding what the best way to proceed might be (Bandura, Langer & Chanowitz, this volume). Just precisely how this is happening is worked out in detail by Bandura et al. later. For the present, we can summarily say that perceptual judgments, cog-nitive evaluations and action decisions pass from a conscious, reflective level to an automatic, pre-reflective level and back again, depending on changing circumstances (Carver & Scheier, this vol-ume). However, conscious processing is <u>always</u> taking place against the pre-reflective background of tacit assumptions, knowledge, rules, beliefs, etc., which by definition, are not themselves the focus of attention, but provide the frame or schema for under-standing events now attended to. As Arnkoff (1980) says, there are no particulars without reference to abstract structures.

The distinction between two levels of mutually interactive processing has been developed in theory and research by a number of investigators. Schneider and Shiffrin (1977) termed them automatic versus con-trolled processing, and Mandler (1976) stated the functional efficiency of such a system. There is an abundance of evidence from these and other invest-igators (e.g., Bowers, 1981) to show that automatic cognitive processing, much of it dysfunctional (Beck, 1976), goes on at a level below conscious awareness, and it is obvious that individuals, unaware at the reflective level of how they actually processed events, will often invent plausible explanations (Nisbett & Wilson, 1977), often of the internally or externally controlled "organism" type, especially when automated patterns fail to fit changing circum-stances. Since failures trigger self-awareness and since self-awareness leads to causal attribution to self (Duval & Wicklund, 1972), the stage is set for global self-evaluation as helpless (environmentally controlled) and/or useless (unchangeable psychic disposition). This surely is the bottom line in the conceptualization of self-as-organism, and is a product of dysfunction at the reflective level.

CONCLUSIONS FOR THERAPY

A fully functioning agent must "mindfully" desire and

set some goal or realistic standard, believe he can perform or learn the appropriate skills to achieve the goal, and attribute failures to the appropriate points in the process of carrying out the plan. Loss of agency can, therefore, involve all or some of the following: having no conscious aims or wants, or being unable to specify what goals would be desired, or demanding unrealistic goals; believing he does not know what action is required and believing he lacks and cannot learn the necessary skill (behaviour outcome and efficacy outcome expectancies respectively); attributing failed acts to self and generalizing to total failure of the self. Loss of agency involves even more than this, however, since many of these dysfuncntional processes will be automatic, out of conscious awareness, giving the individual the illusion that he is under external or "internal" (e.g., personality or illness) control and is powerless to change his condition.

Therapy must involve uncovering aims and desires, specification of practical goals, establishment and acceptance of realistic rather than idealistic standards, acquiring of behaviour-outcome knowledge and the building of efficacy expectations. Therapy must tackle the cognitive blocks to carrying out these aims. These include distortional perceptions and thoughts, like selective perception - e.g., the selection of failed rather than successful social acts - and faulty inferences, like the prediction of catastrophic consequences. Other blocking inferences like generalization, personalization, dichotomous thinking and magnification (Beck, 1976) must be assessed and included as part of the therapeutic process of restoring agency.

Therapy must address not only these perceptual and inferential blocks but, even more importantly, the client's negative evaluations. For example, faulty attributional styles lead clients to attribute failure (e.g., in social skill homework assignments) to the self but successes to others or luck - the reverse of the self-serving bias. Through generalization clients soon arrive at global self-condemnation. Self concepts of worthlessness, helplessness and so on then become continuously reinforced in self-fulfilling cycles as they block further intentional actions, and serve to prevent, at source, the development of agency. Therapy must aim to help the client become mindful of his automatic cognitive blocks and behavioural responses, to identify elusive "emotional episodes" (Wessler & Wessler, 1980) when they occur, to be a vigilant

A Radical Critique

monitor of such processes in his social experiments, and to systematically use "agency" cognitions in self-instruction exercises.

SST cannot well succeed while the cognitive processes of agency are dysfunctional, and while SST may facilitate the growth of agency by chance and nonspecific factors, therapy had best be applied purposefully and systematically to resolving cognitive blocks, lest training becomes another of the client's failed experiences, and leaves him worse off than before.

Once the client begins to carry out and to recognize successful social acts, his negative expectancy hypotheses will be challenged and may change, and he will respond to realistic feedback. He has then started on the path of the agent as problem solver and skill generator. The therapist can intervene whenever the client starts to distort the evidence, by challenging and disputing, and pressing the client into social mini-experiments designed to contradict dysfunctional assumptions and build tolerance of discomfort. This way the therapist gets the client to think and act like an agent, i.e., fully reflectively, and to give up thinking like an "organism". For practical guidance the practitioner is referred to the chapters by Shepherd and Dryden in Part II.

REFERENCES

Argyle, M. Personality and social behaviour. In R. Harre (Ed.), Personality. Oxford: Blackwell, 1976

Argyle, M., & Kendon, A. The experimental analysis of social performance. In L. Berkowitz (Ed.), Advances in experimental social psychology, (Vol. 3). New York: Academic Press, 1967

Arnkoff, D. B. Psychotherapy from the perspective of cognitive theory. In M.J. Mahoney (Ed.), Psychotherapy process. New York: Plenum Press 1980

Bartley, W.W. The retreat to commitment. New York: Alfred A. Knopf, 1962

Baumeister, R.F. A self-presentationaal view of social phenomena. Psychological Bulletin, 1982 91, 3-26

Beck, A.T. Cognitive therapy and the emotional disorders. New York: International Universities Press, 1976

Bellack, A.S. Behavioral assessment of social skills. In: A.S. Bellack & M. Hersen (Eds.), Research

and practice in social skills training. New
York: Plenum Press, 1979,(a)

Bellack, A.S. A critical appraisal of strategies for
assessing social skill. Behavioral Assessment,
1979, 1, 157-176,(b)

Bellack, A.S. Recurrent problems in the behavioral
assessment of social skill. Behaviour Research
and Therapy, 1983, 21, 29-42

Berger, P.L. & Luckmann, T. The social construction of reality. Harmondsworth, Middx.:
Penguin, 1966

Bhasker, R. The possibility of naturalism. Hassocks:
Harvester Press, 1979

Bothwell, S., & Weissman, M.M. Social impairments
four years after an acute depressive episode.
American Journal of Orthopsychiatry, 1977, 47,
231-237

Bower, G.H., Black, J.B., & Turner, T.J. Scripts in
memory for texts. Cognitive Psychology, 1979,
11, 177-220

Bowers, K.S. Knowing more than we can say leads to
saying more than we can know: On being implicitly informed. In D. Magnusson (Eds.), Toward a
psychology of situations. New Jersey: Erlbaum,
1981

Brazil, D., Coulthard, M., & Johns, C. Discourse
intonation and language teaching. London:
Longman, 1980

Brenner, M. Actors' powers. In M. von Cranach & R.
Harre (Eds.), The analysis of action. Cambridge:
Cambridge University Press, 1982

Brown, G., Birley, J.L.T., & Wing, J.K. Influence of
family life on the course of schizophrenia.
British Journal of Psychiatry, 1972, 121, 241-
258

Campbell, D.T. A phenomenology of the other one:
Corrigible, hypothetical and critical. In T.
Mischel (Ed.), Human action. New York: Academic
Press, 1975

Cantor, N., & Mischel, W. Prototypes in person perception. In L. Berkowitz (Ed.), Advances in
experimental social psychology (Vol. 12). New
York: Academic Press, 1979

Collett, P. Segmenting the behaviour stream. In M.
Brenner (Ed.), The structure of action. Oxford:
Blackwell, 1980

Coulter, J. The social construction of mind. London:
Macmillan, 1979

Coyne, J.L. Depression and the response of others.
Journal of Abnormal Psychology, 1976, 85, 186-
193

von Cranach, M., & Harre, R. (Eds.) The analysis of action. Cambridge: Cambridge University Press, 1982

Curran, J.P. Pandora's box reopened? The assessment of social skills. Journal of Behavioral Assessment, 1979, 1, 55-72, (a)

Curran, J.P. Social skills: Methodological issues and future directions. In A.S. Bellack & M. Hersen (Eds.), Research and practice in social skills training. New York: Plenum, 1979, (b)

Douglas, J.D. Deviance and respectability: The social construction of moral meanings. In J.D. Douglas (Ed.), Deviance and respectability. New York: Basic Books, 1970

Duval, S. & Wicklund, R.A. A theory of objective self-awareness. New York: Academic Press, 1972

D'Zurilla, T.J. & Nezu, A. Social problem solving in adults. In P.C. Kendall (Ed.), Advances in cognitive behavioral research and therapy. New York: Academic Press, 1982

Eisler, R.M., Hersen, M., Miller, P.M., & Blanchard, E.B. Situational determinants of assertive Behaviors. Journal of Consulting and Clinical Psychology, 1975, 43, 330-340

Goffman, E. Behavior in public places. Glencoe, Ill.: Free Press, 1963

Goffman, E. The presentation of self in everyday life. Harmondsworth, Middx.: Penguin, 1971

Hampshire, S. Thought and action. London: Chatto and Windus, 1982

Harre, R. The ethogenic approach: Theory and practice. In L. Berkowitz (Ed.), Advances in experimental social psychology (Vol. 10). New York: Academic Press, 1977

Harre, R. Social being. Oxford: Blackwell, 1979

Harre, R., & Madden, E.H. Causal powers. Oxford: Blackwell, 1975

Harre, R., & Secord, P.F. The explanation of social behaviour, Oxford: Blackwell, 1972

Howes, M.J., & Hokanson, J.E. Conversational and social responses to depressive interpersonal behavior. Journal of Abnormal Psychology, 1979, 88, 205-208

Ingleby, D. Critical psychiatry: The politics of mental health. Harmondsworth, Middx.: Penguin. 1981

Kanfer, F.H. & Busemeyer, J.R. The use of problem solving and decision making in behavior therapy. Clinical Psychology Review, 1982, 2, 239-266

Kendon, A., & Ferber, A.A. A description of some human greetings. In R.P. Michael & J.H. Crook

(Eds.), Comparative ecology and behaviour of primates. London: Academic Press, 1973

Kirschenbaum, D.S., & Tomarken, A.J. On facing the generalization problem: The study of self-regulatory failure. In P.C. Kendall (Ed.), Advances in cognitive behavioral research and therapy. New York: Academic Press, 1982

Laing, R.D., & Esterson, A. Sanity, madness and the family: Families of schizophrenics. London: Tavistock, 1964

Libet, J.M., & Lewinsohn, P.M. Concept of social skill with special reference to the behavior of depressed persons. Journal of Consulting and Clinical Psychology. 1973, 40, 304-312

McFall, R.M. A review and reformulation of the concept of social skills. Behavioral Assessment, 1982, 4, 1-34

Magnusson, D. & Ekehammer, B. Similar situations - similar behaviors? Journal of Research in Personality, 1978, 12, 41-48

Mahoney, M.J. Scientist as subject: The psychological imperative. Cambridge, Mass.: Ballinger, 1976

Mandler, G. Consciousness: Respectable, useful and probably necessary. In R.L. Solso (Ed.), Information processing and cognition. Hillsdale, N.J.: Erlbaum, 1976

Marzillier, J. Outcome studies of skills training: A review. In P. Trower, B.M. Bryant & M. Argyle (Eds.), Social skills and mental health. London: Methuen, 1978

Mischel, T. Human action, New York: Academic Press, 1975

Mischel, W. Toward a cognitive-social learning reconceptualization of personality. Psychological Review, 1973, 80, 252-283

Natsoulas, T. Basic problems of consciousness. Journal of Personality and Social Psychology, 1981, 41, 132-178

Neisser, V. Cognition and reality. San Francisco: Freeman, 1976

Nisbett, R.E., & Wilson, T.D. Telling more than we can know: Verbal reports on mental processes. Psychological Review, 1977, 14, 231-259

Nisbett, R.E., & Ross, L.D. Human inference: Strategies and shortcomings of social judgement. Englewood Cliffs, N.J.: Prentice Hall, 1980

Quine, W.V.O. Ontological relativity and other essays. New York: Columbia University Press, 1969

Ross, L. The intuitive psychologist and his short-comings: Distortions in the attribution process. In L. Berkowitz (Ed.), Advances in experimental social psychology (Vol.10). New York: Academic Press, 1977

Schank, R.C., & Abelson, R.P. Scripts, plans, goals, and understanding. Hillsdale, N.J.: Erlbaum, 1977

Scheflen, A.E., & Scheflen, A. Body language and the social order. Englewood Cliffs, N.J.: Prentice Hall, 1972

Schneider, W., & Shiffrin, R.M. Controlled and automatic human information processing: 1. Detection, search and attention. Psychological Review, 1977, 84, 1-66

Shaffer, J.A. Philosophy of mind. Englewood Cliffs, N.J.: Prentice Hall, 1969

Shepherd, G.W. Social skills training: The generalization problem: Some further data. Behaviour Research and Therapy, 1978, 16, 287-288

Sinclair, J. McH., & Coulthard, R.M. Towards an analysis of discourse. Oxford: Oxford University Press, 1975

Smail, D.J. Psychotherapy: A personal approach. London: Dent, 1978

Spivack, G., Platt, J.J., & Shure, M.B. The problem-solving approach to adjustment. San Francisco: Jossey Bass, 1976

Strawson, P.F. Individuals. London: Methuen, 1959

Toulmin, S. Concepts and the explanation of human behavior. In T. Mischel (Ed.), Human action. New York: Academic Press, 1975

Trower, P. Situational analysis of the components and processes of behavior of socially skilled and unskilled patients. Journal of Consulting and Clinical Psychology, 1980, 48, 327-339

Trower, P. Towards a generative model of social skills: A critique and synthesis. In J. Curran & P. Monti (Eds.), Social skills training: A practical handbook for assessment and treatment. New York: Guilford, 1982

Trower, P. Social skills and applied linguistics. In R. Ellis and D. Whittington (Eds.), New directions in social skill training. London: Croom Helm, 1983

Trower, P., O'Mahony, J.M., & Dryden, W. Cognitive aspects of social failure: Some implications for social skills training. British Journal of Guidance and Counselling, 1982, 10, 176-184

Twentyman, C.T., & Zimering, R.T. Behavioral
    training of social skills: A critical review.
    In M. Hersen, R.M. Eisler & P.M. Miller (Eds.),
    Progress in behavior modification (Vol.7).
    New York: Academic Press, 1979
Vaughn, C.E., & Leff, J.P. The influence of family
    and social factors on the course of schizo-
    phrenic illness. British Journal of Psychiatry,
    1976, 121, 241-255
Ventola, E. The structure of casual conversation.
    Journal of Pragmatics, 1979, 3, 267-298
Wallace, C.J. The social skills training project of
    the mental health clinical research center for
    the study of schizophrenia. In J.P. Curran & P.
    M. Monti (Eds.), Social skills training: A
    practical handbook for assessment and treat-
    ment. New York: Guilford, 1982
Wegner, D.M., & Vallacher, R.R. The self in social
    psychology. New York: Oxford University Press,
    1980
Weissman, H.M., & Paykel, E.S. The depressed woman:
    A study of social relationships. Chicago: Univ-
    ersity of Chicago Press, 1974
Wessler, R.A., & Wessler, R.L. The principles and
    practice of rational-emotive therapy. San
    Francisco: Jossey-Bass, 1980
Wolpe, J. Cognition and causation in human behav-
    ior and its therapy. American Psychologist,
    1978, 33, 437-446

Editorial Introduction, Chapter Three

PUBLIC-COLLECTIVE PSYCHOLOGICAL PROCESSES AND SOCIAL
SKILLS

Rom Harre

INTRODUCTION

The theme of chapter two is taken a stage further
(chapter three) by Rom Harre, a philosopher of
science specializing in social science. He begins by
briefly restating one principle of his ethogenic
theory, that individual lives are structured as moral
careers, namely people actively present themselves as
worthy, rational, reasonable and so on - the true
meaning of "social competence" within an agency
approach. This idea brings together the aims of both
SST and rational-emotive therapy (see Dryden, this
volume). Harre points out that such psychological
attributes (as worthy, reasonable, etc.) are normally
construed as internal, private phenomena which cannot
be directly observed (like personality traits) and
can only be inferred from behaviour - a step which a
behaviourist is understandably loath to take. Harre
puts forward a two-dimensional conceptual scheme
which entirely dispenses with this fallacious dualism
of inner and outer. In this scheme the attributes
and processes which characterize social competence
are to be found in the public-collective domain and
are created and sustained by collective adherence to
public behaviour-guiding rules of conduct. The main
vehicle for such construction is conversation. Indeed conversation is the main vehicle for the construction of social reality and sustaining and sha-
ping of social identities (see chapter two), hence
its profound importance. From this perspective a
desired attribute can be non-mysteriously described,
because it is located in the public domain.

    Attributes thus located in the public collective
area do, of course, become appropriated in private
thought but retain their publicly verifiable properties, i.e., English people think, as well as talk, in

*English.   This model overcomes objections to so-
called inaccessible cognitive representations (and
abolishes mental entities).*

*Employing his scheme, Harre goes on to develop
the idea of psychological symbiosis, by which people
co-operate in the construction of each other's social
competence, or the reverse - the latter occurring in
places like mental institutions.   Psychological symbiosis is continuously happening - a fact of social
life - and needs to be given a central role in all
social skills assessment and training.*

Chapter Three

PUBLIC-COLLECTIVE PSYCHOLOGICAL PROCESSES AND SOCIAL SKILLS

Rom Harre

INTRODUCTION

In daily life people roughly divide their responses to the social and physical worlds around them into those that are quite automatic and those for which they must take responsibiliy. For human beings the overwhelming bulk of the activities of social life are of the latter kind. Part of what is involved in taking responsibility for one's actions, whether as an individual or as a member of a collective, is to have available an acceptable way of explaining what one did, so as to make it out to be the action of a morally worthy person or group of persons. The study of responsible action and of the ways we produce and defend it, is the subject matter of the "ethogenic" appoach to the understanding of social life.

In this approach it is natural to emphasize the part played by speech and other semiotic activities in the public demonstration of the rationality and propriety of one's actions. Rational and proper actions are the mark of morally acceptable selves. By showing that one's actions are in accordance with a rule or convention one establishes their rationality. By citing a rule or convention that is drawn from the stock of local social norms, so to speak, one demonstrates the rightness or propriety of one's actions. The capacity to produce an account of one's actions in terms of local rules and conventions, is a social skill of paramount importance. In many ways it is more important than skilful action itself, since one can, given a golden tongue, do much to re-create the past.

Our primary emphasis in the early statements of the programme of ethogenic studies (Harre & Secord, 1972) was on the ways one could use justificatory speech, accounting for one's actions, as a prime research object. If the skilful use of normative material is a basic social competence then we should be able to find that normative material in justificatory speech. From the analysis of this speech one should be able to discover the people's systems of beliefs as to what are proper projects and intentions for them, and what are the locally appropriate rules and conventions for realizing their aims. In the early phase we considered only those products of human action that were through and through social, that is collective activities of various kinds. But we developed methodologies that were directed to revealing only the contributions of individuals to such public products as ceremonies and quarrels.

Ethogenics has now entered a second and more radical phase (Harre, 1979) in which we are trying to identify not only social products but public-collective cognitive processes, modes of reasoning, planning and deciding. If these are genuinely group processes of reasoning and not merely sets of people thinking in various similar ways (the basis of Tajfel's idea of social psychology, Tajfel & Fraser, 1978), then collectives that reason, such as families, committees, friends and so on should exemplify such psychological attributes as rationality, knowledge, memory and the like. Once we have become aware that the thought processes involved in producing social action and social entities such as institutions, might not be individual at all, a new dimension of interest opens up. In this chapter I want to emphasize the social skills involved in the construction of public-collective psychological attributes and processes such as collective rationality and collective reasoning. From the point of view of an interest in relieving the troubled mind, it is crucial to identify some of the ways individuals are caught up in the results of collective cognition and in the social processes by which it is created.

By "cognition" and "cognitive process" I mean mainly modes of reasoning, assembling premises and drawing conclusions, making judgments of likeness and difference, identifying a particular instance as falling under a generalization and so on.

My argument moves through two stages. In the first I try to show that a reorganization of our conceptual scheme for "placing" psychological attributes and processes is possible. In the course of it the traditional Cartesian way of locating psychological matters, based on a one dimensional map, running from an inner-subjective to an outer-objective pole is rejected in favour of a two-dimensional

scheme admitting of both public and private psychological processes, located either individually or
collectively.

On the basis of this revision I elaborate, in a
second stage, the idea of psychological symbiosis.
This notion was introduced originally by Shotter and
Newson (Shotter, 1974) for explicating certain
mother-child relations important in developmental
psychology. I generalize this idea into a full blown
theory of the way groups of people publicly construct
psychological attributes for each other. These constructions usually sustain, though sometimes they may
be used to denigrate, a level of "mental" functioning
for each member that sustains the group's conception
of its proper cognitive level and style.

If the argument is successful then there is an
immediately given problem concerning the range of
social skills requisite among group members, as
individuals, to respond to and help create and sustain the required level of psychological functioning
of other members and so of the group as a whole. And
conversely there is the possibility of defining a
life predicament in which a person's right to display
cognitive competence is out of keeping with his or
her capacities, which may far exceed that which he or
she is permitted publicly to display.

WHERE IS THE "COGNITIVE" PRIMARILY TO BE LOCATED?

Recently the idea of a social construction of individual minds has gained renewed currency (see for
instance, Coulter, 1979). According to that way of
thinking the primary location of many important
cognitive processes and attributes, such as rationality, logical argument, contradiction, reason and so
on, is in talk, that is in forms of public discourse.
This move makes cognition part of the social realm.
I hope to demonstrate the correctness of locating
cognitive processes socially rather than personally
in part one of this paper. Only secondarily do
cognitive processes and properties appear in thought
as something private or individual. I propose to try
to demonstrate that the development of cognitive
competence is not to be thought of in terms of the
growing power to construct private individual cognitive properties, such as some alleged personal
rationality, but rather in the skilful appropriation
for private use of public and collective, that is
social, attributes of discourse. Fortunately, I am
not alone in holding this view. Plato, in the
Theatetus, 190A says, "....The soul when thinking,

appears to me to be just talking, asking questions of herself and answering them, affirming and denying.... To form an opinion is to speak....I mean to oneself and in silence, not aloud or to another."

The first move in my argument is the unqualified denial of the viability of any form of a Cartesian distinction between inner and outer processes, particularly when that distinction is mapped onto that between the subjective and the objective, conceived as opposed points of view from which human beings' actions can be observed. The upshot of Cartesianism is a linear opposition of locations on one dimension, with thought at one pole and behaviour at the other. Traditionally, there is supposed to be a partition in this dimension and irresolvable problems for passing from one side of the partition to the other. It is quite crucial to an understanding of the thrust of my argument to see that my aim is to deny the viability of the one-dimensional space created by the opposition of "inner" and "outer" for locating psychological phenomena. I am making no attempt to solve the traditional problems which derive from taking this opposition for granted. Instead I propose to replace the linear opposition by a non-Cartesian, two dimensional space, formed by the orthogonal axes, public-private and collective-individual (Figure 1).

One of the great virtues of the philosophical psychologies of Ryle (1947) and Wittgenstein (1980) was the demonstration that reasoning was at least as much of a public activity, such as talking or working things out on paper, as it was a private activity, experienced only by the thinker him or herself. As a consequence Wittgenstein was able to demonstrate the central role of public criteria for the definition and acceptability of what was to count as meaning, consistency and so on. One way, but only one way of achieving privacy is to keep our thoughts to ourselves by not disclosing some "inner" state. However, one might equally achieve privacy by grimacing behind one's hand. So the privacy or otherwise of thought and feeling is not to be identified with whether it is inside or outside of a person, nor with whether it is subjective or objective, known to that person alone or to anyone who cares to look. The public-private axis represents what I take to be one of the two most important issues involved in deciding where a psychological process should be looked for, since only in the public realm could we have socially enforced criteria as to the nature and propriety of certain forms of reasoning and feeling.

The individual-collective axis represents the

location of a psychological attribute or process, either in a single person - for instance some memories are individual - or in a collective or structured group of people - for instance some bodies of practical knowledge are distributed about a team, so that everyone must be on hand for successful employment of the knowledge in performing the practical task.

Figure 1: Two Dimensional Representation of Psychological Properties and Processes.

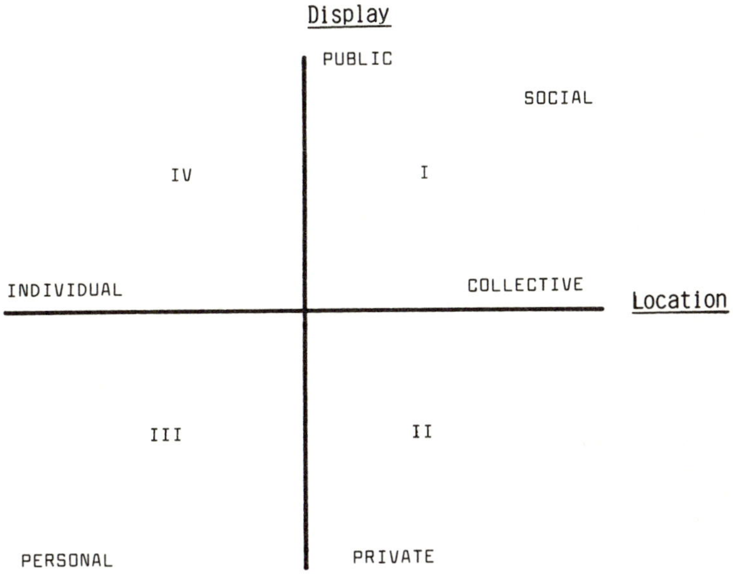

I shall be demonstrating that this organization of psychological properties and processes enables us to understand the process of cognitive development in a much more satisfactory way than using the naive assumption that language is the transparent medium through which we can see the individual "at work". I believe that cognitive processes, states, and so on can be found in each of the four quadrants. One must admit the possibility of there being individual and private (personal) psychological processes, but on the view to be defended in this paper they are the least important aspects of our psychological functioning. For the purposes of this paper I am concerned only with the other three quadrants, public-collective (or social), private-collective and individual-public.

The second background idea in my argument is the Vigotskyan conception of learning (Vigotsky, 1962). The individualist or Cartesian idea of learning is that knowledge is transferred from one inner realm (the mind as a cognitive store) to another inner realm, by some mysterious process of communication. The transfer is said to involve those strange psychological processes Cartesian psychologists have called encoding and decoding. The conception of communicative learning entails the hypothesis that the medium of thought is different from the language of communication, but there is no empirical evidence for the hypothesis that an English speaker does not think in English. The Cartesian conception of learning is to be replaced by the Vigotskyan idea of learning as appropriation, the rendering private of something which is public and collective. But in making something private, it does not lose the properties it derives from its location in a collective. Private uses of public discourse retain properties characteristic of the public discourse, and these properties are essentially referable to the collective.

Great care must be exercised in inferring from attributes of discourse whose propriety is collectively defined, to any allegedly individual cognitive processes, processes which are supposed to be independent of the properties of discourse (cf. Rorty, 1980; Latour & Woolgar, 1979). The cognitive processes by which an individual produces a contribution to a public-collective discourse that displays rationality may not be rational. Business studies of decision-making have shown how a group of people can build up a public discourse which has strong rational /cognitive properties. But individual contributions are made on all kinds of bases, such as social prestige, intuition, hunches, prejudice, power-game strategies, emotion and so on. The public constraints, which reflect the defining properties of the collective, that is if it is conceived as a rational decision-making body, impose constraints on what contributions of individual speakers are allowed to survive as components of the remembered or recorded public discourse (cf. the role of Minutes). It may be only the public discourse that has the cognitive properties of rationality in many cases, and that discourse is itself an attribute of a collective.

The third step in the argument for locating the

cognitive primarily in talk, the main public-collective medium of thought, depends upon observations about phenomenal qualities of thinking itself. I want to consider a form of thought which was of the greatest interest to psychologists of the seventeenth century, particularly those interested in the psychological processes involved in artistic and literary creation. Borrowing from antiquity, they formulated a theory to cope with the recognition that much thought becomes conscious as if from nowhere. Inspirations from the Muses were offered as a metaphor for this sort of thinking, that is the thought was "breathed in" from outside the mind. Lately we have had Julian Jaynes' (1979) theory of the contribution of the right hemisphere to thought. Cognitive work in that hemisphere cannot be experienced by a person as conscious thought, but when transferred across the corpus callosum, the neural transfer is experienced as a sudden realization. This is a form of Muse theory. It shows that individual cognitive processes are not experienced as private individual phenomena. Only their products are so experienced. Ideas, we say "pop up"; forgotten names "come to one"; we wake up with "a solution to a problem"; and so on. There is a great deal of literature on mathematical creation and poetic composition, which reflects this feature of human psychology. In the light of these parsimonious explanations, I can see no justification for projecting back into some mysterious inner realm alleged cognitive processes which are the supposed antecedents of these sudden strokes of inspiration. Cybernetic software models of cognitive processes are another thing however. But I shall not discuss their status in this paper (cf. Broadbent, 1980).

But there are some cognitive processes that are lived as structured and continuous happenings, namely ordinary, everyday thought. It seems to me quite clear that these are privatized forms of talk in some general sense. They are discourses, and though their semiotics might not necessarily be linguistic (other symbolic systems may be used), nevertheless they take the form of cognitive activities which are originally public-collective. The concepts that are employed to describe the cognitive properties of privatized forms of talk such as reason, contradiction, consistency, knowledge, etc., have a primary public-collective, that is social, application. Philosophers have been troubled for centuries about the conditions under which such concepts can have private-individual or personal application. The problematic nature of these applications seems to me to derive almost entirely from uncritical acceptance of a fundamentally Cartesian point of view. For example, "I know...." which is used to make an assertion of authority in the public-collective realm, if transferred to some alleged private-individual application, turns out to be a claim about some form of private-personal store of something mysterious called "knowledge", the status of which is obscure. I do not mean to deny, of course, that there are personal attributes upon which an individual's skills and dispositions depend. One of the best ways of speaking of them, I suppose, is to call them "beliefs", though it is not the only one (Needham, 1972). The idea that some of these beliefs are unproblematically true, that is have some potent epistemic property, is what generates the problem of knowledge. If we see these beliefs simply as individual applications of public-collective concepts a characteristic of which is authority, then we can investigate them straightforwardly by looking at the conditions under which persons have legitimate authority in the assertion of matters of fact. In explicating the concept of knowledge as distinguished from belief, we have turned to a public-collective matter, the right to issue authoritative pronouncements of matters of fact.

Our contributions to conversations are obvious occasions for displaying cognitive attributes. If the argument for the priority of public-collective applications of epistemic and logical concepts such as knowledge and rationality, is correct, then we must surely ask why it is that public discourse, for example conversations, are constructed in such ways as to display the attributes they pick out. What is the point of putting logic, rationality, coherence, etc. into conversations? Or for that matter putting in their opposites? In keeping with the general argument of my Social Being (Harre, 1979), the answer may be that the motivation to display one's personal qualities in the public-collective realm comes from the need to present oneself as a person of good standing, as someone who has the capacity to show himself or herself to be of worth or to display some other form of social propriety in their actions i.e., social competence. This explanation of "putting in the logic" is shown in some recent empirical studies of scientific reasoning. Latour and Woolgar, in their book Laboratory Life and Karin Knorr (1981) in her The Social Manufacture of Scientific Knowledge have examined very closely the process by which the messy results of scientific research and fragments of the existing corpus of public scientific knowledge, are put together into a scientific paper. The writing of a paper involves a sequence of steps in which new and old material is blended in various ways. Only towards the end of the process do authors turn to satisfy the demand for "logic". "Putting in the logic" turns out to be required by the uses to which scientific papers are put in the social processes of the scientific community. A discourse is required to display admired cognitive properties, such as consistency, for the practical social purpose of engaging in agonistic interaction, in debates and disputes with other scientists. I think it is clear from the work of Latour, Woolgar and Knorr, that "logic" is not used for the primary activity of construction of a discourse that eventually appears much modified as a scientific paper, but is added. It is a deliberate injection to further a social project, that of procuring conviction, which itself is achieved by displaying the admired property of rationality in one's discourse and thus showing oneself to be a person of the "right sort". The process in itself, is also to be understood as social. If someone appears at a scientific congress and displays irrationality, and claims to have reached his results by intuition etc., he is hardly likely to be taken seriously. He is not the sort of person who should appear at such a public gathering. Yet, Latour and Woolgar have shown quite clearly that most of those who are present at such gatherings create the impression of their rationality as a deliberate addition to the product for whose actual original production we have no rationale.

A good example from work that I have myself been undertaking recently, concerns not the insertion of logic into discourse, but of illogic. Some people make an effort to display intuition, inconsequentiality, sensibility and so on in their public discourse. There is a great deal of material from the late eighteenth century to the early twentieth century, from which the admired properties of women's speech can be inferred. It seems quite clear that there were social demands that women's discourse should display socially approved qualities of illogic. There is a sharp contrast with the psychological attributes and powers Shakespeare's women are shown to display (cf. Lady Macbeth, Portia, Rosalind, etc.). There is an interesting example of the deliberate display of illogic in the early part of

Jane Austen's <u>Pride and Prejudice</u>. Elizabeth Bennet is staying with the Bingleys and has been talking with Mr. D'arcy. He congratulates her on her accomplishments. It seems that she suddenly realises that she has been displaying far too much rationality, and is altogether too accomplished for the proper public requirements of feminine charm. She inserts into the discourse a claim that what she really likes is feminine chit chat. In <u>Kilvert's Diary</u> similar examples appear of what he considers to be the appropriate way for women to talk. The most striking and clearest description of this can be found in Flora Thompson's (1979) <u>A Country Calendar and other Writings</u>. "As Laura came to know the girls better, she found that much of their frivolity and brainlessness as a group was a pose, an unconscious pose, due to their determination to appear wholly feminine. They had been told, and believed, that serious thought was the prerogative of man; women's part in the scheme of creation was to be charming." Not only are these exemplars of "putting in the illogic" but they also require the theory of "representation sociale", (Moscovici, 1961). Flora Thompson refers to some social process by which the girls acquire the idea that their public display should show these qualities as part of the demonstration of their feminine virtue and womanhood.

There is a most interesting historical problem raised by this example. The women that appear in sixteenth and early seventeenth century literary works such as Shakespeare's plays, display a very striking bouquet of psychological attributes and powers which they generally lack in eighteenth and nineteenth century presentations. In Shakespeare, women are shown to have the power to make decisions and stick to them in ways that men cannot. <u>Love's Labour's Lost</u> is an example of an exquisite formulation of psychological differences between men and women in that the four young men, however powerful their oath, are quite unable to keep it when confronted by the power of the will of women who are determined they shall break it. Portia, Lady Macbeth and many others exemplify a tacit psychological theory about the special properties of women's psychology. Why is there this change? Did the social conventions for the display of femininity change, or did women become less rational? The mistake of transferring a form of thought from discourse to individuals as an individual cognitive property is exemplified most beautifully by the folk theory of a special feminine mode of reaching conclusions - women's intuition. It seems likely that thoughts pop up in the minds of men and women in much the same way. Men, however, are required publicly to display their thoughts embedded in discourse which exhibits the admired property of rationality. Women, on the other hand, have been under no such constraint. A woman can produce a conclusion without being called upon to display the premises. Now since I believe the phenomenology of thinking shows us that in most cases neither men nor women have the premises, the introduction of premises into the discourse is a feature of the talk and not of the individual cognitive process that produced it. If we ascribe to women a special form of cognition we could call intuition, at the very best this is a model of a cognitive process which is analogous to a socially approved mode of displaying personal qualities in speech, and given the thesis that the speech is not transparent, justification for using that model is pretty thin. The first question to be asked about some alleged cognitive attribute, such as an emotion, or cognitive process such as intuition, is this: What sort of contribution does the appearance of this attribute in, for instance, a conversation, make to the personality displayed by the talker? And under what convention is it called for? It may be that sometimes a complete historical explanation can be found for the presence of a certain cognitive property in speech, relieving us of the need to make hazardous guesses as to the individual cognitive attribute or processes which it allegedly reflects. A conversation may have cognitive properties only because there is a socially maintained and promul gated rule that discourse of this sort should have attributes of that sort and a rule may be followed blindly.

We can now tackle the associated developmental question in a true Vigotskyan fashion. Learning is the privatization of features of public-collective episodes of mutual engagement, and individual cognitive processes are just as Plato thought they were – primarily privatized forms of talk. The fact that they display cognitive properties is a collective, not an individual fact. It is a reflection of the social conventions of the time which have very little to with the natural structure of the way human beings would think if it were possible to imagine human individuals engaging in thought independently of society, a feat I am unable to accomplish. Perhaps cognition just is a form of talk and thinking a privatized form of talk. So the research question for those interested in the acquisition of cognitive competence is to be construed along Vigotskyan lines. Under what circumstances are various forms of thought appropriated for private use? What happens to these forms of talk when so appropriated? What modifications occur in them as they are used by individuals in ways that relieve them of continuous public scrutiny?

An extreme form of the dissociation between private thinking and public rationality is to be found in the "Delphi" method for making business decisions. Members of the group contribute a random collection of sentences. The public-collective sanction that the group should display rationality requires them to sort out a product as a discourse and this product, it has been demonstrated, can have all the attributes of high rationality.

PSYCHOLOGICAL SYMBIOSIS

In this section I want to begin to develop an application of the idea of cognitive psychology as the study of the attributes of public talk to the investigation of the development of human beings as persons within a moral order, processes by which merely animate beings become responsible and "socially competent" agents. The idea of psychological symbiosis is due to Shotter and Newson (e.g. Shotter,1974) and came from the study of the kind of talk in which mothers embed their infant offspring. What, then, is psychological symbiosis? I define it as a permanent interactive relation between two persons, in the course of which one supplements the psychological attributes of the other as they are displayed in social, i.e., public-collective performances, so as to present a complete and competent social and psychological being. In this first definition, the relationship between the two persons who form the symbiotic dyad is not specified. There are many possibilities. For example, there are cases of considerable practical importance where though the supplementations are mutual, the power-relations in the dyad are asymmetrical. The symbiotic dyad is to be conceived as a single social being. There is plenty of evidence from the work of Richards (1974) and others that the dyad as a social being may interact socially with one of its own constituent persons, who display individually proper attributes and powers.

The phenomenon of mother-talk has been noticed by psychologists other than Richards, Shotter and Newson, but not correctly described. Snow is reported in Bruner and Garten (1979, p.76) as saying, "mothers constantly talked about the child's wishes, needs and intentions". The use of "about" in this sentence misconstrues the relationship completely. In psychological symbiosis mothers do not talk about the child's wishes; they supply the child with wishes, needs and intentions, wants and so on, and interact with the child as if it had them. Psychological symbiosis is a supplementation to the person's public display in order to achieve completeness with respect to the criteria of personhood in day-to-day use in a particular society in this or that specific social milieu. A mother may undertake to supplement her daughter's psychology differently in a medical consultation from the way she does it for a visiting relative. I want to enlarge the idea of psychological symbiosis far beyond the sense in which it was originally introduced, namely for the ways mothers supplement the psychology of their children to complete acceptable social and psychological beings. The concept can be generalized to include all those kinds of public performances by which inadequate personal displays are supplemented by others by whatever means. There may be several persons involved in the supplementation process.

Why do these practices exist? I believe that the answer can be found in turning to the necessities of moral orders as they are defined and sustained in particular collectives. For the purposes of this chapter it will be sufficient to understand by a moral order a collectively maintained system of public demonstrations of respect and contempt in terms of which the moral value of persons and their actions are publicly displayed; for example, by being deferential to someone, by censuring someone, by trials, by punishments, by insults, by apologies, by psychological supplementation, and so on.

The idea of psychological symbiosis as defined in this section is that of Shotter and Newson. However, the term has been used by Margaret Mahler et al. (1975). The remarkable thing about that work is that so far as I can discover it does not refer in any way to the properties of the flow of talk in which the caretakers embed an infant. Mahler's world is, for the most part, an almost silent world. Psychological symbiosis in her conception is somewhat similar to the emotional bond of attachment and loss so vividly described by Bowlby (1971). Psychological symbiosis in my sense has nothing much to do with emotion as a bond, though it is vitally important in the process by which mere affect is defined as emotion. It is an act of psychological symbiosis to define a display of feeling as anger, or hunger, or frustration, or misery, etc.; the definienda, of course, are the referents of concepts of a very high order of sophistication and are properly applied only in the dyad created by the symbiotic relationship.

Profound implications for the development of social skills follow from admitting the existence of psychological symbiosis.

(a) No inferences can be permitted from the kind of rationality or other cognitive mode displayed by an isolated individual, as to how that individual would be allowed to appear vis-a-vis the same cognitive mode in his/her own social world. For in his/her social world his/her displays may be routinely completed in the talk of others so that he/she is seen as displaying the required standard of rationality, for example, for that social milieu and its moral order. An isolated individual may appear quite incompetent at a certain level of cognitive functioning, but once embedded in symbiotic dyads and triads etc., of the actual social world in which the cognitive processes proper to that order are collectively and publicly created, the individual will disappear into a dyad or triad etc., in which he/she as the physical embodiment of the composite psychological being will appear to have adequate cognitive powers. Had the cognitive display of the dyad been performed by a psycholgical individual, it would have called for the attribution to that individual of cognitive capacities of a very high order.

A similar point can be made about public displays of social competence. Socially naive persons may perform as competent social beings at a formal dinner party with the efforts of the host, hostess and staff to guide them tactfully to give a performance exhibiting the highest social graces. Indeed, such a naive person may never realize that their performance has been supplemented. Goffman (1969) amongst others, has pointed out the ways in which waiters in "posh" restaurants ensure that the proper level of social competence is displayed by their clients however naive they may be. Similarly, nurses in mental hospitals are said to train patients in the "correct" displays of the forms of madness favoured by the medical staff of particular institutions.

Inadequate performance from an isolated individual does not entail that that person, when in his/her usual symbiotic relationship will be equally incompetent.

(b) No inferences can be permitted from the level of cognitive sophistication routinely displayed by a person in the social world or moral order in which that person usually lives, as to how they would be seen to perform in isolation. In real life they may have to allow their displays to be complemented, to seem more naive or sophisticated than they know they are. A powerful mother and a biddable daughter may form a symbiotic dyad relative to the daughter, in which the daughter deliberately adopts a naive posture and perhaps, in the end, comes to assume it in her privatized forms of thought, so that the mother can supplement the daughter's displays of rationality by her own. These complicated relationships are only too readily observable. They have been little studied, largely I believe, because it has been taken for granted that cognitions which count are located in individuals, as the private workings of the mind.

It follows from these corollaries that not only is it fallacious to infer from the displays of an isolated individual how that individual will appear in their normal social milieu, but it is fallacious to infer what the normal level of cognitive competence displayed in a typical social milieu in which that person usually operates is likely to be. Cognitive moral development theory commits just this fallacy and professes to be astonished at the disparity between levels of moral reasoning and types of moral action, but empirical investigations of moral reasoning involve individuals isolated from their psychological symbiotic relationships, particularly if one uses the methods of Kohlberg (1969). We can tell virtually nothing about the practical production of the self as a rational being in public displays in the course of normal social relations, from how an individual appears when detached from those relations. These remarks are only too obviously empirically grounded to anyone who cares to look closely at small-scale interactions in social worlds, in which people maintain lasting relations, such as husband and wife, teacher and pupil, etc.

There is a yet more subtle matter involved in psychological symbiosis. Some years ago I was studying the way young children construed an environ-ment in the Skovengveg Bornhaven in Aarhus in Denmark. In the course of this study I had occasion to watch the arrival and departure of the children from the kindergarten. A new feature of social psychological symbiosis emerged. I had to take account of the

105

social structure within the symbiotic dyad to understand the particular form the symbiosis took. In Denmark, egalitarianism and sexual equality are publicly proclaimed as social norms. This claim is false, as can be readily seen in the case I looked at. When a mother collected a child and the time came to leave, the Danish word "Farvel" (Goodbye) was exchanged between the mother, as representative of the dyad, and the kindergarten leader. The child received no ritual acknowledgement of departure. Only the mother had the right to speak "Farvel". On the other hand, when the father collected the child, the kindergarten leader "Farvel"ed both the father and child individually, and both had the right of reply. This opened up an issue of great importance to developmental psychology and for social skills training. There is a difference between the capacity to display social knowledge of skill and the right to display it. The failure to display some piece of knowledge or to employ a skill, cannot be used as an index of individual cognitive development. The attempt to study the capacities of actors as displayed in social events of various kinds, must involve both actors' understanding of the power relations in their symbiotic N-ads and whether they have a right to display a certain kind of knowledge or skill. Cognitive competence will change, but those rights will also change in the course of the social development of the individual. Not only will a person become more competent at various levels of social cognitive attainment, but, via the local "rites de passage" will be progressively legitimized as a person who rightly displays that knowledge or skill.

Some very beautiful empirical work has been published which illustrates this distinction most elegantly. Bronwen Davies (1980) has examined how children use their understanding of an adult rule-system for purposes of social irony. But adult rule-systems, according to a simple-minded Kohlbergian staging cognitive development theory, ought not to be known, and certainly could not be used by those of tender age. The children know that they have no right to display their knowledge of rules and modes of reasoning appropriate to adult moral issues. However, for one reason or another, they are sometimes obliged to show that they are competent in the adult forms of a moral order. They do this by ironizing their knowledge of the rules. They talk something like this: "You think you have a right to do something because relative to the rules according to you, that govern your relations with us, we are supposed to accept that your action - let us say walking through a piece of territory private to us - is not legitimate." Adults in one system of childhood moral order, have the right of transgression. "However, we want to let you know that we know that had we been adults you would not have had that right and that your transgression is, according to your own moral order, a moral fault." Notice how this displays Kohlbergian Stage 4 reasoning, and awareness that as children they are supposed to display only Stage 2. All this is conveyed in subtle and economical ways. A similar interpretation seems to be able to be given to some of the material published by Much and Shweder (1978).

Figure 2: Two-Dimensional Representation of Cognitive Moral Development.

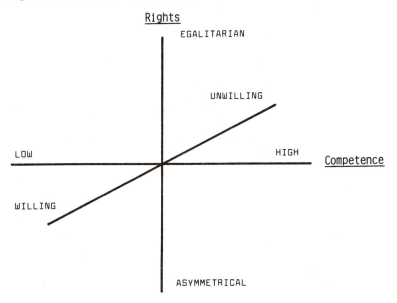

Cognitive moral development, then, must be graphed on at least a two-dimensional plane, marked with orthogonal axes, one representing the degree of individual right to display knowledge of adult rule-systems and adult cognitive capacities, and on the other the level of cognitive development. Some informal observations suggest that the phenomenon noticed by Labov and by the critics of Bernstein, that is that whether people are willing to display valued attributes in talk which has grammatical sophistication, depends on the social inter-relations between the interrogator and the individual. It would make good sense to add a third orthogonal axis representing the degree of willingness to display valued attributes that an individual is likely to feel.

CONCLUSION

Two main ideas have emerged from this discussion that I believe are particularly relevant to the concerns of this volume. The first is the importance of paying attention to the way psychological attributes appear in discourse, and particularly in conversations. It is not just that the person who can talk skilfully seems rational. To talk skilfully _is_ to display an admired psychological attribute. But if conversation is the main locus of many psychological processes and attributes the fact that talk is usually a socially structured affair with more than one contributor allows for unequal distributions of rights to display favoured attributes, and to the opportunity for powerful persons to create "psychologies" for others whether these are wanted or not. Here is a field of great theoretical and practical interest to the practitioners of social skills training, a field which has not yet had the attention it deserves.

REFERENCES

Bowlby, J. Attachment and loss (Vols. 1 & 2). Harmondsworth, Middx.: Penguin, 1971

Broadbent, D. Herbert Spencer Lecture, University of Oxford, 1980

Bruner, J., & Garten, A. Human growth and development. Oxford: Clarendon Press, 1979

Coulter, J. The social construction of mind. London: Macmillan, 1979

Davies, B. An analysis of primary school children's accounts of classroom interaction. British Journal of Sociology of Education, 1980, 1, 257-278

Goffman, E. The presentation of self in everyday life. Harmondsworth, Middx.: Penguin, 1969

Harre, R. Social being. Oxford: Blackwell,1979

Harre, R., & Secord, P.F. The explanation of social behaviour. Oxford: Blackwell, 1972

Jaynes, J. The origins of consciousness in the breakdown of the bicameral mind. Harmondsworth, Middx.:Penguin, 1979

Kilvert, F. Kilvert's diary: 1837 - 1840 W. Plomer (Ed.). London: Cape, 1944

Knorr, The social manufacture of scientific knowledge. Oxford: Pergamon Press, 1981

Kohlberg, L. Stage and sequence: The cognitive-developmental approach in socialization. In D. Goslin (Ed.), Handbook of socialization theory and research. Chicago: Rand McNally, 1969

Latour, B., & Woolgar, S. Laboratory life. Beverly Hills, Calif.: Sage, 1979

Mahler, M., Pine, F., & Bergman, A. The psychological birth of the human infant. London: Hutchinson, 1975

Moscovici, S. La psychoanalyse: Son image et son publique. Paris: Presses Universitaire de France, 1961

Much, N.O., & Schweder, R.H. Speaking of rules: The analysis of culture in breach. In W. Damon (Ed.), Moral development. San Francisco: Jossey-Bass, 1978

Needham, R. Belief, language and experience. Oxford: Blackwell, 1972

Richards, M.P.M. The integration of a child into a social world. Cambridge: Cambridge University Press, 1974

Rorty, R. Philosophy and the mirror of nature. Oxford: Blackwell, 1980

Ryle, G. The concept of mind. London: Hutchinson, 1947

Shotter, J. The development of personal powers. In M.P.M. Richards (Ed.), The integration of the child into a social world. Cambridge: Cambridge University Press, 1974

Tajfel, H.J., & Fraser, C. Introduction to social psychology. Harmonsworth: Penguin, 1978

Thompson, F. A country calendar and other writings. Oxford: Oxford University Press, 1979

Vigotsky, L.S. Thought and language. Cambridge, Mass.: MIT Press, 1962

Wittgenstein, L. Remarks on philosophical psychology. Translated by G.E.M. Anscombe & G.H. von Wright. Oxford: Blackwell, 1980

Editorial Introduction, Chapter Four

*COGNITIVE-SOCIAL PSYCHOLOGICAL THEORIES AND
SOCIAL SKILLS: A REVIEW*

Richard Wessler

*Following the advocacy of a paradigm shift to an
agency approach in the last two chapters, the next
chapter by Richard Wessler reviews the various
cognitive-social theories in psychology which exemplify various aspects of this approach, from the broad
map of Kelly's personal construct theory, through the
social learning theories, attribution theories and
the self-fulfilling prophecy and interpersonal
theories. In his review Wessler (a social and
clinical psychologist) extracts insights from these
theories about the production of effective and
ineffective social behaviour. A theme which runs
thoughout these theories is the emphasis on the
unique role of the agent construing and predicting
events, and responding on the basis of these constructions. Another and related theme, is the interactional one, emphasizing the intrinsic bond between
persons and situations rather than exclusively focussing on one or the other - a theme also emphasized in
the preceding three chapters. Wessler concludes that
the production of skills must depend on the individual's cognitive constructions, and that progress in
SST necessarily implies an assessment and modification of such constructions. The next two chapters
explore this idea in more detail.*

Chapter Four

COGNITIVE-SOCIAL PSYCHOLOGICAL THEORIES AND
SOCIAL SKILLS: A REVIEW

Richard Wessler

INTRODUCTION

How can we explain instances of social competence and
social failure? The answer must be found in individual differences among people, for the simple reason
that a majority of persons act competently in any
given social situation.
     This chapter presents several cognitive-social
psychological models whose principles explain how
socially skilled behavior is produced and what is at
fault when there are social deficits. Included
amongst the social learning theories under discussion
are those of Rotter (1954), Bandura (1977) and
Mischel (1968, 1973). To complete the roster of
related cognitive approaches, personal construct
theory (Kelly, 1955), attribution theory, interpersonal theory, ecological considerations, and the
role of the self-fulfilling prophecy are also
included. The major points of each position are
presented and their implications for understanding
individual problems and their remediation are
explored. One of the main themes is that humans are
information processors who seek to understand their
own and others' actions, and who find satisfaction in
successfully predicting behavioral outcomes. While
social behaviors are learned phenomena, their performance depends upon subjective estimates of probable
reinforcement, and reinforcement must be viewed from
the person's, not the observer's, perspective.

PERSONAL CONSTRUCT THEORY

George Kelly's theory of human behavior starts with
an assumption that the individual's actions proceed
from his or her unique ways of anticipating events.
From Kelly's point of view, people approach the

world as scientists to construct a satisfying version of reality. Like scientists, each individual proposes hypotheses, acts in ways to test them, and uses the results to improve predictive efficiency. Personal constructs, like scientific ones, are used to summarize observations, organize them into a more or less coherent whole, explain phenomena, and predict future events.

Social interactions are governed by the construct systems of the persons involved. Successful interactions result from each person's construing the construction process of the other(s), for such construing allows accurate prediction of the other person's behavior. Adams-Webber (1979) found that predictions about the social behavior of the other person will be more accurate if the person's construct system is known. Kelly (1955) reported on the process of initial social interactions among strangers. Social interaction was found to depend on initial discovery or assumption of similarities, followed by discovery of differences, but in either instance the discovery of the construct system of another person.

In order to grasp the personal constructs of another person, one must have experiences that render the personal constructs recognizable and understandable. Rigidity in holding to one or at best a few constructs, will result in being able to know the constructs of but a few other people and to misconstrue and thus interact poorly with most other people. Continued social interactions are possible only when both (or all) parties can adopt significant portions of the others' personal construct systems. In other words, in order to interact successfully and repeatedly with the same persons, one must have the capacity to form cognitive conceptions of the others' cognitive conceptions; such capacity, it may be hypothesized, depends on both ability and previous experience.

The sources of constructs are the usual socializing agencies in society. Social institutions, such as church and school, provide large amounts of data which the developing individual actively organizes into meaningful, abstract conceptual categories. Using data furnished by the socialization process, they create a personal version of reality.

Physical reality can be objectively verified; social reality cannot (Festinger, 1954). The individual validates his or her view of the world in two ways. First, there can be validation by consensus; well-socialized members of a group or society share many common views, particularly ones which allow them to easily get along with each other. Persons with similar data inputs from society can readily generate similar constructions of reality, provided they fall within a normal range of intellectual abilities.

Second and perhaps more important in personal construct theory, social reality can be validated by the experience of having one's predictions confirmed. Kelly assumed that all persons hold predictive efficiency as a value, and that all personal constructs must eventually be validated or revised in relation to predictive efficiency. The person most fully believes in those constructs he or she finds most useful in predicting events.

Social success and failure (i.e., performing skillfully or not in social situations) result in part from predictions about one's performance and the reactions to one's performance by other persons. Success in social situations depends, therefore, in part on one's belief that he or she will perform successfully, or at least adequately and appropriately.

Social failure is explained as the inability of the individual to use his or her own construct system to make appropriate predictions about social situations. What Kelly termed disorders of construction occur when an inappropriate amount of permeability in the constructs causes the person to view events in too tight or too loose a manner. Disorders of transition occur when a person has difficulty in the process of changing constructs, and thus is more likely to have problems in dealing with situations that appear, subjectively, to be radically new. In either event, the probable result is social behavior that appears inappropriate or inadequate or both. What is not as clear is the causes of the disorders, or how corrective interventions can be made.

SOCIAL LEARNING THEORY

Two names stand out in the development of a theoretical position called social learning theory. They are Julian Rotter and Albert Bandura.

In Rotter's theory of personality, the concept of expectancy plays a central role. Expectancies are ideas one has about what reinforcers might result from a course of action. This assumption is congruent with Kelly's notion of behavior directed by the way an individual anticipates events. The critical component of the anticipating of events is their potential to reward or penalize the individual, in Rotter's view.

Whether an outcome is rewarding or penalizing depends on one's values, for they determine the extent to which an anticipated consequence is appraised as favorable by the individual. Behavior, then, is guided by the person's desiring and seeking positive consequences.

A key concept, and the one for which Rotter is best known, has to do with one's perceived ability to control the reinforcing consequences in one's life. This concept, called locus of control, affects the motivation of behavior and, in turn, the behavior itself.

Locus of control refers to the extent to which one generally believes that one is capable of influencing the environment so that it will provide desired reinforcers. A person with an internal locus of control believes that he or she has, in the most extreme form, total control over the environment, and that what he or she does is the sole factor in obtaining reinforcers. The prototype of the person who has an external locus of control sees him or herself at the mercy of the environment and unable to influence the obtaining of reinforcers. The subjective estimate of ability to control reinforcers does not necessarily correspond to the actual ability to control them. In reality, no one has complete control over the environment nor is completely dependent on it.

A significant portion of the environment consists of other people. Here, then, is the relevance of Rotter's theory for social skills. Socially appropriate behavior, it may be hypothesized, will be effective in producing reinforcers for the individual. Compliance with social norms and with the expectations of other people, is more likely to be rewarded than socially deviant behavior, which is more likely to be penalized.

However, an individual may desire social responses that are uniquely reinforcing. A behavior that seems unproductive of reinforcers in a certain situation (if viewed from the perspective of the majority) may in fact produce reinforcers wanted by the individual. Lack of social skills must be interpreted in terms of whether and to what extent the individual is dissatisfied with the results. If the individual is seemingly satisfied with the results he or she obtains, then questions of personal values, goals and motivations can be raised. If the person is dissatisfied with results of behavior, then questions other than motivation may be raised. The two main questions are: does the individual have the requisite behaviors in his or her repertoire, and does the individual believe he or she can employ those skills instrumentally to obtain desired results?

In the first instance, an individual may want reinforcers available in the environment, but lack the skills to attain them, despite holding the belief that he or she can attain them (i.e., has an internal locus of control). In the second, the individual might actually have the necessary skills to attain reinforcers, but not use them because he or she believes that the environment can manipulate him or her like a chess pawn and feels powerless to prevent it (i.e., has an external locus of control).

In order for these two possibilities to occur, the source of perceived locus of control must be examined. Expectancies and values, which shape the choices people make, are learned. Learning is based on past experience. Hence, it is unlikely that a person who has successfully operated on a reinforcing environment will develop an external locus of control unless he or she fails to learn from past experiences. People fail to learn from past experiences when they have a learning disability or when anxiety or some other psychopathological factor interferes with learning.

Bandura's work suggests another way of explaining failures to learn. For Bandura, much behavior is learned from the observation of other people and of the consequences of their behavior. The results of one's own actions may be less important initially than the observed results of other people's actions. Without an initial model to imitate and learn from, the individual might well not acquire behaviors or the idea that certain behaviors can effectively bring rewards.

Observations of the behavior of others are mentally encoded, either through imagination or verbalization and thereby become available for the observer to perform, provided the consequences are believed to be rewarding. If the consequences are regarded as non-rewarding, the observed behavior serves as a model for non-performance. This process is termed modeling, and forms one of the foundations of Bandura's theory. Modeling is, in short, the acquisition of behavior through the observation of others. The learning of social behavior involves the observation of the behavior of parents, peers, and other persons with whom the individual identifies in everyday social situations. In addition, symbolic modeling may occur from reading books and other printed materials, and from films, television programs, and other media-presented information.

Bandura (1977) postulates four processes involved in modeling or observational learning. The first step is attention, and this is influenced by such factors as perceived similarities to the model, intelligence and other capacities, past experience and awareness of what specific behaviors result in reinforcement.

The second step is retention, in words or images, so that information will be available in the future when it can no longer be observed.

The third step is the motor capability to reproduce desired behavior. When there is a deficiency in the behavior repertoire, either through lack of opportunity to observe, inattention, or poor retention, it is necessary to seek additional modeling experiences. Rehearsal, both overt and covert (mental), is necessary to develop the skill.

The fourth and final step is motivation. A person is more likely to reproduce those observed behaviors for which others receive rewards. Reinforcement changes behavior because it supplies information on likely outcomes, i.e., behavior is predicted on anticipated outcomes. Private thoughts have the capacity to regulate and control behavior because they make it possible for one to select responses and to decide to act or not to act in the absence of external reinforcement (McLaughlin, 1971). Such decisions about the selection of behaviors also mean that new behaviors can emerge from new combinations of behaviors represented in memory.

The choosing of good models to learn from is essential for effective social behavior. Socially incompetent behavior results from exposure to poor models, when those models receive rewards. If both poor and good models are reinforced, imitations of both are equally likely to be reproduced (Bandura, 1977).

Socially incompetent behavior may result from failure to be exposed to models of relevant skills. But, even if exposure occurs, the individual might not attend to or represent in memory what he or she has been exposed to. Assuming that the necessary behaviors have been learned, they still might not be called upon.

The social learning approach to personality differs considerably from a pure or radical behavior approach, in that the person's actual behaviors need not have been rewarded directly in order to acquire a

response. What is learned are ideas about responses
and reward contingencies, rather than the responses
per se. Forecasts about the future have a central
role; what one thinks will happen controls behavior,
and thoughts are continually revised using the data
of new experiences.

Bandura distinguishes between outcome expectancies and efficacy expectancies. The former are
simply the understanding that certain behaviors lead
to certain outcomes. Efficacy expectancies are
beliefs one has that he or she can in fact enact the
behaviors required to produce the predicted results.
When people speak of self-confidence they refer to
these subjective estimates of personal or self-
efficacy. Unfortunately, self-confidence is an over-
generalized label. One of the first steps in helping
persons who lack self-confidence in social skills is
to encourage them to particularize their deficits and
redefine them as lack of task confidence - deficiency
in a particular skill.

Remediation, or revision of faulty predictions,
occurs according to Bandura, as a result of observations of new models. As in the original acquisition of responses, the new models should appear
relevant to the observer, should be rewarded for
their actions, and the contingency between specific
action and reward should be made clear. The model
need not be present but can be observed symbolically,
through reading or watching and listening to audio-
visual presentations, which suggests methods of
training in social skills that do not require the
presence of another person, and are, therefore, potentially cost-effective. It also explains how
persons with no live contact with certain social situations, learn to perform adequately in those situations. Thus, appropriate behavior in a strange
environment can be learned by reading guidebooks and
instructional manuals. Or, one can be coached on
proper manners, etiquette, and conduct. One can also
learn a general rule, e.g., to watch and imitate a
socially skilled person when confronted with an unfamiliar situation. But in order to benefit from
knowing this rule, one must have the skill to select
a good model rather than a poor one, and have the
cognitive capabilities to attend to and mentally
store what one witnesses. The learning through
modeling, in other words, can be deliberate as well
as accidental, but still depends on the successful
processing of information through the four steps -
attention, representation, memory and motivation - in
order to perform subsequent behaviors at the correct

time and place.

However, this process of remediation also crucially involves changing negative expectancies. Bandura lists four sources of information on which expectations of personal efficacy are based and therefore can be modified. In addition to modeling, they are verbal persuasion, emotional arousal and performance accomplishments as most important; the cognitive expectations that determine behavior may be "altered most readily by experiences of mastery arising from successful performance" (Bandura, 1977, p.79).

Perceptions of self-efficacy will affect people's willingness to attempt new behaviors needed to provide corrective experiences of mastery, as well as influence their persistence following poor first results. Since it is not the magnitude of the threat but one's conviction about personal efficacy that determines whether tasks will be undertaken, it is important in social skills training to create conditions that promote positive (or at least, realistic) expectations. Support of a trainer and peer group are frequently used tactics to reduce the uncertainty and anxiety stimulated by the threatening situation. Among other approaches this writer has used successfully to reduce initial reluctance are: behavioral rehearsal, cognitive rehearsal, time projection imagery and exploring worst possible outcomes and how to cope with them (Wessler, 1979).

PERSON AND SITUATION

Walter Mischel (1973) proposes an account of social behavior that includes both characteristics of the person and the situation in its explanation of human behavior. In so doing, he has worked within the psychological tradition of Kurt Lewin. Lewin's position is summarized by his well-known formula $B = f(p,e)$ - behavior is a function of the characteristics of the person and of the person's perception of the immediate environment.

The most extensive attempt to specify the impact of the environment on the individual is that of Roger Barker (1968). For several decades Barker worked in the small American town of Oskaloosa, Kansas and devised methods for describing environments and their impact on individuals. Barker's key concept is the behavior setting which consists of a standing pattern of behavior whose existence does not depend on any particular individual; it has a temporal beginning and ending, recurs predictably and has specific

118

physical boundaries and characteristic physical objects used in the activities that form the pattern of behavior.

A game, such as football, is one example, since it has a beginning and end, is played on a field within well-marked boundaries, employs a ball and other special equipment, e.g., shoes and uniforms; the activities of running and kicking are character-istic of the game, and do not depend on the presence of any particular player.

The game has impact on the individual partic-ipant, provided he or she knows the appropriate behaviors to perform. Thus the question, why is that person running and kicking? has a clear answer: because it is appropriate for the behavior setting. Barker described individuals as the medium on which a behavior setting impresses its distinctive features - the setting molds the behavior of the individual. This is done in part by the physical environment, which makes some activities possible and others dif-ficult or impossible.

The second way is entirely social - appropriate and inappropriate behavior in the setting is rewarded and punished respectively by other people. Barker identifies two mechanisms that keep activities appropriate to the setting: vetoing and exclusion.

Vetoing is a familiar process in groups. A deviant in any group will have verbal and non-verbal messages directed toward him or her that are designed to promote conforming to the norms of the setting. The messages may teach or threaten. Teaching appropriate behaviors is done when participants think the person deficient in his or her behavior reper-toire. Participants might, for example, teach the rules of football, skills required for the game, and strategy and tactics of play. Threats of negative sanctions or penalties will be made if participants think the person has the skills but does not use them. Threats might range from mild statements that say in effect, "we don't do that (deviant action) here", to stronger statements about penalties for non-compliance.

The ultimate penalty is exclusion from the setting. The deviant person may be ignored by the rest (such as the practice of Meidung or shunning em-ployed by the Old Order Amish in America, in which the person is literally treated as though he or she does not exist), or physically removed.

Barker has also shown that persons may take roles in a setting that are more or less essential to it. For example, players are more important to the football game than are spectators. This is termed depth of penetration, and the deeper one penetrates a setting the more power he or she has in it. Barker (1968) presents data to show that settings are affected by the number of participants (without a minimum number of players the game cannot continue except in highly modified form) and that the setting affects the individual's decision to participate in it (the fewer performers per required performance, the greater the setting's influence on the individual's decision to participate). Persons who realize their power in the setting, or that the setting depends upon their participation feel subjectively important; thus the setting can impact the individual's self-evaluations.

Behavior settings may be classified according to their similarities. A college course in French resembles a course in German more than it resembles one in comparative anatomy. Settings can appear subjectively dissimilar to the individual, who, due to lack of knowledge about appropriate behaviors, develops feelings of discomfort and anxiety. Such anxiety may promote or interfere with the learning of the behaviors needed in the setting, depending on its intensity.

Social skills consist of having a repertoire of behaviors that "fit" the setting. Behavior repertoires depend on past learning and possibilities for learning, but also on one's physical capabilities. Successful performance in a setting consists of knowing how to act and recognizing when to produce the actions in one's repertoire (i.e., skill in discriminating one setting from another).

Barker's behavior setting theory has cognitive implications - the person must perceive and make judgments about the setting - and is interactional, in Lewin's tradition.

Mischel's interest is this interaction between person and situation. Noting that it is easier to describe such interactions than to explain them, he seeks person variables that account for how people react to the numerous stimuli in any given situation. He employs cognitive or information-processing concepts to do so.

Mischel postulates five cognitive social learning variables. These can also be seen in the work of Rotter, Bandura and Barker, and have already been discussed in this chapter. The five are: competencies; encoding strategies and personal constructs; expectancies; subjective values; and self-regulatory systems and plans.

Competencies are the ability to transform and use information actively, rather than merely to store past learned responses in a personal memory bank. Individual differences in ability to generate new solutions are due to innate ability, past learning and learning to learn, and to non-intellectual psychological factors.

The second variable concerns the manner in which people attend to different aspects of situations, and the categories they employ to evaluate information. One spectator, for example, may describe a football game as "exciting", while another may call it "boring", due to their individual interpretations of the stimulus. As Mahoney (1977) points out in the context of psychotherapy, humans respond primarily to cognitive representations of their environments not to their environments per se. People make inferences, create abstractions, and organize their experiences rather than view each experience as a unique event.

When people categorize their own behavior and personal qualities they abstract from their behavior, they form self-categorizations. In this view, the self exists as the result of an encoding process, using categories created by the individual. Such self-categorizations are usually made in relatively stable trait terms, and can have considerable impact on the person's behavior.

The third variable, expectancies (like Rotter's notion of expectancies and Bandura's notion of anticipated outcomes), concerns the individual's predictions about the consequences of behavior. Objective reality is not the critical determinant, perceived reality is; the belief that a football game will be boring (expectancy) is sufficient to influence one to avoid it (behavior). Past experience guides choices.

Poor social performance may be due to one's employing expectations based on old categories that do not apply to new situations. Such failure to discriminate occurs when one has a generalized rule that fails to account for exceptions. A woman might believe that all men are chauvinistic oppressors, fail to generate positive expectations in interactions with any man, and consequently miss potentially satisfying relationships. Mischel notes that outcome expectancies may be idiosyncratic, but many are widely shared by members of the same culture who use a common language for verbal and non-verbal communication (e.g., taking eye-contact as a signal of interest and permission to continue talking).

The fourth variable is subjective values. The

identical forecasting of outcomes does not assure similar behavior among people, for they may appraise them differently. One person may value the approval he or she expects from others, while another may be indifferent to it.

The fifth variable is labeled self-regulatory systems and plans. This variable focuses on the individual's own ideas about goals and standards of performance, and his or her self-reward or self-criticism for attaining or failing to attain self-imposed goals and standards. Here Mischel presents a picture of the individual as a self-regulating system, which like other cybernetic devices, has mechanisms for gathering information about performance and making (or attempting) corrections to ensure adequate performance (see Carver and Scheier, this volume). This is the critical process for overcoming the control by the environment (stimulus control of behavior). The person is seen as active rather than passive in selecting environments to enter, and in deciding what to do and what not to do. Here the human is clearly described as a thinking agent not an empty organism; as a creature who chooses, not a conditioned organism that automatically responds to an external environment.

Situations provide information that may affect each of the five person variables. Situations are termed powerful when almost everyone construes them the same way, agrees about the most proper behavior in the situations, has adequate competence to enact proper behaviors and incentives to carry them out. Failure to exhibit correct social behavior in a "powerful" situation leads one to raise questions about which of the five variables is involved, and how.

The analysis has implications for remediation. Some typical questions to generate about the individual are: does he or she have competencies requisite to the construction of situationally correct cognitions and behaviors? Are failures to generate consensual categories due to low intelligence, lack of prior experience, specific cognitive deficit or psychopathology? Does the person have non-consensual outcome-expectancies in situations where he or she fails to perform adequately? Does the person have non-consensual values, due, say, to an unusual family or subcultural background? Or, might psychopathology be an explanation? Does the person approach the task of self-monitoring in a causal fashion?

Powerful situations constrain individual behaviors and because they command consensual agreement about appropriate behavior tend to be seen by persons as potentially embarrassing (Price & Bouffard, 1974). Thus, another pertinent question is: does the person inhibit his or her behavior due to anxiety about potential embarrassment? As Barker suggested, constraints do not come automatically from the situation, but from the other persons who can give or withhold social rewards. Predictions about such behavior of other people seems a crucial variable.

Knowledge of what a person hopes to achieve by his or her actions is a key variable in understanding and predicting those actions. At what point does inaction become the preferred course of "action" by the individual? The answer will furnish important clues for the remediation of poor social performances. For example, if knowledge about when saving oneself from embarrassment is more important than gaining the rewards the situation can offer, a useful prediction about behavior on an action-inaction dimension will result.

ATTRIBUTION THEORY

Attribution theory (Harvey & Weary, 1981) is not a coherent body of theoretical propositions, but rather is a label given to a set of interrelated attempts to understand the processes by which people understand and explain their own and other people's behavior. Thus, it is relevant for understanding the ways people develop personal constructs. Fritz Heider (1958) introduced the attributional approach to psychology, and echoing Kelly, suggested that persons function as lay scientists who strive for a causal understanding of events, including personal events. Subsequent research and theorizing have emphasized the role of cognitions in human behavior, especially causal attribution.

A causal attribution is an inference about the reason(s) an event occurred or about one's personal dispositions. Heider suggested that persons search for explanations (logically, these are post-dictions, as contrasted with pre-dictions that form an important part of social learning theory). Persons may explain events by attributing their causes to the environment (external attribution) or to personal characteristics within the individual (internal attribution). Persons are hypothesized to function in scientific ways, insofar as they attempt to make cause-and-effect connections.

Weiner (1974) has followed Heider's suggestion in a series of studies of achievement motivation. He proposes four ways commonly used by people to explain their successes and failures: the difficulty of the task and luck are external attributions; personal ability and degree of effort are internal attributions.

The four attributions can also be arrayed along a dimension of variability-stability. Luck and effort are relatively variable; personal ability and task difficulty are relatively stable. Rosenbaum (1972) has added controllability as a causal dimension, and Abramson, Seligman and Teasdale (1978) have introduced global versus specific attributions.

These attributional types have relevance for remediation of social skills deficits. A person who attributes his or her lack of social success to external causes that are relatively stable, beyond control and pervasive (global), is unlikely to be motivated to acquire new behaviors. His or her explanation might sound like this: the task is too difficult, will remain so for it is beyond anyone's control, and is just like all other similar tasks - impossible! In order for such a person to be ready to acquire new skills and to try them in actual situations, the attributions must change to their opposites, e.g., it is not the task that is impossible it is the case that I am as yet unskilled (internal attribution), but I can become skilled (variable attribution), and with practice learn to succeed (controllability attribution) in certain situations for which I have trained (specific attribution) (see also Bandura et al. this volume). Several studies report attempts to change achievement strivings by teaching subjects to attribute failure to lack of effort rather than to lack of ability (Dweck, 1975; Heckhausen,1975; Andrews & Debus, 1978). However, for some already overachieving persons, training them to attribute failure to lack of effort seems to result in unrealistic persistence. The making of internal attributions seems necessary for the self-modification of behavior, but such attributions can also lead to low motivation to make changes (Seligman, 1975).

Forsterling (1983) proposes a scheme to broaden the application of attributional principles to cognitively-based remediation efforts, and presents a hypothetical example that has relevance for social skills training. A person who often acts inappropriately at parties and blames the resulting rejection on the other people (external attribution) could benefit from adopting the attitude that people are the way they are (external attribution) and therefore it would be best to learn and change his or her behaviors to suit them and gain acceptance (internal variable attribution).

Following the explanation of how attributions are formed put forth by H.H. Kelley (1967), Forsterling hypothesizes that individuals use co-variation, distinctiveness, and consistency of events to reach their understandings of them. A person who experiences extreme social anxiety, might start to think about how many other people are equally as tense at a party and thus focuses on consensus infor-mation. He or she might decide that consensus is low (only a few people are anxious) and attribute the presence of anxiety to factors within him or herself. The person may experience anxiety in many social situations (e.g., at work as well as at parties); therefore, the situation is not a distinctive one, and an internal attribution is facilitated. If con-sistency is high, such as when the individual con-cludes that he or she usually experiences anxiety in social situations, an internal attribution is more likely.

How people come to learn to make certain types of attributions is a complicated issue for which no definitive answers exist. Forsterling suggests that misattributions are likely to occur in areas of life where important information is withheld, such as specific information about how one performs socially (due to social norms about politely refraining from such criticism). Kelley (1972) suggests that it may often be too time-consuming to seek consensus infor-mation, and data about distinctivenes and insistency and so persons mistakenly apply causal schemata to their situations or uncritically adopt causal cog-nitions from other people who have significance in their lives.

However, Nisbett and Wilson (1977) show that people easily err in ·forming judgments, making pre-dictions and attributions. In effect, they say that people are poor introspective subjects, that they cannot report on critical stimuli that affect them, that they may not report events but theories of events as they already hold them, or achieve ac-curacy by accident.

In an extensive review, Nisbett and Ross (1980) show that people are very sloppy in behaving like the lay scientists Heider, Kelley and others would have them be. Drawing on the work of Tversky and Kahneman (1981), they show that people often ignore evidence in favor of either unreliable data or adopt view-points for reasons totally unrelated to evidence.

Instead of believing the results of a well-controlled
study, people as easily (if not more so) believe
their friends, who have far less reliable data. They
may believe what they want to believe because it
satisfies an existing set of personal constructs or
worldview, and blithely ignore contradictory data.
They may be motivated by their predictions, but seek
data that confirm those predictions rather than
revise their personal theoretical scheme.

In short, people's personal biases interfere
with the logical processing of reliable information.
The difficulty may reside in the question of whom to
trust for reliable information. Scientists, probably
more than any other category of persons, trust
scientific information. Indeed, there is more than
one basis for knowledge, and scientific knowledge is
but one among several. This writer was once a
faculty member at an American Jesuit university whose
credo contained the statement that divine revelation
had equal standing with science. Artists and persons
in the humanities no doubt want equal status as well.

Confidence in the person who presents information probably outweighs the objective goodness
(according to logical or scientific criteria) in influencing people's beliefs. Janis (1981) makes this
point: non-rational, non-evidential processes are at
work in the counseling situation, and therefore a
relationship in which the client trusts, likes and
believes the counselor is essential. The argument is
less important than its proponent. The implication
for remediation of social skills deficits is clear
(if you trust the writer): training will be more
effective if the trainees trust, like, and have
confidence in the trainer. They are more likely to
learn and more likely to take the risks involved (at
least psychologically) in applying what they have
learned. Their success in applying their learning
will further enhance the relationship, but the
competent trainer will attribute success to the
trainees' personal efforts. The trainees are, in
turn, likely to adopt the same attributions, not
because they are objectively correct, but because
they are psychologically correct.

INTERPERSONAL THEORY

Thus far the discussion of what determines socially
appropriate behavior has omitted emotional styles
with which situationally relevant actions are carried
out. The same words may be uttered in a friendly
fashion or a hostile one, in an assertive manner or

an acquiescent one. These affective interpersonal styles and their impact on other people have been described by Carson (1969) based on the early work of Leary (1957). The basic assumption is that certain behaviors cause other people to react in predictable ways.

Carson describes two intersecting dimensions which form four general categories of interpersonal behavior. One dimension is labeled dominant-submissive, and the other friendly-hostile. The rationale for these dimensions may be found in Leary's work, and subsequent independent lines of evidence have given them futher credence. Small group research has shown that interactions can be usefully arrayed along a continuum of power and of affect and Osgood's (1952) extensive research into the connotative meaning of concepts reveals, from factor analysis, two similar dimensions - evaluative and potency factors.

The four general categories fit together in a complementary fashion. On the power dimension, dominant behavior is reciprocated by submissive behavior. Leary describes this as a process of "pulling" behaviors from others; submissive behavior forms an invitation for the other person to behave in a relatively more dominant manner. Failure to behave reciprocally is said to lead to dissatisfaction and probable termination of the interaction. On the affective dimension, hostile behavior tends to pull hostile responses, and friendly pulls friendly.

Using the hypothesis that a person develops an interpersonal style that results in predictable responses from other people, Carson shows how people with complementary interpersonal styles can satisfy each other. The main assumptions of Carson's theory are a combination of the dynamic interpersonal theory of Harry Stack Sullivan and the interaction approach of Thibaut and Kelley (1959). It is non-cognitive insofar as it assumes unconscious motivation of behavior, whereas a cognitive approach, almost by definition, assumes conscious motivation. However, Carson's theory can be restated in terms that are consistent with social learning theory. The person can be said to seek rewards that are idiosyncratic, to predict the availability of those rewards, and to act in ways to obtain rewarding responses from other people.

In the writings of Kelly, Rotter, Bandura and Mischel, there is an assumption that people find it rewarding to predict successfully, even if what they predict is not in itself very satisfying to them.

Successful prediction is its own reward.

Carson goes further and suggests that people behave in ways that are designed to produce predicted (and desired for their familiarity) responses from other people. Thus, one develops a characteristic style of interaction that Carson calls personality. A person who has a lifelong experience of getting hostile-dominant responses feels rewarded when he or she continues to get them, and will work at getting them. The same can be said for the other categories in the fourfold scheme.

However, some interpersonal styles are more appropriate for a majority of situations than are others. In general, some degree of friendliness is more appropriate than hostility. Behavior that is neither too dominant nor too submissive seems more generally acceptable than either extreme. Producing an inappropriate affective response is another example of social skills deficit.

When the rewarding responses are appropriate (i.e., the "correct" amount of power and affect), the question of lack of social skills does not arise. However, those behaviors that fail to "fit" the situation call attention to themselves and are seen as abnormal. Neurotic behavior, in the interpersonal scheme, consists of rigid adherence to one style of interpersonal behavior. Instead of adjusting one's behavior to each situation, the neurotically rigid individual continues to display but one form of social action. This behavior is especially obvious when extreme. The reason for extreme, rigid behavior is that the individual seeks certain types of satisfying responses, continues to try to attain them when not readily available, (unconsciously) forces other people to behaviors they rarely display or breaks off the interaction, and finds little or no satisfaction in any other type of interpersonal response.

Normal personality styles are typified by an individual's preferring one type of interpersonal response, but having the flexibility to behave in ways that fall anywhere along the two dimensions of dominant-submissive, and hostile-friendly. Thus, a normal (non-neurotic) individual might prefer somewhat friendly, somewhat submissive responses from other people and therefore display somewhat friendly, somewhat dominant behavior in order to maximize the probability of receiving them. But, a normal non-neurotic individual will be able to display other styles of behaving should he deem it appropriate to do so. By contrast, the neurotic person seems unable to alter his behavior.

The neurotic person, in this analysis, gets what he or she wants, but often at a high cost. He or she may succeed in finally obtaining the interpersonal response desired, but expend great effort in so doing, and feel unhappy because other motives remain unsatisfied. How this might occur can be seen from an examination of typical neurotic styles.

Persons who rigidly adhere to extreme forms of friendly submissiveness are typical anxiety neurotics. They, according to Carson's theory, act in submissive but friendly ways, as if to say to other people, I am weak and harmless; be kind to me and tell me what to do. If they enter social situations that call for other responses such as taking responsibility for some task or acting assertively, they do not. If they also have motives for achievement or other goals that benefit from responsible, assertive behavior, they become frustrated and feel unhappy.

Persons who are termed passive-aggressive fall into the extreme category of hostile-submissive. Their behavior tends to pull hostility from other people as well as actions that are more dominant than theirs. According to Carson's theory, they have learned to fear openly expressing their hostile feelings and therefore do so in subtle ways. Their weak self-presentation allows avoidance of feared open conflict. When they also desire, say, affection from other people, they may get frustruated because their interpersonal style does not encourage friendliness on the part of other people. The result is unhappiness, but theoretically at least, the satisfaction of their predictions. They can reassure themselves that other people are indeed unfriendly if not hostile, and that their view of the world is correct.

There is a further complicated strategy in which the individual gains reinforcement by first adopting a weak but friendly approach to other people, and ultimately displays unfriendly dominant behavior which he or she can justify to him or herself. This process is similar to what Eric Berne (1964) described as a "game", an interpersonal transaction that results in ego-enhancing thoughts which the person finds rewarding. Berne, using his colorful terminology, called the game, why-don't-you-yes-but. In it the person presents him or herself as weak, friendly, and in need of help. This "pulls" helping behavior - typically friendly, dominant advice from the other person(s). However, every attempt to help is rejected as inadequate, naive or inappropriate.

Cognitive-Social Theories and Social Skills

Finally, with all suggestions demolished by the "weak" victim, he or she feels triumphant and free to criticize the helper, who by now is acting inadequately if not badly. These games were proposed as scenarios by which the individual gets psychological satisfactions but at a high interpersonal cost; they are maladaptive because they interfere with close and effective interpersonal relations.

In terms of the remediation of social skill deficits, these games may block the learning and/or performing of new behaviors. The person may lack competencies, not because of low intelligence or other learning deficits of an intellectual nature, but because of neurotic interpersonal strategies. If this occurs, remediation efforts will fail because the person already has one set of motives satisfied by his or her interpersonal style. Thus remediation of social skills deficits may require counseling or psychotherapeutic intervention as well as education and training in social skills themselves.

Therefore, it is advisable to assume that no behavior is totally ineffective; it is effective in bringing some rewards the individual holds to be valuable. By taking this approach, which is basically a functional analysis of behavior, interventions can be planned based on either (1) aiding the individual to examine and perhaps change his or her motivational structure, or (2) aiding the individual to develop less neurotic and psychologically costly interpersonal strategies and tactics for satisfaction of his or her motives.

Assessment of the causes of social skills deficits should precede intervention attempts, just as every modification attempt can be done more effectively following proper understanding of the malfunction of difficulty. Some persons lack socially skilled behavior, despite having cognitive knowledge of the requisite skills. It has been this writer's experience in teaching assertive behaviors (and has been found in a number of studies) that many unassertive people actually know how to act assertively and what to say, how to say it, etc. But they fail to enact what they know because of emotional factors. Some fear to act assertively because they fear other people's responses or fear acting in (for them) novel ways; others fear they will not get what they want. The former are anxious and underassertive, the latter are aggressive and overassertive.

This writer has used Carson's fourfold scheme to teach appropriately assertive responses (those that are neither too dominant nor too submissive, and are neither too friendly nor too hostile), and to analyze the individual's current interpersonal style and the reasons underlying it. Persons who are not neurotically committed to an interpersonal style benefit from such an explanation and analysis. Persons who are more rigid do not benefit from assertiveness training unless it is coupled with counseling or psychotherapy.

SELF-FULFILLING PROPHECY

Weary and Arkin (1981) have proposed a model of the self-presentation process in social situations. Like Carson's interpersonal theory, they begin with an assumption that people attempt to control the responses of others by establishing a particular identity and that the identity is established in part by the individual's self-attributions. The process of establishing an identity is broken into five analytic components: (1) The strategically controlled behavior of the presenter; (2) his or her perceptions of his or her behavior and the social context in which it is enacted; (3) the actual reactions of the audience to the presenter's behavior; (4) the presenter's attributions about the audience's reactions; (5) the presenter's self-concept.

There are five major categories of variables that might influence the nature of causal judgments strategically presented to others: (1) aspects of the task performance and outcome, and nature of attributional activities; (2) presenter's goals (avoid disapproval, gain approval, convey desired impression); (3) social norms; (4) individual differences (excluding expectancies, self-monitoring, anxiety, empathetic ability); and (5) real or imagined characteristics of the audience. They report that research generally supports the model, and that the model is a major effort to integrate an attributional approach with the closely-related symbolic interactionist tradition found in sociological social psychology based on the ideas of George Herbert Mead.

The classical statement of the definition of the situation is usually attributed to the American sociologist W.I. Thomas; to paraphrase his dictum: if people define situations as real, they are real in their consequences. It is one thing to say that an individual's social behavior is based on his or her unique perceptions, perceptions which need not have much to do with the reality of the situation as defined by consensus. It is quite another matter to show that personal definitions lead to expected outcomes. The self-fulfilling prophecy claims that expectations affect subsequent developments.

The term self-fulfilling prophecy was first used by Robert Merton who said of it,

> ....in the beginning, a _false_ definition of the situation (evokes) a new behavior which makes the originally false conception come _true_ ....the prophet will cite the actual course of events as proof that he was right from the very beginning.
> (Merton, 1957, p.423)

While it is possible that the prophet only imagines or misperceives the response of other people, Merton clearly intended that one person's expectancy actually affects another person's actions.

Rosenthal (1976) used the self-fulfilling prophecy to summarize his program of research into the unintended consequences of experimenters' hypotheses on the outcome of their research (Wessler, 1969), and of teachers' impressions of pupils' abilities and pupils' performance, and of examiners' expectations about the test results of persons they examine (Wessler, 1970). In general, these and other studies confirm the general proposition that expectancy affects actual performance by other people.

Of relevance to social skills, Mark Snyder in a series of studies, investigated personal hypotheses and their effects on social interaction (Snyder, Tanke & Berscheid, 1977; Snyder & Swann, 1978; Snyder & Cunningham, 1975; Snyder & Frankel, 1976; Snyder & Jones, 1974; and elsewhere). The data supports the hypothesis that the perceiver tends to draw stereotypic inferences about a target person, typically on the basis of physical attributes (sex, ethnic features), assigns these inferences to all members of that group, and makes inferences about individual members of that group. Social stereotypes are, as a rule, simple, widely accepted over generalizations, but usually not accurate; nonetheless, they are highly influential in social behavior. Memory of past events serves to confirm such beliefs and what gaps in evidence that might exist are conveniently filled in by preconceived notions of what ought to be.

In a study of male-female pairs, Snyder et al. (1977) found that persons considered physically attractive often behaved in a cordial, agreeable manner due to the behavior of perceivers who saw them as attractive and behaved accordingly. The perceivers' inferences initiated a sequence of events which resulted in confirmation of the inferences - the self-fulfilling prophecy.

The perceivers' stereotypic thinking about target persons receives behavioral confirmation and thus strengthens or bolsters the stereotype. Expectations guide interaction in such a way as to create their own social reality. Expectations are influenced by selective remembering of information consistent with current interpretations of the target person, or selective re-interpretations of past events to give them meanings that are consistent with current interpretations of the target person or both.

Darley and Fazio have tried to specify in great detail the steps involved in self-fulfilling interactional sequences. They identify the following steps in a general social interaction sequence between two people:

> (1) Either because of past observations of the other or because of the categories into which he or she has encoded the other, a perceiver develops a set of expectations about the other person. (2) The perceiver then acts toward the target person with his or her expectations of the target person. (3) Next, the target interprets the meaning of the perceiver's action. (4) Based on the interpretation, the target responds to the perceiver's action, and (5) the perceiver interprets the target's action. At this point the perceiver again acts toward the target person and so can be regarded as re-entering the interaction sequence loop at Stage 2. (Darley & Fazio, 1980, p.868)

Darley and Fazio add a sixth step, "after acting toward the perceiver, the target person interprets the meaning of his or her own action" (p.868). Throughout this account, there is a clearly stated emphasis on the meanings imposed by both persons on their own and others' actions; the actions do not automatically convey meanings. Meanings - interpretations and evaluations - are crucial to the process, and are potential sources of misunderstanding between the persons, and of disrupted and ill-fated attempts at social interaction.

The perceiver's expectancies are formed from a sample of the target's behavior, and are subject to the dispositional error discussed in attribution theory (Harvey & Weary, 1981): the perceiver is likely to consider personality rather than situation as the "cause" of the target's actions. Expectations may be based on category-based expectations, as Snyder has shown, or on the perceiver's implicit theory of personality (Tagiuri, 1968). The target's interpretations of the perceiver's actions may be similarly affected. However, the meanings the target imposes might also be based on attributions to the situation, awareness of his or her own characteristics, or more complex attributions.

Actual behaviors will be based on meanings assigned by both perceiver and target. The perceiver may avoid or terminate interaction with the target. The target may act in ways that are consistent with expectations, and thus strengthen them, or the target may behave in disconfirming or ambiguous ways. But even if disconfirming responses result, the perceiver may still be able to rationalize them, discount them, or attribute them in such a way that they become exceptions to the rule. When the target conforms to expectations, the perceiver may ignore or minimize his or her role in the process, thus strengthening the expectations. In other words, there are powerful processes involved in maintaining one's expectations and cleverly but unwittingly distorting the data.

In its most grotesque form, this model suggests that people go to great lengths to maintain their expectations and fail to revise them despite contrary evidence. The data reviewed by Darley and Fazio tell what people can do; what they actually do in natural settings is a question of prevalence that cannot be addressed here, probably because data do not exist. But, are people doomed to interact with their constructions of other people rather than with people themselves, and are they doomed to roam the labyrinth of their own unrevised categories?

The answer is that they are not. Explicit in social learning theory is the notion of revising of categories, of modifying conceptions. It is a question, in part, of vigilance (Janis, 1981). Just as Darwin is said to have written down criticisms of his work so that he would not (unintentionally but conveniently) forget them, people can monitor their environment and the effects of their behavior on other people. The extreme of failing to monitor and use information provided by other people's responses is autism. Encounter groups and some forms of group therapy represent explicit efforts to help people monitor their own actions and their reception by other people. Such groups are necessary, one might speculate, because the social norms of interaction exclude the giving of such feedback. It is considered impolite (if not actually rude) because it is assumed that one would offend if he or she gave such feedback, or that the other person would feel emotionally wounded by the information.

So, except in group therapy or among friends who have agreed to speak frankly with each other, one must create his or her own opportunities to discover the appropriateness of his or her actions. A self-imposed commitment to self-monitoring seems called for, since the social environment may ignore inappropriate behavior (in an attempt to extinguish it?), or resort to avoidance without helping persons first make corrections.

The tendency to ascribe the causes of others' actions to their personal characteristics rather than to environmental variables - including one's own actions, is another source of failure to change. If the responses of others are thought to be due to their personalities rather than to the effects of one's own actions, there is little motivation for revision. When this tendency is also applied to one's self, the error is additionally compounded. Consistency of self is both a socially approved idea and the goal of some psychotherapy and counseling systems (e.g., client-centered, Gestalt). The idea of adjusting one's behavior to fit different situations seems to clash with the ideal of "being oneself" in each and all situations. The result of such an attitude might be consistency, but it is better termed rigidity. The person who is consistent in this sense behaves autistically rather than authentically; in following the cliche "to thine own self be true" he or she succeeds in performing poorly in social situations.

DISCUSSION AND CONCLUSIONS

Trower (1981) has proposed that a highly socially skilled person will monitor the external events in which he or she participates, and look for situational data rather than being self-oriented. Such a person can adjust his or her behavior and learn to modify it. Why then are there persons who are internal monitors and self-oriented?

The answer to this question is not simple, but a review of the principles and findings presented in this chapter points toward an answer.

First, the answer can be found within the individual. The word skills implies a characteristic of persons. This assumption also suggests that remedies are to be sought in programs that attempt to modify characteristics of the person, not the situation.

Are there adequate incentives to perform appropriately? Social learning theory states that rewarding events are those that are defined as rewarding by the individual, given his or her values. Further, rewards fall into several categories, as most persons have many values, not one or two, and these are hierarchically arranged. Thus, a person may complain that he or she does not get good results in social situations, but at some level actually does get reinforced. It seems safe to say that recurring actions are those that bring desired results.

The results that unskilled social behavior may bring, include predictable actions by other people (thus satisfying one's conception of self and of the world). Some people would rather be right than happy. Careful analyses of the consequences of behavior in relation to the person's stated and unstated (but inferred from his or her actions) goals applies here. Confirmation of one's expectations or of a negative self-image may override the more obvious (to the casual observer) benefits of appropriate behavior.

Are rewards not expected? Since expectation of reinforcement rather than reinforcment per se looms importantly in social learning theory, it is essential to examine expectations about rewards. Since people seem so resistant to revising their conceptualizations, it is likely that many people suffer from unrealistically evaluating the environment's potential to furnish rewards. Other persons may have a negative self-image that includes the idea that others get rewarded for actions he or she gets penalized for. Alternatively, one might not expect rewards due to an external locus of control.

Does the person know how to perform appropriately? Before automatically adopting the position that social skills deficits are due to emotional or self-image problems, it is advisable to inventory the person's behavior repertoire. Simple knowledge deficits might be revealed. Spivack, Platt and Shure (1976) have shown that in many instances psychopathology is not the reason for inappropriate behavior, but failure to think in causal terms or to anticipate the results of one's actions before doing them, is. Their remedy is cognitive skills training with an ultimate goal of the subject's generalizing what they have learned into useful strategies.

The writer knows of a highly successful social

skills training program conducted on a U.S. Army base in West Germany. The participants in this program are coerced into acquiring certain behaviors that previous socializing agencies failed to instill; the participants could ignore their teachers and avoid school, but they cannot ignore their Army superiors without significant penalty. They quickly acquire skills that they easily evade in their usual subcultural environment.

Does the person have the capacity to learn? Here is the most important and at the same time most complicated question to answer. Several factors may interfere with the capacity to benefit from experience. Emotional and self-image factors have already been discussed. Neurosis and the need to maintain predictability have likewise been shown to interfere with learning (and performance). In addition, intellectual factors, easily overlooked in a misplaced spirit of democracy, are important cognitive variables. Overall intelligence must be considered; some persons may lack, either through education or genetics, basic intellectual abilities needed to acquire social information. They then have no or little information to use, or lack the additional ability to use it well.

Some persons may perform intellectual tasks poorly due to some other condition, e.g., psychosis or nervous system impairment. These conditions may be permanent or temporary, but can and most likely do interfere with learning.

Some persons may have specific learning disabilities that make it difficult or impossible to learn certain tasks. Developmental aphasias are one example. This is a matter of neuropsychology, but should be taken seriously in attempting to understand the failure to learn social skills. This writer hypothesizes that in those cases in which there are no other psychological factors to which poor social learning can be attributed, there will be found a high proportion of neurological deficits among persons identified as having social skills deficits.

The implication of the foregoing for remediation is clear: no intervention plan should be implemented without a careful assessment of each individual. It is pointless to teach skills to people who already have them, but who, for psychological reasons, do not use them. It seems strange enough that psychologists now do what experts on social etiquette did generations ago - teach proper social conduct. But, to do so without careful psychological assessment, seems stranger still. Assessment should include examination for psychopathology and, where indicated, neurological deficit. Only then should an educational approach be adopted.

The theories reviewed in this chapter offer many clues about poor social performance, but their application requires sound clinical judgment and additional research to make the psychological, physical, and social causes of poor social performance better understood.

In summary, this chapter has presented several cognitive models that account for social skills acquisition and performance. Their implications for improving the performance of persons deficient in social skills was discussed, along with some factors that pose difficulties for successful remediation attempts. The thread that joins these models is the generation of predictions about reinforcement outcomes, especially the behavior of other people. Most of the models posit humans as information processors and scientists who explain their own and others' behavior. (Attribution theory has much to contribute in this area.) Explanations are post-dictions that may lead to predictions; each model assumes that predictions motivate behavior. Bandura distinguishes between knowing what actions will produce outcomes and knowing that one can successfully display these needed behaviors; uncertainty about either type of knowing yields anxiety and avoidance. Many different motives can be satisfied by one's actions, and what appears to be unrewarding behavior may actually satisfy the "need to predict accurately" and the security it brings. In addition, the self-fulfilling prophecy research and Carson's interpersonal theory assume that people work to make their predictions come true, even when they predict unfavorable outcomes. Social learning theories emphasize that skills are characteristic of the person, even though situational variables are important. Skills depend on past learning, on opportunities to learn and capacity for learning. Capacity depends on innate potentials, which should be assessed before initiating remediation attempts.

REFERENCES

Abramson, L.Y., Seligman, M.E.P., & Teasdale, J.D. Learned helplessness in humans: Critique and reformulation. Journal of Abnormal Psychology, 1978, 87, 49-57

Adams-Webber, J.R. Personal construct theory: Concepts and applications. Chichester: Wiley, 1979

Andrews, G.R., & Debus, R.L. Persistence and causal
    perceptions of failure: Modifying cognitive
    attributions. Journal of Educational Psychol-
    ogy, 1978, 70, 154-166
Bandura, A. Social learning theory. Englewood
    Cliffs, N.J.: Prentice Hall, 1977
Bandura, A., & Walters, R.H. Social learning and
    personality development. New York: Holt, Rine-
    hart, Winston, 1963
Barker, R.G. Ecological psychology: Concepts and
    methods for studying the environment of human
    behavior. Stanford, Calif.: Stanford University
    Press, 1968
Berne, E. Games people play: The psychology of hu-
    man relationships. London: Andre Deutsch, 1964
Carson, R.C. Interaction concepts of personality.
    Chicago: Aldine, 1969
Darley, J.M., & Fazio, R.H. Expectancy confirmation
    arising in the social interaction sequence.
    American Psychologist, 1980, 35, 867-881
Dweck, C.S. The role of expectations and attrib-
    utions in the alleviation of learned helpless-
    ness. Journal of Personality and Social Psych-
    ology, 1975, 31, 674-685
Festinger, L. A theory of social comparison proc-
    esses. Human Relations, 1954, 7, 117-140
Forsterling, F. Interdependencies among different
    depressogenic cognitions. Rational Living,
    1983, 18, 13-15
Harvey, J.H., & Weary, G. Perspectives on attrib-
    utional processes. Dubuque, Iowa: Wm. C.
    Brown, 1981
Heckhausen, H. Fear of failure as self-reinforcing
    motive system. In I.G. Sarason & C. Spiel-
    berger (Eds.), Stress and anxiety (Vol. 1).
    Washington, D.C.: Hemisphere, 1975
Heider, F. The psychology of interpersonal relat-
    ions. New York: Wiley, 1958
Janis, I. Counseling for personal decisions. New
    Haven: Yale University Press, 1981
Kelley, H.H. Attribution theory in social psych-
    ology. In D. Levine (Ed.), Nebraska symposium
    on motivation (Vol.15). Lincoln: University of
    Nebraska Press, 1967
Kelley, H.H. Causal schemata and the attribution
    process. In E.E. Jones, D.E. Kanouse, H.H.
    Kelley, R.E. Nisbett, S. Valins, & B. Weiner
    (Eds.), Attribution: Perceiving the causes of
    behavior. Morristown, N.J.: General Learning
    Press, 1972
Kelly, G.A. The psychology of personal constructs.

New York: W.W. Norton, 1955

Leary, T. The interpersonal diagnosis of behavior. New York: Ronald Press, 1957

Mahoney, M.J. Reflections on the cognitive-learning trend in psychotherapy. American Psychologist, 1977, 32, 5-13

McLaughlin, B. Learning and social behavior. New York: The Free Press, 1971

Merton, R.K. Social theory and social structure. New York: The Free Press, 1957

Mischel, W. Personality and assessment. New York: Wiley, 1968

Mischel, W. Toward a cognitive social learning reconceptualization of personality. Psychological Review, 1973, 80, 252-283

Nisbett, R.E., & Ross, L. Human inference: Strategies and shortcomings of social judgment. Englewood Cliffs, N.J.: Prentice Hall, 1980

Nisbett, R.E., & Wilson, T.D. Telling more than we can know: Verbal reports on mental processes. Psychological Review, 1977, 84, 231-259

Osgood, C.E. The nature and measurement of meaning. Psychological Bulletin, 1952, 49, 197-237

Price, R.H., & Bouffard, D.L. Behavioral appropriateness and situational constraint as dimensions of social behavior. Journal of Personality and Social Psychology, 1974, 30, 579-586

Rosenbaum, R.M. A dimensional analysis of the perceived causes of success and failure. Unpublished doctoral disseertation, University of California, Los Angeles, 1972

Rosenthal, R. Experimenter effects in behavioral research. New York: Irvington, 1976

Rotter, J.B. Social learning and clinical psychology. Englewood Cliffs, N.J.: Prentice Hall, 1954

Seligman, M.E.P. Helplessness: On depression, development, and death. San Francisco: Freeman, 1975

Snyder, M.L., & Cunningham, M.R. To comply or not to comply: Testing the self-perception explanation of the "foot-in-the-door" phenomenon. Journal of Personality and Social Psychology, 1975, 31, 64-67

Snyder, M.L., & Frankel, A. Observer bias: The stringent test of behavior engulfing the field. Journal of Personality and Social Psychology, 1976, 34, 857-864

Snyder, M.L., & Jones, E.E. Attitude attribution when behavior is constrained. Journal of Experimental Social Psychology, 1974, 10, 585-600

Snyder, M.L., & Swann, W.B. Behavioral confirmation

in social interaction: From social perception to social reality. *Journal of Experimental Psychology*, 1978, 14, 148-162

Snyder, M.L., Tanke, E.D., & Berscheid, E. Social perception and interpersonal behavior: On the self-fulfilling nature of social stereotypes. *Journal of Personality and Social Psychology*, 1977, 35, 656-666

Spivack, G., Platt, J., & Shure, M. *The social problem solving approach to adjustment*. San Francisco: Jossey-Bass, 1976

Tagiuri, R. Person perception. In G. Lindzey & E. Aronson (Eds.), *The handbook of social psychology* (2nd ed., vol. 3). Reading, Mass.: Addison-Wesley, 1968

Thibaut, J.W., & Kelley, H.H. *The social psychology of groups*. New York: Wiley, 1959

Trower, P. Toward a generative model of social skills: A critique and synthesis. In J.P. Curran & P. Monti (Eds.), *Social skills training: A practical handbook for assessment and treatment*. New York: Guilford Press, 1981

Tversky, A., & Kahneman, D. The framing of decisions and the psychology of choice. *Science*, 1981, 211, 453-458

Weary, G., & Arkin, R.M. Attributional self-presentation. In J.H. Harvey, W. Ickes & R.F. Kidd (Eds.), *New directions in attribution research* (Vol. 3). Hillsdale, N.J.: Erlbaum, 1981

Weiner, B. *Achievement motivation and attribution theory*. Morristown, N.J.: General Learning Press, 1974

Wessler, R.L. Experimenter expectancy effects in three dissimilar tasks. *Journal of Psychology*, 1969, 71, 63-67

Wessler, R.L. Estimating I.Q.: Expertise or examiner effect? *Perceptual and Motor Skills*, 1970, 30, 268

Wessler, R.L. Direct and indirect influence tactics in cognitive-behavior therapy. Paper presented at symposium: When psychotherapy stalls: Behavioral guidelines for responsible therapist action. Division 29, American Psychological Association 87th annual convention, New York, 1979

Editorial Introduction, Chapter Five

*A CONTROL-THEORY APPROACH TO BEHAVIOR, AND SOME
IMPLICATIONS FOR SOCIAL SKILLS TRAINING*

Charles S. Carver and Michael F. Scheier

*In the last chapter Wessler gives an overview of the
various facets of the person as agent, as exemplified
in some prominent cognitive-social psychological
theories. In this chapter Carver and Scheier focus
on certain of these facets which are most germane to
a reformulated social skill model.*

*One of the most valuable theories for providing
a clear and simple understanding of social skill
process is the social skill model of Argyle and
Kendon (1967). At that time it was a conceptual
breakthrough and gave rise to a decade or more of
productive research. Although some of the earlier
findings and emphases may need to be modified in the
light of some recent work the main ideas remain conceptually valid and empirically well founded. However, the model does not deal with (and does not
claim to deal with) the many complicating but
important phenomena such as attributional style,
self-consciousness processes, evaluation, emotion and
so on which we need to take account of in an agency
approach. A model which does take account of these
processes is the "control theory" developed by Carver
(1979) and further developed here for SST by Carver
and Scheier (who are social and personality psychologists).*

*The theory describes not only the basic cyber-
netic or TOTE principle of matching-to-standard (by
input, comparison and output), but shows how interruption of this process leads to an assessment
phase, and a resultant outcome expectancy. If the
expectancy is unfavourable (i.e., failure), this will
lead to behavioural withdrawal, or "giving up". Such
negative expectancies result in (and in time are
caused by) poor self-evaluation (or low perceived
self-efficacy) whenever such failures to reduce discrepancies are attributed to self rather than*

situation. This theory fits conceptually with the practical procedures developed by Shepherd and Dryden in part II.

Chapter Five

A CONTROL-THEORY APPROACH TO BEHAVIOR AND SOME
IMPLICATIONS FOR SOCIAL SKILLS TRAINING

Charles S. Carver and Michael F. Scheier

INTRODUCTION

In the course of normal human activity, behavior
usually flows more or less effortlessly, as plans and
intentions are formulated and carried out, and new
ones easily take their place. Though the carrying-
out of behavioral sequences is often relatively
"mindless", in the sense of not being very carefully
monitored (see Bandura et al., this volume), there
typically is a coherent underlying structure to the
behavior. Even when problems occur, and goals are
unattainable for one reason or another (either temporarily or more permanently), people usually rebound
from these obstacles quickly, readjusting their
sights on new goals, and starting off again.
    It sometimes happens, of course, that this sense
of efficiency and continuity is lacking in behavior.
Sometimes people are unable to negotiate significant
aspects of their social environments successfully.
Often this inefficiency is due to the absence or
deficiency of some behavior that is needed. Sometimes the disruption is a product of the "mindless"
execution of maladaptive behavior patterns, actions
that the person would recognize as disruptive but has
failed to monitor and prevent. In either case, there
may be a need for some sort of social skills training
as a vehicle for altering the person's behavior.
    As with any behavior-change device, social
skills training can be a set of ad hoc procedures -
doing whatever seems to "work" - or it can be grounded in a set of more general assumptions about how
behavior is organized. This is the point at which
the two of us enter the picture. We are not experts

Preparation of this chapter was facilitated by NSF
grants BNS 80-21859 and BNS 81-07236.

in techniques of behavior change; we are personality/social psychologists. We have, however, been working with a rather general model of how behavior is structured. And we think that the nature of that model may have implications for the conceptualization of problems in the area of social skills training. Describing that model, and pointing briefly to several of its implications, are the dual purposes of this chapter.

ORIGINS

Self-awareness

The background to the model we are about to present derives from two sources. The first is a body of research findings concerning the effects of directing one's attention inward to the self. This research stemmed from Duval and Wicklund's (1972) self-awareness theory, the origins of which can be traced in turn to the writings of Mead (1934) and Cooley (1902). The essence of self-awareness theory is contained in the following assumption: that inward focus of attention leads a person to compare his or her present behavior or state with whatever standard of comparison is salient. One potential result of this comparison is a tendency to alter the present behavior so that it conforms more closely to the comparison value.

That such effects upon behavior do occur as a result of self-focus seems beyond dispute. Experimental manipulations such as the presence of a wall mirror, a T.V. camera, and a live observer have been validated as producing states of increased self-focus (Carver & Scheier, 1978; Davis & Brock, 1975; Geller & Shaver, 1976; or see Carver & Scheier, 1981a, for a comprehensive review). And such stimuli have, on a great many occasions, have been found to produce enhanced behavioral conformity to salient standards of behavior (e.g., Carver, 1974, 1975; Gibbons, 1978; Greenberg, 1980; Scheier, Fenigstein, & Buss, 1974; Wicklund & Duval, 1971).

Though these behavioral effects seem to be reliable in their occurrence, the precise mechanism by which they occur has been a matter of great controversy. Our own position on the matter derives from an examination of the processes of control theory, or cybernetics (Wiener, 1948). Control theory thus represents the second source of background information underlying our general approach.

Control Theory

The principles of cybernetics are principles of self-regulating systems. They are applicable to self-regulation of many kinds of systems, including living ones. Indeed, among living systems, control principles seem applicable at a great many levels of analysis, which has led some theorists to propose that control principles are ubiquitous in their functioning. This position has become known as "general systems theory" (see, e.g., Buckley, 1968; Kuhn, 1974; Miller, 1978; von Bertalanffy, 1968). Our emphasis here, however, will not be on the possibility that control principles are universally applicable. Instead, we will focus on the utility of cybernetics in analyzing human behavior at the level of abstraction that is of greatest interest to personality and social psychologists. Let us begin by reducing control theory to its simplest ingredients.

Feedback loops. The basic unit of cybernetic control is the negative feedback loop. It is called a negative or discrepancy reducing loop because its function is to negate or minimize any sensed difference between two values. Though the concept of "feedback" or "control" may seem forbidding at first exposure, a negative feedback loop is actually quite simple (see Figure 1). A feedback loop comprises a closed loop of control. Thus it does not really have a beginning or an end. But perhaps the most intuitive place to strart in examining functioning is with what is labeled "input function" in Figure 1 (the left box). The input function comprises the sensing of some existing state or quality. This perception then, is transferred to a second component of the loop, termed a "comparator". This element is so named because its function is to compare the sensed value against a reference value, or standard of comparison. (Some readers may be familiar with the comparison function under the designation "test", a term used by Miller, Galanter, & Pribram, 1960, in their discussion of the behavior of feedback systems.)

This comparison process can yield either of two outcomes. If the values are not discriminably different from each other, no further action is called for. If there is a discrepancy between the two values, however, control is transferred to an "output function" (what Miller et al., 1960, labeled "operate"). The output function is behavior, in the most general sense of the word. As we shall see later on, outputs are not always literally behavior,

Control-Theory and Social Skills Training

but they always have some impact on the system's environment - i.e., anything external to the system itself.

Figure 1: The Feedback Loop: The Basic Unit of Cybernetic Control.

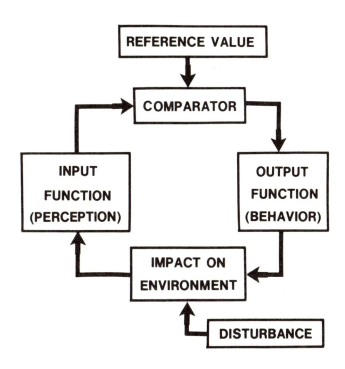

The output function represents an attempt to counter the sensed discrepancy, by bringing the existing state closer to the standard of comparison. The output function does not attain this goal directly, however, but does so instead by having an impact on its environment. Thus it is possible for outputs that might seem quite unrelated to the "present state" to have a major impact on that state, but an impact that is very indirect. As the present state changes, the result is a change in the perception that constitutes the input function. This perception is compared anew with the reference value, and the cycle continues.

In order to provide readers with an intuitive "feel" for how these functions can be realized in a physical system, authors commonly take the behavior of a room thermostat as an illustration. A thermostat senses the temperature of the air in a room. If the temperature departs discriminably from the value at which the device has been set, the thermostat turns on a furnace (or an air conditioner, depending upon the application). The furnace (or air conditioner) changes the temperature of some air and dumps the air into the room. As the overall temperature of the room becomes indistinguishable from the reference point, the action of the furnace (or air conditioner) is terminated.

As we indicated above, the feedback principle is not really complex. But it does have one implication that seems to run contrary to many people's intuitions. Specifically, the central purpose of a control system is not to "emit behavior". Rather, its function is to reduce sensed discrepancies, to maintain the perception of a present state as close as possible to a reference value. As viewed from this perspective, human behavior is a process of establishing goals - reference values - and shifting one's present state to more closely approximate the goals.

Self-focus and feedback loops. Let us now step back for a moment to draw a connection between the two preceding sections. In the first of those sections we described one of the effects of self-directed attention: i.e., that such a state leads to a comparison between one's present behavior and whatever is salient as a standard of comparison. The result is a tendency to alter the behavior so that it conforms more closely to the standard. In the second section we described the essential elements of a feedback system: the comparison of a sensed present state with a reference value, and the output of behavior which compensates for any sensed discrepancy. The parallels between the two should by now be apparent. To be explicit about the matter, we view the focusing of attention inward to the self (when a behavioral standard is salient) as engaging a feedback loop. More specifically, we view self-focus as a precursor to the operation of the comparator of such a loop (see Carver, 1979; Carver & Scheier, 1981a, 1981b).

This relatively simple statement leaves a lot of ground uncovered, a lot of important questions unanswered. It is a first approximation to a cybernetic model of behavior, but only that. In order to provide a more detailed picture, we must introduce at least two more basic notions concerning control

148

therapy. Both of them stem from the fact that feedback systems can be connected to each other.

Branching Chains and Hierarchies

The simpler of these two points is easiest to illustrate by treating the feedback loop as if it were a series of discrete steps, executed in sequence - essentially the position that was taken by Miller et al. (1960) in discussing their TOTE construct (see Figure 2).*   The comparator of a feedback loop, when

Figure 2: The TOTE unit of Miller, Galanter and Pribram (1960), which comprises a sequential description of the behavior of a feedback system (adapted from Miller et al., 1960).

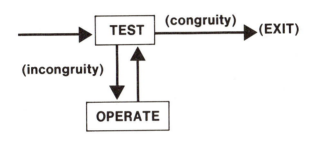

it engages in its activity, is making a yes-or-no binary decision. That is, either the values being compared are the same, or they are different.   If they are different, control is transferred to an output function - what Miller et al. termed "operate". If they are the same, control is not transferred to this function.   Instead, in Miller et al.'s terms, control may be transferred to an "exit" function, thereby freeing this loop for other applications.

---

* There are certainly some systems in which sequential processing is the more accurate depiction - e.g., a digital computer. But in many systems the functions occur simultaneously. There is some difference of opinion about the circumstances under which one depiction or the other is more accurate (see Powers, 1973a). For present purposes, the basis of this disagreement is less important than is the fact that at least some systems are best viewed as being sequential in their operation.

Based on this characterization, the feedback system
thus may be construed as a decision-making device.
   Here is where the complexity comes in. If
control is transferred out of the first loop, where
does it go? Typically to _another_ loop, where another
binary decision is made. In fact, it is perfectly
sensible to imagine that an "operate" called for by a
given loop may entail many sub-components, each of
which incorporates another decision-making loop. The
result of connecting several systems together in this
fashion is an ever-branching "decision tree". Such
networks can be quite elaborate. They are, for
example, the basis for digital computers. And they
are clearly visible in a great many human activities.
Perhaps the easiest illustration of a decision tree
is the sort of "trouble-shooting" guide that amateur
handymen use to try to figure out what is wrong with
electrical or mechanical devices in order to repair
them. The guide consists of a series of checks. If
the first check reveals nothing wrong, you go to the
next one, and so on.
   There is also a second way in which feedback
systems can be interconnected, a way that is a bit
less intuitive. Specifically, feedback systems can
be ordered in a hierarchy (see Figure 3). In a
hierarchical organization, the output of a superordinate system is not literally behavior. The high-
order system acts by specifying a goal - a reference
value, or standard - to the system that is immediately subordinate to it. That system then acts by
specifying reference values to the next lower level,
and so on. The standards that are specified are
becoming more concrete and restricted as one moves
down the hierarchy. At the very bottom, the reference values to be matched are physical ones, and the
behavioral output may be more obviously seen as
behavior. At each level, attainment of reference
values is monitored by checking on the perceptual
input relevant to that level.
   Note that the functioning of any superordinate
system presupposes the functioning of all systems
that are subordinate to it. Their action is a
relatively automatic consequence of the action of the
higher order system. The opposite is not necessarily
true, however. That is, whereas the operation of
level 3 in the hierarchy of Figure 3 would seem to
ensure the involvement of levels 2 and 1, it does
not seem that it would automatically ensure the
involvement of level 4.

Figure 3: A Hierarchy of Feedback Loops. The
behavioral output of a superordinate system consists
of the resetting of a reference value at the next
lower level. Goal attainment is monitored at each
level via perceptual input information appropriate
to that level. The boxed "C" at each level is that
level's comparator. (Adapted from Carver & Scheier,
1981a.)

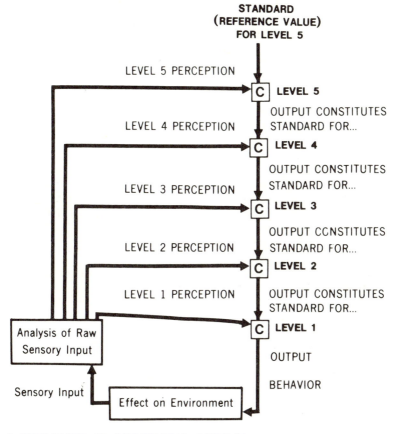

A HIERARCHY OF BEHAVIORAL CONTROL

Just what does this notion of a hierarchy of control
have to do with human behavior? Perhaps a good deal.
William Powers (1973a, 1973b) has suggested that the
human nervous system incorporates such a hierarchy of
feedback structures, and that this sort of organization is in fact what allows people to execute in

physical action what are often very abstract and ephemeral behavior prescriptions.*

In order to illustrate the levels of the model that Powers proposed, let us take an instance of a common behavior, and follow it through the hierarchy. We borrow this particular example from our more extended discussion of control theory and behavior published elsewhere (Carver & Scheier, 1981a). The example is the behavior of a person who has had guests drop in unexpectedly, and is making coffee for them.

In order to treat the full range of the levels that Powers postulated, we will assume that the person in our example is regulating his behavior with regard to a very abstract reference value: his concept of who he thinks he ought to be, his "ideal self". This self-image is one instance of what Powers termed a <u>system</u> concept, and the regulation of one's outgoing behavior with respect to such a value represents control at the level of system concepts. (Note that there are other potential system concepts to serve as highest-order guides for behavior, including idealized group identifications.)

The person in our example conceives of himself - when at his best - as an urbane and civilized person. But what does that mean? How is that reflected in behavior? Powers' answer is that conformity to a system concept is attained via the specification of <u>principles</u> in behavior. Principles are general guiding rules. Since those rules are specified by the system concept to which they are subordinate, they represent manifestations of the essence of that system concept. One principle held by the man in our example (specified by the civilized, urbane system concept) is that of graciousness. He should normally behave in a gracious manner, even toward unexpected visitors. Doing this represents control at the principle level. (From this point onward, our example is illustrated graphically in Figure 4.)

---

* We should note that the Powers model is a specific example of a more general class of possibilities (cf. discussions of "productive systems" by Newell, 1973; Newell & Simon, 1972; Simon, 1975, and of "action identification" by Wegner & Vallacher, 1980). We are focusing on the Powers hierarchy here for two reasons. First we are more familiar with his organization than with the alternatives. And second, we find aspects of his nomenclature to nicely capture the essence of certain qualities of human action.

Figure 4: Diagram of the Hierarchy Implicit in the Behavior of a Person Making Coffee for Unexpected Guests (from Carver & Scheier, 1981a).

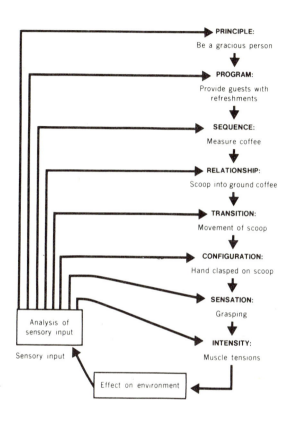

And how does one behave in a "gracious" manner? Graciousness is really a "quality" of behavior, rather than being a behavior itself. And this quality could be expressed in any number of ways. Powers argues that such principle-based qualities are realized by the carrying out of specific programs of activity. (Power's programs seem virtually identical to Schank & Abelsons's, 1977, "script", by the way.) Thus, program control is directly subordinate to principle control. Programs are organizations of behaviors, with specific goal states, but with a lot of potential ways of attaining those states. The program of activity in which the person in our example is engaged is "serving refreshments."

As this example indicates, by the time we have reached the level of program control, there is beginning to be "content" in behavior. But it is important to realize that not all of the acts to be engaged in are specified in a concrete way in a program. A program is not simply a list of acts. To the contrary, the most notable quality of program control is its "if-then" character. That is, what behavior is done at any given point depends partly on the overall goal, and partly upon what conditions are encountered along the way. For example, if your goal is to go to a specific restaurant, how you will get there is not rigidly determined. If it is a pleasant evening, you might walk; if it is pouring rain you would probably take a car. Similarly, "providing refreshments" is not a simple linear specification of acts. What the man in our example is providing is dictated partly by what was in the pantry and partly by the time of day. These considerations have led him into the sub-program "making coffee".

Though we are now closer to behavior, we are by no means there yet. Programs are physically executed by the production of yet more and more restricted aspects of behavior. For example, certain actions within a program must be organized in specific sequences; a given act represents a transition between specific orientations of the body; and all of this must be carried out by very elaborate patterns of very simple instances of physical, overt behavior - i.e., changes in muscle tensions. All of these characteristics of behavior reflect lower and lower levels of control in the hierarchy (see Figure 4).

And now mentally stand back and consider the total picture. As the man scoops into the ground coffee, what reference value is he matching? Is he creating muscle tensions? Is he holding onto the scoop? Is he measuring coffee? Providing refreshments? Being gracious? Or living up to his self-image? Given our construction of the situation, he is doing all of these simultaneously.

We have taken the position that self-regulation within this hierarchy is partially dependent upon the person's focus of attention. More specifically, we have assumed that the level of the hierarchy that is the object of the person's focus is functionally superordinate at that moment. We also assume, however, that in a good deal of human behavior, the program level of control is functionally superordinate though the capability of self-regulation with respect to principles and system concept is also present. Those levels will be involved in behavior when something makes a reference value salient at those levels. Why is the program level so often focal in behavioral regulation? Perhaps because of its "if-then" character, the maze of decisions that must implicitly be negotiated in executing a program successfully.

There are two more issues that we must broach (psychological issues, really, rather than cybernetic), before we can have a sense of closure on the basic element of the model with which we are working. The first issue is this: we have described a self-regulatory system that sets up goal states for itself (at several levels of abstraction) and behaves in such a way as to more closely approximate those goal states. But we have not yet suggested how this system goes about dealing with goals that it cannot attain, reference values it cannot match. Without some vehicle for responding to that sort of situation any system organized in the way we have outlined would continue to trudge forward, endlessly attempting the impossible, once such a task has been undertaken.

Disengagement From Behavioral Attempts

Our response to this difficulty is to assume that the behavior-regulating process can be interrupted by several kinds of conditions, and that this interruption leads to an assessment of how likely discrepancy reduction is to occur, based on the present situation and the person's resources (see Figure 5). If this judgment yields a favorable outcome, the result is continued attempts at discrepancy reduction. If the judgment is sufficiently unfavorable, the result is an impetus to withdraw from further attempts. This may be expressed behaviorally in terms of overt, physical withdrawal from the scene; withdrawal of effort in subsequent task attempts; or mental withdrawal and refusal to consider further (cf. Lewin, 1935; see also Heckhausen, 1967). We assume that these two responses - renewed efforts and withdrawal - comprise a rough dichotomy among potential responses. The "waters" point at which they diverge will presumably vary (in terms of subjective probability of goal attainment) as a function of the importance of the behavioral goal in question.

It should be noted that the elements that stem from the postulated interruption are not unique to our theory. We are squarely in the camp of expectancy-value theories in this regard, theories which have had a long history in psychology. However, it is also worthy of note that the sort of dichotomy

Figure 5:   Flow Diagram of the Attempt-Versus-
Disengagement Decision that takes place when Goal-
Directed Behavior is Interrupted by a Condition
such as Rising Anxiety or Frustated Efforts.
(Adapted from Carver, 1979)

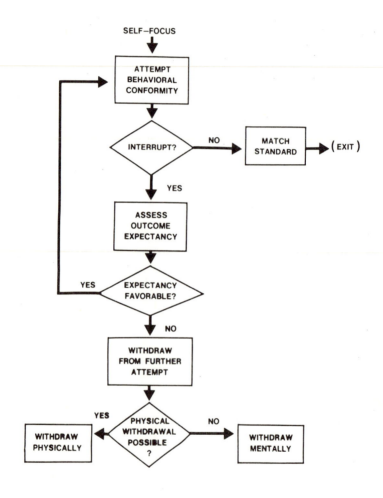

among responses that we are proposing seems easily
amenable to conceptualization within an information-
processing framework.   That is, as we discussed
earlier, the operation of a feedback loop - if viewed
in sequential terms - can be seen as a simple
decision, with two possible outcomes.   Either two

values match, or they do not. Similarly, in the postulated assessment process, a decision is being made as to whether or not it is worthwhile to continue, a decision that in some sense at least is reducible to an implicit yes or no.

What kinds of stimuli induce an interruption of this sort? This process can occur prior to a task attempt if, for example, the person knows ahead of time that the task will be difficult. It can occur during the behavior, if something is frustrating the person's attempt (cf. Kimble & Perlmuter, 1970). The frustrating condition can, of course, be either an environmental impediment of some sort, or a deficiency within the person that is preventing discrepancy reduction.

Another important class of interrupting stimuli is the rising of a strong emotion. As Simon (1967) has argued, one function of emotion is to serve notice that one's present goal is not the only thing that is deserving of one's attention. Of particular interest and importance to self-regulation is the emotion of fear, or anxiety. Many of the actions that people undertake are stressful, threatening, in one way or another. As anxiety mounts, the person may interrupt the attempt to assess whether he or she can cope with the rising fear well enough to successfully carry off the desired behavior. If the assessment is favorable, the effort will ensue. If it is unfavorable, the effort may be half-hearted, or it may even be given up altogether.

Public and Private Selves

A final point that we need to address derives from the fact that the self is multifaceted. A useful distinction, in this regard, can be made between private aspects of the self and public aspects of the self (cf. Buss, 1980; Carver & Scheier, 1981a; Fenigstein, Scheier, & Buss, 1975; Scheier & Carver, 1981). The private self consists of personal feelings, attitudes and other covert and hidden self aspects. The public self consists of those aspects of a person that are overt: displays and presentations of self to other people in the social matrix of which one is a part.

Goals that are "personal", in the sense that they do not depend upon the tacit approval of other people, are directly relevant to the private self. This sort of goal would seem to be implicit, for example, in competence strivings: internally motivated attempts to become more proficient at something (cf. White, 1959). An individual's attitudes also specify goal states relevant to the private self, in that they suggest the seeking out of persons, objects and events that are disliked. Such personal likes and dislikes do not depend upon the social context, and when behavior is based upon one's attitudes, the preferences of other people are not necessarily taken into consideration.

There are, however, many goals for which the social context and the opinions of other people are quite important. These goals are tied to the public self. A great deal of theory and research makes this point quite strongly: a substantial amount of human behavior seems motivated by a desire to project a particular image of the self (e.g., Goffman, 1959, 1967), or to "manage" the impression that one is conveying to others (e.g., Schlenker, 1980; Tedeschi, 1980). It thus should come as no surprise to find that people quite often choose how to behave on the basis of the nature of the social context (see, e.g., Scheier & Carver, 1981; Snyder, 1979).

In many cases, goals which are relevant to one's private and public self-aspect are quite similar to each other. Consider, for example, a person who often goes out of his way to be helpful to others. Helping others makes this person feel good (a private consideration), and it also makes him look good to others (a public consideration). Either or both of these considerations may be relevant to his behavior. Furthermore, each would tend to induce a greater amount of helping.

In other cases, however, self-presentational goals and private goals can differ from each other quite substantially. Consider, for example, a person who would prefer to act in one fashion, but is surrounded by (esteemed) other people who are behaving quite differently. In this situation, the goal that is relevant to the public self is to fit in with the group. The goal that is relevant to the private self is to behave in accord with one's attitudes. And the two goals sometimes are mutually exclusive.

The public-private distinction is quite an important one in predicting and understanding behavior. Moreover, as was implicit in the preceding paragraphs, the distinction is easily incorporated into a control-theory model of self-regulation. That is some reference values for behavior stem from the superordinate goal of creating and maintaining a desired personal image of oneself. Other reference values stem from the superordinate goal of creating and maintaining a desired public image. But both sorts of goals imply hierarchical organizations of

Control-Theory and Social Skills Training

behavior, entailing the specification of principles, programs of action, etc., and the matching of behavior to those reference values.

EVIDENCE

The two preceding sections have, in effect, sketched out a second-order approximation of control-theory approach to behavior, elaborating upon the simpler model that we presented initially. In the first of these sections we presented one possible way in which a hierarchy of control processes might be viewed as being embodied in behavior. We repeated there our earlier argument that focus of attention has an important impact on the self-regulation of behavior. But we added the following assumption: that the level of control structure at which attention is focused is functionally superordinate in the guidance of behavior.

In the second section we introduced two other important embellishments. The first was the notion that people disengage from attempts to match reference values when those attempts seem sufficiently likely to fail. This argument allows our model to account for withdrawal as well as reassertion, when a person is confronted by adversity. We also suggested that a meaningful and useful distinction can be made between the private image of what one should be, and the public image that one would like to display to others. Both of these can serve as relatively superordinate guides to behavior, but their influences on behavior are often quite divergent.

Having developed a more elaborate theoretical position in the two preceding sections, we now turn to a brief consideration of evidence that tends to establish the credibility of the model. We begin by examining the behavioral standard as a construct.

Behavioral Standards
As noted earlier, we assume that whatever level of behavioral control is being attended to is functionally superordinate at that time. Self-regulation at lower levels typically follows automatically, but self regulation at higher levels presumably is suspended temporarily. The level of control that is functionally superordinate need not be the highest level of control of which the person is _capable_. But one problem still remains: whatever level is being treated as superordinate at a given time needs to be provided with a behavioral standard to use as a reference value. An important question

that we have avoided until now is where does this standard come from?

A partial answer to this question is suggested by theories devised by cognitive psychologists to account for the development and use of categories in memory. Though the theories differ from each other in important ways (cf. Anderson, 1980), what is most important in the present context is their commonality. To oversimplify somewhat, the various theorists all assume that people encode elements of their experience fairly continously, and that those stored records are organized in some manner over time and experience (e.g., Neumann, 1977; Posner & Keele, 1968; Reitman & Bower, 1973; Rosch & Mervis, 1975). These organizations of knowledge - which generically are often termed schemas (cf. Bartlett, 1932) - are then used in the processing of new experiences. Specifically, those new experiences are "perceived" or "recognized" or "categorized" by reference to the preexisting schemas. When attributes of the new experience are the same as those of a knowledge structure, the new experience tends to evoke the structure, completely or partially, depending upon the degree of fit.*

The evoking of a schema appears to have at least two consequences. The more obvious is an implicit or explicit identification of the stimulus being experienced. The second, less obvious effect is this: the accessing of information from a schema appears to result in enhanced access to other aspects of the schema. This may lead the person to be more likely to seek out and notice other schema-relevant characteristics of the stimulus (e.g., Rothbart, Evans, & Fulero, 1979; Srull & Wyer, 1980; Wilder & Allen, 1978; Zadney & Gerard, 1974). It may even lead the person to assume the presence of schema-consistent attributes that have not been observed (e.g., Bransford & Franks, 1971; Cantor & Mischel, 1977; Hastorf, Schneider & Polefka, 1970).

What does all of this have to do with behavioral reference values? The answer is that many cognitive theorists assume that knowledge structures used to identify stimuli can also incorporate or imply information specifying behaviors (see, e.g., Rosch, 1978).

---

* Note that the process of perceiving or construing a stimulus may not be well represented in awareness. People do not always sift carefully through the elements of their sensory input to decide what they are perceiving (though they are capable of doing so, if need be).

These behavioral prescriptions presumably are acquired in the same fashion as are other attributes of the category that the knowledge structure represents. And they help to define the schema just as do the more perceptual or conceptual attributes that comprise it (cf. Ginsburg & Opper, 1969; Piaget, 1971). Thus, for example, the category "apples" typically includes the following attributes: round-ish, often red, grows on trees, and you can eat them.

When a schema incorporating behavioral information is evoked we assume that the behavioral information is thereby made more accessible (just as is true of other schema-consistent information). If it is accessed, it becomes the reference value for a feedback loop. We assume that in normal adult self-regulation, the schemas evoked by the implicit identification and categorization of the social (and physical) context are usually schemas with abstract overtones. That is, the perception of a room that one is entering is not only a pattern of colors, shades, and angle. It is also the perception of the room as a grocery store, or a dentist's office. When such categorizations imply behavior, the behaviors thus are themselves typically abstract - i.e., spec-ifications of programs, or sometimes of principles.

Is this reasoning viable? There is at least some evidence that it is. For example, Price (1974) had subjects rate the appropriateness of a series of behaviors occurring in a series of settings. He found a clear consensus that certain classes of actions were linked to certain classes of settings. Research on the association of behavioral prescrip-tions with environmental categories appears to be limited to that sort of data. But there is a greater diversity of research linking behavioral biases with classifications of persons. For example, arbitrary group assignments (i.e., the target person is made a member of the subject's group, or a different group) have had predictable influences on how subjects allocate money (e.g., Allen & Wilder, 1975; Billig & Tajfel, 1973). Racial categorizations lead to variations in behavior (Rubovits & Maehr, 1973), as do variations in perceived physical attractiveness (Snyder, Tanke, & Berscheid, 1977). Even perceiving the same person in two different ways - i.e., in terms of a role versus as a unique individual - has led to variations in allocation of resources (Carles & Carver, 1979). All of these effects represent acts of behavior stemming from initial categorizations. This suggests that behavior-specifying information is linked in memory with category membership information

Self-focus, Discrepancy Reduction and Disengagement

Once a behavioral standard has become salient, we have argued, self-focus induces a tendency to match one's behavior to the standard. As we indicated earlier in the chapter, there is substantial support for this argument, and we will not review that support in any detail here. What we will address here instead is support that has been gathered for the more elaborate version of that argument: i.e., that self-focus leads to enhanced discrepancy reduction when the person anticipates being able to do so successfully, and leads to a greater tendency to disengage from discrepancy reduction attempts when such attempts are seen as futile.

Data from several studies converge in support of this point. Though the studies were conducted for varying reasons, and many of them were conducted by investigators other than ourselves (e.g., Brockner, 1979; Gibbons & Wicklund, 1976; Steenbarger & Aderman, 1979), two of our own studies serve as simple and straightforward illustrations of the point. In one of the studies (Carver, Blaney, & Scheier, 1979a), subjects were persons who had earlier reported having a moderately intense fear of non-poisonous snakes. They differed from each other, however, in terms of how well they thought they could cope with their fear. "Confident" subjects thought that if asked to approach and pick up a snake they would be able to do so, though it would clearly be uncomfortable for them. "Doubtful" subjects reported being not at all sure that they could do that. All subjects later attempted (in individual sessions) to do the behavior in question, after the experimenter had indicated the importance of approaching as far as possible.

Nine levels of approach behavior had been predefined, ranging from coming to within two feet of the aquarium in which the snake was resting, to holding the snake in the air for fifteen seconds. Self-focus was varied within each subject group by the presence of a mirror at the level of the subject's face and shoulders. We expected this stimulus to make subjects more aware of their rising anxiety, as well as their goal of holding the snake (cf. Scheier, 1976; Scheier & Carver, 1977; Scheier, Carver, & Gibbons, 1981). This prediction was confirmed by subjects' post-experimental self-reports: more anxiety was reported overall among mirror-condition subjects than among no-mirror subjects. This awareness of anxiety was expected to cause subjects to interrupt their task attempts momentarily, and consider whether or not they could cope with the anxiety. Subjects' responses to that interruption, then, were expected to be predictable from their earlier levels of self-reported confidence. That is self-focus condition was expected to interact with premeasured confidence. This indeed proved to be the case. Doubtful subjects disengaged from the approach attempt earlier in the sequence when self-focus was high than when it was lower. And the opposite tendency occurred among confident subjects.

A conceptually similar finding was obtained in a subsequent study of persistence at an insoluble problem (Carver, Blaney, & Scheier, 1979b). A substantial discrepancy was created for each subject in this study by causing them to experience an unanticipated failure on an initial task. Following this, some subjects were led to expect to be able to redress the failure by performing well at a second task and others were led to expect continued failure on the second task. Mirror-enhanced self-focus led to less persistence on the second task among subjects with unfavorable expectancies. And, once the constraints of a too-short time limit had been removed (Carver et al., 1979b, Experiment 2), self-focus led to increased persistence among subjects with favorable expectancies. Finally, we should repeat that findings similar to those discussed here have also been reported by several other researchers (see Carver & Scheier, 1981a, for a comprehensive review).

Private and Public Self-Aspects

The final theoretical embellishment that was introduced into the model in the previous section (or at least embellishment for which there are data available) is the distinction between private and public aspects of the self. In making this distinction, we indicated that values associated with each of these facets of oneself can have an impact on behavior. Furthermore, we asserted that under some circumstances, at least, the impacts can be quite divergent. Finally, we argued that a given aspect of the self (and the reference values that are associated with it) influences behavior only when that aspect of self is taken as the object of one's attention.

Evidence supporting these assertions comes from several sources, utilizing two fundamentally differerent research techniques. The first technique - which involves experimental manipulations - is based upon a body of evidence indicating that stimuli such as small mirrors tend to focus attention selectively onto the private self, whereas stimuli such as T.V.

cameras or an audience of observers tend to focus attention onto more public self-aspects. The second technique makes use of chronic individual differences in the tendency to focus attention inward to the self. The Self-Consciousness Scale, which is used to assess this disposition (Fenigstein et al., 1975), incorporates a measure of private self-consciousness composed of items such as "I'm generally attentive to my inner feelings", and a measure of public self-consciousness composed of items such as "I'm concerned about the way I present myself". These two scales are factorially sound, and are relatively independent of each other (see Fenigstein et al., 1975). This makes it relatively easy to use the instrument in examining the separate effects on behavior that are associated with attending to the public and private self-aspects of oneself.

Studies using the Self-Consciousness Scale have uncovered several instances in which these two self-aspects influence behavior in quite different ways. In one project (Carver & Scheier, 1981c) subjects were exposed to a manipulation of psychological reactance (Brehm, 1966), in a fashion that involved interpersonal communications. Private self-consciousness was associated with a high degree of resistance to the reactance manipulation. Said differently, private self-consciousness intensified the normal reactance effect, apparently by making subjects more aware of the aversiveness of having their personal freedom threatened. Independent of this effect, public self-consciousness was associated with a _moderation_ of the reactance effect, apparently by sensitizing subjects to the potential interpersonal consequences of overreacting (see Carver & Scheier, 1981c, for greater detail).

In another study (Froming & Carver, 1981), subjects were exposed to conformity pressure that was implicit rather than explicit. This pressure took the form of unanimous but incorrect responses made to perceptual-judgment problems on the part of ostensible co-subjects (cf. Asch, 1951). In this circumstance, private self-consciousness was associated with a tendency to disregard the others' responses. Public self-consciousness, independently, was associated with a tendency to go along with the incorrect majority.

Yet a third project (Scheier & Carver, 1980) investigated cognitive reorganization following a voluntarily undertaken counter-attitudinal behavior (cf. Festinger, 1957). Private self-consciousness was found to be associated with a tendency among

164

subjects to retain their original attitudes, and to bring their perceptions of their (public) behavior into line with those attitudes. Public self-consciousness, in contrast, was associated with a tendency to acknowledge the public behavior, and to bring their attitudes into line with the behavior. This project also examined the effects of experimental manipulations on subjects' cognitive reorganizations. In brief, the presence of a mirror produced effects that were quite comparable to those of high private self-consciousness, and the presence of a T.V. camera produced effects that were quite comparable to those of high public self-consciousness.

At least one more research project has used experimental manipulations to examine the divergent effects of focusing on the private versus public self. In this research (Froming, Walker, & Lopyan, 1982) subjects were selected as having a specific opinion about the utility and desirability of using punishment as a teaching technique, but as also believing that "most people" held the opposite opinion. These subjects later were given the opportunity to deliver punishments to another person in a presumed experiment on learning. The presence of a mirror in front of subjects during that session caused them to conform more closely to their own personal opinions (whether pro-punishment or anti-punishment) than when the mirror was absent. The presence of several observers, on the other hand, caused increased conformity to the opinions that subjects attributed to "most people".

These examples illustrate the kinds of situations in which focusing on the private self leads to effects quite different from the effects created by focusing on the public self. Though these examples do not by any means exhaust the research illustrations of this point (see Scheier & Carver, 1981, for a more complete review), they do indicate that the public-private distinction is an important one, with very real behavioral implications.

Section Summary
In this section of the chapter we have reviewed part of the available research support for several aspects of the theoretical model that was outlined earlier. We suggested that behavioral standards are encoded in memory along with other information that comprises the schemas with which people organize and catalogue their experiences, and we discussed several sources of evidence that this might be so. We also described

a pair of studies that appear to indicate that conformity to a behavioral standard (once that standard has become salient) is influenced both by self-focus and by the person's expectancy of being able to do the behavior that will attain the goal. Finally, we reviewed studies that contrasted focus on the private self with focus on the public self. These studies appear to indicate that each self-aspect can have an important impact on behavior, but each does so only when it is taken as the specific object of one's focus. Taken together, these various studies offer considerable support for the theoretical perspective we have adopted. We should note quite explicitly however, that one facet of this perspective has not been subjected to experimental tests. That facet is the hierarchical organization of control structures proposed by Powers (1973a). Though we feel that his ideas have merit, we have not yet attempted to verify their utility empirically.

IMPLICATIONS

Now that we have described our general approach to behavioral self-regulation and reviewed portions of the support for that approach, let us adopt for the moment a broader perspective and consider a different question: specifically, what might be the implications of this approach for the conceptualization of problems in the area of social skills training? Three sets of rather basic implications seem apparent to us. One of them stems from the notion that behavior is organized in a hierarchy of control structures. The second concerns the role of expectancies in self-regulation. And the third derives from the distinction between public and private aspects of the self. These are taken up, in turn, in the following sections.

Hierarchical Organization and Maladaptive Behavior
Consider once again the hierarchy of control proposed by Powers (1973a). In ordinary adult behavior (and in the behavior of children past a certain age) it seems likely that reference values for the behavioral qualities occurring at very <u>low</u> levels in the hierarchy are usually specified easily and automatically by the higher-level structures. That is, the behavioral qualities that are being specified at those lower levels are component elements of a great many kinds of action. They occur repeatedly, and in widely diverse contexts. Those low-level goal specifications - and their ultimate realization in

physical action - thus are typically well programmed. This has consequences that are easily observed. It is commonly noted, for example, that muscle coordinations generalize across different domains of activity. The more similar the domain, the more complete the generalization, of course. But it is really only when one considers domains such as sport, dance, the playing of musical instruments, and the like, that highly specialized patterns of action seem to be needed at all. Most human action is comprised of relatively simple behavioral qualities. And it is our assumption that those qualities are called for by higher-order structures with a high degree of automaticity in normal behavior.

The same thing can not necessarily be said of behavioral specifications at higher levels, however. Indeed, it seems likely that a good deal of the behavioral disruption that is viewed as neurotic or maladaptive stems from an inability to specify reference values from the level of system concepts (or principles) down to - and through - the program level. That is, many people have abstract images of what they think they should be - "happy", "likeable", "successful", "popular", and so on - but have no idea what concrete actions will move them in the direction of those higher-order goals. Indeed, they may even lack guides as to how to go about determining what concrete steps will help to match reference values at the more abstract levels. This can be quite distressing, of course, when the abstract goals are highly valued.

Conceptualizing the behavioral problem in this fashion also yields suggestions for the process of behavior change. Specifically, a useful way of approaching a psychological problem would seem to be (a) to induce the person to analyze the abstract complaint ("I'm terrible at getting along with others") in terms of the concrete acts of ineffective self-regulation that are associated with it - indeed, may compromise it (e.g., "I don't speak up very often when I'm with other people") - and (b) to respecify those component acts in more effective ways. It is interesting to us that this line of argument has considerable similarity to some of the reasoning underlying the so-called "cognitive" therapies (cf. Beck, 1976; Meichenbaum, 1977).

Conclusions derived from recent research on problem solving in intellectual domains are also of interest in this context. Such research typically finds evidence of a sort of "bootstrapping" effect (see, e.g., Anzai & Simon, 1979; Larkin, McDermott,

Simon, & Simon, 1980). That is, the way in which an initial problem is approached differs markedly from the way problems are approached after gaining some experience. The initial attempt involves generating small components of behavior strategy. Once a component structure is incorporated into the behavioral stream, it is then used as a vehicle for the generation of higher-order structures. Ironically, once a sophisticated understanding of the task at hand has been developed, the very initial component behavior which led to the development of the more abstract behavior may even be abandoned, because it turns out to be less efficient than a previously unconsidered alternative. The long-term result of this process is that the person is not just capable of solving a specific problem. Instead, the person has learned a general approach to a class of problems. This sort of process also has implications for therapy. If the bootstrapping effect generalizes to solving problems in one's behavioral self-management, a properly focused therapy should naturally induce in clients a greater ability to analyze and resolve their problems in different domains.

We should not leave our discussion of the control hierarchy without making one more point. The cases under discussion have implicitly involved the absence of a strategy for translating higher-level goals into concrete action specifications. But there are also cases in which an action strategy is being actively used despite the fact that it is demonstrably ineffective. This typically occurs when an individual either is failing to monitor the effects of his or her behavior, or is monitoring those effects via perceptual input that is actually irrelevant to the higher-order goal attainment. In this "misregulation" of behavior, the person continues to act in inappropriate ways, because he or she literally does not realize that the actions are inappropriate.

As a simple example of this process consider the person who enters every social gathering by acting in a loud, raucous and overbearing manner. He is convinced that such behavior makes him appear to others to be the "life of the party", an image that he holds dear and very much wishes to project. Because the people with whom he interacts consistently fail to disabuse him of this notion, he never realizes that the public image he is creating is actually that of an obnoxious boor.

Expectancies, Goal Setting and Goal Attainment

A second set of considerations revolves around

the notion that people will not make serious attempts when they believe those attempts will be futile. Our earlier discussion of research relating to this point concerned moment-to-moment self-regulation. We presented evidence, for example, that when doing a fear-inducing behavior people's actions depend upon whether or not they feel they can cope successfully with their fear. If they think they <u>can</u>, they strive toward the goal. If they have sufficient doubts, efforts cease and they disengage from the attempt.

One can easily see a sort of self-fulfilling quality in this sort of sequence. When a person assesses outcome expectancy, finds it to be bleak and then ceases to try, the result is usually a bad outcome. This, in turn, further reinforces the person's doubts about his or her ability to perform the desired behavior. The result is an ingrained tendency to withdraw from the difficult situation at the earliest opportunity (cf. Kanfer & Hagerman, 1981).

This same general line of reasoning is applicable at other levels of analysis, as well. In particular, it has been known for some time that "therapy expectancy" - the expectancy that some treatment procedure will reduce the severity of one's problem - plays a role in the therapy process (cf. Murray & Jacobson, 1978). It seems a straightforward inference that the effect of such an expectancy is to keep the person involved in the process of therapy, even when the process is difficult and painful, and even when progress is slow and tortuous. Without the expectancy of gain, on the other hand, the person is more apt to withdraw effort and involvement when difficulties are encountered. Indeed some authors (e.g., Bandura, 1977; Kanfer, 1977; Kanfer & Hagerman, 1981) have discussed the process of effective behavior change as involving the alteration of one's perceptions of being able to <u>effect</u> the needed change (i.e., self-efficacy perceptions). Everything else presumably depends upon that reorganization and reorientation.

It should be noted, however, that expectancy assessment occurs in many forms, in part because most goals of human endeavor have component subgoals. That is, any time people assess the likelihood of moving forward to goal attainment, they may do this with regard to the overall goal, or with regard to some temporarily salient subgoal. It seems likely that the result of the assessment process may depend very much upon which of those is done. Specifically, all other things being equal, expectancies of being able to do a discrete, restricted behavior should be more favorable than expectancies of being able to attain a more abstract, psychologically distant goal of which the discrete behavior is a component. This directly implies the importance of breaking any difficult behavior (or indeed the process of behavioral change) into a series of discrete, manageable steps, no one of which is too forbidding by itself. It may also suggest the importance of making the component steps concrete, rather than abstract and "conceptual" (cf. Leventhal, Meyer, & Nerenz, 1980; Leventhal, Brown, Shacham & Engquist, 1979).

There is another side to this issue, as well. Specifically, it is important that the person's expectancies be realistic as well as concrete. That is, even in cases where the behavior of interest is clearly defined (for example, in controlling one's weight through dietary adjustment and monitoring of calories), it is often sufficiently difficult that the person needs to be aware that the path will not be easy. Too-easy acceptance of a favorable prognosis may otherwise lead to disillusionment, discouragement and ultimately to disengagement (cf. Kirschenbaum, Humphrey, & Malett, 1981).

Social Skills and Aspects of Self

The final set of considerations that we will address here stem from the distinction made earlier between private and public aspects of the self. As a general rule, any mention of "social skills" as a problem area brings to mind the public self. It is, after all, the public self that is involved in the matrix of interaction with other people (cf. Leary & Schlenker, 1981). In discussing this issue in greater depth, however, we find it useful to make a second distinction, this one among the problems to which social skills training might be applied. We see two classes of problems here. In the first category is the person who is acutely aware that some needed behavior or skill is either deficient or lacking. This leads to an anticipation of bad outcomes, and chronic anxiety over impending social interactions. In the second category is the person who is not really aware that needed social skills are lacking. Indeed, the skill that may be most lacking is the ability to recognize when a given behavior is or is not appropriate. This person is disruptive in social encounters, but some such people are blissfully unaware that they are having that effect on others.

The first of these two problem classes has a familiar ring, conceptually. Indeed, we see this category as nicely illustrating the two sets of ideas just discussed. The person who perceives a self-deficiency wants to be successful, but either does not know what to do, or else has doubts about having the ability to do it. With doubts about the ability to cope, the result is a vicious cycle of disengagement without further doubts. Shyness, and the more extreme forms of social anxiety would all seem to fit this pattern to some degree (see, e.g., Buss, 1980; Leary & Schlenker, 1981; Pilkonis, 1977a, 1977b).

We would assume that such problems are exacerbated by high degrees of focus on the public self, because such focus makes salient the desired goals (cf. Leary & Schlenker, 1981), and is likely to lead to interruption and outcome-expectancy assessment. But because these problems also involve an affective reaction, they can also be exacerbated by focusing on the private self. That is, when anxiety becomes strong, private self-consciousness is associated with greater awareness of the anxiety (cf. Carver et al., 1979a; Scheier et al., 1981). If the person is someone with severe doubts about coping, the result of this enhanced awareness of the anxiety engendered by the situation will be an impetus to withdraw from the situation. Whether the problem is viewed as associated with private or public self-consciousness, however, the mode of approaching treatment of such problems would seem to be the same: i.e., develop the necessary skills in the person, and the confidence that is needed to deploy these skills.

Although there is certainly more complexity in this class of problems that we have addressed here (see Buss, 1980; Crozier, 1979; Leary & Schlenker, 1981), the second category is perhaps even more complex. That is, it probably includes at least two subclasses which have quite divergent underlying dynamics. The overt display of inappropriate social behavior may in some instances reflect an abnormally low level of focus on the public self. That is, the person may simply not be thinking about how he or she is appearing to others, as behavior is guided instead by purely personal desires. Such a person might benefit from reminders that there is a society out there; that it can be important to attend to self-presentational concerns, if one's behavior is to be effective. In some cases, this means going further than mere reminders, of course. Some people can be described without too much hyperbole as having little or nothing in the way of a social self, at the point of clinical intervention. The social self must almost literally be extracted from them by the intervention process.

There is, however, another sub-class of instances of disruptive and inappropriate behavior,
instances in which attention to the public self is
high, rather than low. This is the case of the
person who actively uses such behavior as a tool to
mainipulate others. Disruptive behavior receives
attention; it can be used to bully one's peers; and
however much one may deplore the use of such tactics,
one must also recognize that they exist. The sort of
person who uses such tactics regularly would seem to
have an unusually strong overlap between public and
private self-aspects, in terms of the component goals
that they incorporate. That is, such a person is
using the public self and its goal specifications in
the furtherance of very personal, private ends.
Whether this class of events is one that is subject
to social skills training would seem to depend upon
how one defines social skills training. It seems
clear, however, that the distinction being made here
between the person who is unwillingly disruptive and
the person who is intentionally disruptive is an
important one, both theoretically and practically.

Section Summary

In this closing section of the chapter we have
attempted to indicate, in general terms, what sort of
implications our approach to self-regulation might
have for social skills deficits and social skills
training. We suggested that in many social skills
problems there exists an abstract, high-order reference value, but with inadequate specification of
concrete component reference values. Thus, the hierarchical organization of behavior cannot function
effectively. In other problems goals are specified
rather completely, but the person has chronic and
severe doubts about being able to attain the goals.
The result is disengagement from the attempt, and a
continuing spiral of doubt and withdrawal. Finally,
we indicated the importance of recognizing that
problems in social skills are problems associated
with the public self. In some cases the difficulties
are created by an inability or a perceived inability
to project oneself effectively, despite a high degree
of self-awareness. In other cases, the difficulties
can be traced to an inattention to the self as part
of the social matrix.

None of these connections between our theoretical approach and the practical reality of social
skills training is so simple as to indicate "the"
answer to a given problem in research or application.

Moreover, many of the ideas we have advanced could easily be generated from alternative formulations. Thus we are not likely to be sending social skills practitioners off into fundamentally new directions. Finally, we should acknowledge that these implications are at this point speculative. They have not yet been tested by ourselves or anyone else, to our knowledge. Nevertheless, they arise from a model of behavior that we perceive as having reasonable internal consistencies, and a model that has had considerable support from the laboratories of social and personality psychology. Thus, we feel that it has promise. We hope that these speculations will prove interesting to workers in the area of social skills, and we hope that they may suggest useful hypotheses to those workers for future investigation.

REFERENCES

Allen, V.L., & Wilder, D.A. Categorization, belief similarity, and intergroup discrimination. Journal of Personality and Social Psychology, 1975, 32, 971-977

Anderson, J.R. Cognitive psychology and its implications. San Francisco: Freeman, 1980

Annett, J. Feedback and human behavior. Baltimore, Md.: Penguin, 1969

Anzai, Y., & Simon, H.A. The theory of the learning by doing. Psychological Review, 1979, 86, 124-140

Argyle, M. & Kendon, A. The experimental analysis of social performance. Advances in Experimental Social Psychology, 1967, 3, 55-98

Asch, S. Effects of group pressure upon the modification and distortion of judgments. In H. Guetzkow (Ed.), Group, leadership, and man. Pittsburgh, Pa.: Carnegie Press, 1951

Bandura, A. Self-efficacy: Toward a unifying theory of behavior change. Psychological Review, 1977, 84, 191-215

Bartlett, F.C. Remembering: A study in experimental and social psychology. Cambridge: Cambridge University Press, 1932

Beck, A.T. Cognitive therapy and the emotional disorders. New York: International Universities Press, 1976

Billig, M., & Tajfel, H. Social categorization and similarity in intergroup behavior. European Journal of Social Psychology. 1973, 3, 27-52

Bransford, J.D., & Franks, J.J. The abstraction of linguistic ideas. Cognitive Psychology 1971,

        2, 331-350
Brehm, J.W. A theory of psychological reactance.
    New York: Academic Press, 1966
Brockner, J. The effects of self-esteem, success-
    failure, and self-consciousness on task perform-
    ance. Journal of Personality and Social Psych-
    ology, 1979, 37, 1732-1741
Buckley, W. Modern systems research for the be-
    havioral scientist. Chicago: Aldine, 1968
Buss, A.H. Self-consciousness and social anxiety.
    San Francisco: Freeman, 1980
Cantor, N., & Mischel, W. Traits as prototypes:
    Effects on recognition memory. Journal of Per-
    sonality and Social Psychology, 1977, 35, 38-48
Carles, E.M., & Carver, C.S. Effects of person sal-
    ience versus role salience on reward allocation
    in a dyad. Journal of Personality and Social
    Psychology, 1979, 37, 2071-2080
Carver, C.S. Facilitation of physical aggression
    through objective self-awareness. Journal of
    Experimental Social Psychology, 1974, 10, 365-
    370
Carver, C.S. Physical aggression as a function of
    objective self-awareness and attitudes toward
    punishment. Journal of Experimental Social Psy-
    chology, 1975, 11, 510-519
Carver, C.S. A cybernetic model of self-attention
    process. Journal of Personality and Social
    Psychology, 1979, 37, 1251-1281
Carver, C.S., Blaney, P.H., & Scheier, M.F. Focus
    of attention, chronic expectancy, and respon-
    ses to a feared stimulus. Journal of Person-
    ality and Social Psychology, 1979, 37, 1186-
    1195 (a)
Carver, C.S., Blaney, P.H., & Scheier, M.F. Reass-
    ertion and giving up: The interactive role of
    self-directed attention and outcome expectancy.
    Journal of Personality and Social Psychology,
    1979, 37, 1859-1870 (b)
Carver, C.S., & Scheier, M.F. Self-focusing effects
    of dispositional self-consciousness, mirror pre-
    sence, and audience presence. Journal of Per-
    sonality and Social Psychology, 1978, 36, 324-
    332
Carver, C.S., & Scheier, M.F. Attention and self-
    regulation: A control-theory approach to human
    behavior. New York: Springer-Verlag, 1981 (a)
Carver, C.S., & Scheier, M.F. A control-systems
    approach to behavioral self-regulation. In L.
    Wheeler (Ed.), Review of personality and
    social psychology (Vol.2). Beverly Hills,

Calif: Sage, 1981 (b)

Carver, C.S., & Scheier, M.F. Self-consciousness and reactance. Journal of Research in Personality, 1981, 15, 16-29 (c)

Cooley, C.H. Human nature and the social order. New York: Scribners, 1902

Crozier, W.R. Shyness as a dimension of personality. British Journal of Social and Clinical Psychology, 1979, 18, 121-128

Davis, D., & Brock, T.C. Use of first person pronouns as a function of increased objective self-awareness and prior feedback. Journal of Experimental Social Psychology, 1975, 11, 381-388

Duval, S., & Wicklund, R.A. A theory of objective self-awareness. New York: Academic Press, 1972

Fenigstein, A., Scheier, M.F., & Buss, A.H. Public and private self-consciousness: Assessment and theory. Journal of Consulting and Clinical Psychology, 1975, 43, 522-527

Festinger, L. A theory of cognitive dissonance. Stanford, Calif: Stanford University Press, 1957

Froming, W.J., & Carver, C.S. Divergent influences of private and public self-consciousness in a compliance paradigm. Journal of Research in Personality, 1981, 15, 115-121

Froming, W.J., Walker, G.R., & Lopyan, K. Public and private self-awareness: When personal attitudes conflict with societal expectancies. Journal of Experimental Social Psychology, 1982, 18, 476-487

Geller, V. & Shaver, P. Cognitive consequences of self-awareness. Journal of Experimental Social Psychology, 1976, 12, 99-108

Gibbons, F.X. Sexual standards and reactions to pornography: Enhancing behavioral consistency through self-focused attention. Journal of Personality and Social Psychology, 1978, 36, 976-987

Gibbons, F.X., & Wicklund, R.A. Selective exposure to the self. Journal of Research in Personality, 1976, 10, 98-106

Ginsburg, H., & Opper, S. Piaget's theory of intellectual development: An introduction. Englewood Cliffs, N.J.: Prentice-Hall, 1969

Goffman, E. The presentation of self in everyday life. New York: Doubleday-Anchor, 1959

Goffman, E. Interaction ritual: Essays on face-to-face behavior. Garden City, N.Y.: Doubleday-Anchor, 1967

Greenberg, J. Attentional focus and locus of performance causality as determinants of equity behavior. Journal of Personality and Social Psychology, 1980, 38, 579-585

Hastorf, A.H., Schneider, D., & Polefka, J. Person perception. Menlo Park, Calif.: Addison-Wesley, 1970

Heckhausen, H. The anatomy of achievement motivation. New York: Academic Press, 1967

Kanfer, F.H. The many faces of self-control, or behavior modification changes its focus. In R.B. Stuart (Ed.), Behavioral self-management: Strategies, techniques, and outcomes. New York: Brunner/Mazel, 1977

Kanfer, F.H., & Hagerman, S. The role of self-regulation. In L.P. Rehm (Ed.), Behavior therapy for depression: Present status and future directions. New York: Academic Press, 1981

Kimble, G.A., & Perlmuter, L.C. The problem of volition. Psychological Review, 1970, 77, 361-384

Kirschenbaum, D.S., Humphrey, L.L., & Malett, S.D. Specificity of planning in adult self-control: An applied investigation. Journal of Personality and Social Psychology, 1981, 40, 941-950

Kuhn, A. The logic of social systems. San Francisco: Jossey-Bass, 1974

Larkin, J., McDermott, J., Simon, D.P., & Simon, H.A. Expert and novice performance in solving physics problems. Science, 1980, 208, 1335-1342

Leary, M.R., & Schlenker, B.R. The social psychology of shyness: A self-presentation model. In J.T. Tedeschi (Ed.), Impression management theory and social psychological research. New York: Academic Press, 1981

Leventhal, H., Brown, D., Shacham, S., & Engquist, G. Effects of preparatory information about sensations, threat of pain, and attention on cold pressor distress. Journal of Personality and Social Psychology, 1979, 37, 688-714

Leventhal, H., Meyer, D., & Nerenz, D. The common sense representation of illness danger. In S. Rachman (Ed.), Medical psychology (Vol.2). New York: Pergamon, 1980

Lewin, K. A dynamic theory of personality. New York: McGraw-Hill, 1935

Mead, G.H. Mind, self and society. Chicago: University of Chicago Press, 1934

Meichenbaum, D. Cognitive behavior modification: An integrative approach. New York: Plenum, 1977

Miller, G.A., Galanter, E., & Pribram, K.H. Plans and the structure of behavior. New York: Holt, Rinehart, & Winston, 1960

Miller, J.G. Living systems. New York: McGraw-Hill,

1978

Murray, E.J., & Jacobson, L.I. Cognition and learning in traditional and behavioral therapy. In
S.L. Garfield & A.E. Bergin (Eds.), Handbook
of psychotherapy and behavior change (2nd ed.).
New York: Wiley, 1978

Neumann, P.G. Visual prototype formation with dis-
continuous representation of dimensions of variability. Memory and Cognition, 1977, 5, 187-197

Newell, A. Production systems: Models of control
structures. In W.G. Chase (Ed.), Visual information processing. New York: Academic Press 1973

Newell, A., & Simon, H.A. Human problem solving.
Englewood Cliffs, N.J.: Prentice-Hall, 1972

Piaget, J. Biology and knowledge: An essay on the
relations between organic regulations and cognitive processes. Chicago: University of Chicago
Press, 1971

Pilkonis, P.A. Shyness, public and private, and its
relationship to other measures of social behavior. Journal of Personality, 1977, 45, 585-
595,(a)

Pilkonis, P.A. The behavioral consequences of shyness. Journal of Personality, 1977, 45, 596-
611,(b)

Posner, M.I., & Keele, S.W. On the genesis of abstract ideas. Journal of Experimental Psychology, 1968, 77, 353-363

Powers, W.T. Behavior: The control of perception
Chicago: Aldine, 1973 (a)

Powers, W.T. Feedback: Beyond behaviourism. Science
1973, 179, 351-356 (b)

Price, R.H. The taxonomic classification of behaviors
and situations and the problem of behaviour-
environment congruence. Human Relations, 1974,
27, 567-585

Reitman, J.S., & Bower, G.H. Storage and later recognition of exemplars of concepts. Cognitive
Psychology, 1973, 4, 194-206

Rosch, E. Principles of categorization. In E. Rosch
& B.B. Lloyd (Eds.), Cognition and categorization. Hillsdale, N.J.: Erlbaum, 1978

Rosch, E., & Mervis, C. Family resemblances: Studies
in the internal structure of categories. Cognitive Psychology, 1975, 7, 573-605

Rothbart, M., Evans, M., & Fulero, S. Recall for
confirming events: Memory processes and the
maintaining of social stereotypes. Journal of
Experimental Social Psychology, 1979, 15, 343-
355

Rubovits, P.C., & Maehr, M.L. Pygmalion black and

white. Journal of Personality and Social Psychology, 1973, 25, 210-218

Schank, R.C., & Abelson, R.P. Scripts, plans, goals, and understanding. Hillsdale, N.J.: Erlbaum, 1977

Scheier, M.F. Self-awareness, self-consciousness, and angry aggression. Journal of Personality. 1976, 44, 627-644

Scheier, M.F., & Carver, C.S. Self-focused attention and the experience of emotion: Attraction, repulsion, elation, and depression. Journal of Personality and Social Psychology, 1977, 35, 625-636

Scheier, M.F., & Carver, C.S. Private and public self-attention, resistance to change, and dissonance reduction. Journal of Personality and Social Psychology, 1980, 39, 390-405

Scheier, M.F., & Carver, C.S. Private and public aspects of the self. In L. Wheeler (Ed.), Review of personality and social psychology (Vol. 2). Beverly Hills, Calif.: Sage, 1981

Scheier, M.F., Carver, C.S., & Gibbons, F.X. Self-focused attention and reactions to fear. Journal of Research in Personality, 1981, 15, 1-15

Scheier, M.F., Fenigstein, A., & Buss, A.H. Self-awareness and physical aggression. Journal of Experimental Social Psychology, 1974, 10, 264-273

Schlenker, B.R. Impression management: The self-concept, social identity, and interpersonal relations. Monterey, Calif.: Brooks/Cole, 1980

Simon, H.A. Motivational and emotional controls of cognition. Psychological Review, 1967, 74, 29-39

Simon, H.A. The functional equivalence of problem-solving skills. Cognitive Psychology, 1975, 7, 268-288

Snyder, M. Self-monitoring processes. In L. Berkowitz (Ed.), Advances in experimental social psychology (Vol.12). New York: Academic Press, 1979

Snyder, M., Tanke, E.D., & Berscheid, E. Social perception and interpersonal behavior: On the self-fulfilling nature of social stereotypes. Journal of Personality and Social Psychology, 1977, 35, 656-666

Srull, T.K., & Wyer, R.S., Jr. Category accessibility and social perception: Some implications for the study of person memory and interpersonal judgments. Journal of Personality and Social Psychology, 1980, 38, 841-856

Steenbarger, B.N., & Aderman, D. Objective self-awareness as a nonaversive state. Effect of anticipating discrepancy reduction. Journal of Personality, 1979, 47, 330-339

Tedeschi, J.T. (Ed.) Impression management theory and social psychological research. New York: Academic Press. 1980

von Bertalanffy, L. General systems theory. New York: Braziller, 1968

Wegner, D.M., & Vallacher, R.R. Action identification and self-regulation. Paper presented at the meeting of the American Psychological Association, Montreal, 1980

White, R.W. Motivation reconsidered: The concept of competence. Psychological Review, 1959, 66, 297-333

Wicklund, R.A., & Duval, S. Opinion change and performance facilitation as a result of objective self-awareness. Journal of Experimental Social Psychology, 1971, 7, 319-342

Wiener, N. Cybernetics: Control and communication in the animal and machine. Cambridge, Ma.: M.I.T. Press, 1948

Wilder, D.A., & Allen, V.L. Group membership and preference for information about others. Personality and Social Psychology Bulletin, 1978, 4, 106-110

Zadney, J., & Gerard, H.B. Attributed intentions and informational selectivity. Journal of Experimental Social Psychology, 1974, 10, 34-52

Editorial Introduction, Chapter Six

INTERPERSONAL EFFECTIVENESS FROM A MINDLESSNESS/
MINDFULNESS PERSPECTIVE

Mary M. Bandura, Ellen J. Langer and Benzion Chanowitz

*In chapter five, Carver and Scheier give us a model
of efficient skill learning and how this process may
fail. But an agency approach to social skills training (SST) needs to explain precisely how this process
fails in order to rectify it. This is the topic to
which Bandura, Langer and Chanowitz (who are clinical
and social psychologists) address themselves in the
following chapter. Their account may be partly summarized as follows.*

*Control theory describes an efficient system of
social adaptation (which can go wrong in the ways described). As an efficient system it requires a constantly vigilant monitor - the active, perceiving,
choosing, goal-seeking agent described in chapter
two. But not all behaviour is controlled in this
aware and "mindful" way, but is emitted automatically
and "mindlessly". This is more the picture of man
the passive organism, pushed and pulled by external
and internal forces. In this state, action and perception are guided by ingrained beliefs (or what Beck
(1976) describes as automatic thoughts) rather than
facts, and when the beliefs and thoughts are "dysfunctional" or "irrational" (e.g., as in paranoia)
the system becomes inefficient and maladaptive.*

*Bandura et al. argue and demonstrate that the
mindlessness/mindfulness distinction is crucial to an
understanding of good and poor social skills. They
say that the mindlessness mode engenders inaccurate
social inferences, severely curtails the range of
modes of interaction and invariably leads to negative
self-evaluation. They say that mindfulness underlies
the production of socially effective behaviour, and
the implications for training are clear. What it
entails is the conscious focussing on the <u>process</u> of
goal-attainment - the actual steps involved, the process of actually how-to-do-it. It involves the*

constant monitoring, for example, of cues in the situation and the flow of discourse. To achieve this they (the clients) need to be guided to the appropriate information and rules in situations and conversational exchanges.

This chapter, then, highlights the point at which training in productive cognitions can be interfaced with training in actual behavioural skills. It also reveals the weakness of research in SST which separates the "cognitive" from the "behavioural" approaches to SST, pitting one against the other. The two are here thoroughly integrated.

Chapter Six

INTERPERSONAL EFFECTIVENESS FROM A MINDLESSNESS/
MINDFULNESS PERSPECTIVE

Mary M.Bandura, Ellen J. Langer and Benzion Chanowitz

INTRODUCTION

An examination of how psychologists have conceptualized social skills leaves the reader with two
distinct impressions. The first concerns the description of what the socially skilled individual
does, a point upon which consensual agreement is
evident. In essence, this person is one who behaves
effectively in social interactions, with effectiveness defined relative to the context of an interaction (Hersen & Bellack, 1977). The second impression concerns the delineation of the skills exercised
in the production of socially effective behavior.
The definition of social skills, however, is plagued
by considerable conceptual ambiguity. These skills
have been variously conceptualized in terms of
motoric or verbal elements, cognitive capabilities,
regulation of arousal or some combination of these
three factors (Curran, 1977; Linehan, 1979). One
problem consistently encountered in definitional
attempts reflects the context-specificity of social
behavior. As pointed out by Curran (1977), for
instance, teaching people specific behaviors does not
guarantee that they will use them in situationally
appropriate ways. Any definition of social skills
would have to account for the situational specificity
of social effectiveness. In a similar vein, Hersen
and Bellack (1977) state that "the socially skilled
individual is attuned to the realities of the situation and is aware when he is likely to be reinforced for his efforts" (p.512). In the light of
these concerns, some clinical approaches to training
social effectiveness have focused on the acquisition
of discriminating skills. From this perspective, for
example, training in assertiveness should include
teaching people to identify situations in which

assertive behavior is appropriate (Lange & Jakubowski 1976).

In this chapter, we wish to deal with some of the difficulties encountered in specifying the nature of social skills. We will first attempt to identify some of the problems inherent in the analysis of social interaction that render such a definition elusive. Our goal is to provide a perspective from which an adequate psychological analysis of social skills may be obtained.

PHYSICAL VS. SOCIAL SKILLS: A HEURISTIC DIFFERENCE

In comparing the acquisition and exercise of physical skills with the generation of effective social behavior, it seems intuitively obvious that there are no differences that extend beyond those of content. Examining some of these differences suggests properties unique to the domain of social interaction, and is useful in specifying the nature of social skills.

When we speak of mastering a set of particular physical skills, such as carpentry, it makes sense to talk about learning to apply the tools of the trade to particular materials to produce specific products. Over time, the activity assumes a static structure, and demonstration of expertise is easily accomplished by wielding the tools in known ways. However, the mastery and exercise of social skills is not so easily described. First, it is necessary to consider what the tools of social interactions are, and second, to specify the structural character of social involvement. With reference to the first requirement, there are certainly no visible instruments we can point to; rather, the tools are conceptual in nature. With regard to the structural character of social involvement, it is certainly the case that it is not static. In principle, it can be said that the conceptual schemes utilized by individuals to lend definition to a social situation must be constantly up for revision, as there is no fixed structure that characterizes these situations. Herein lies the central problem plaguing attempts to define social skills. When Hersen and Bellack (1977) state that the socially skilled individual is "attuned to the realities of a situation", one may infer that the individual has formed a set of expectancies that specify the consequences associated with particular actions, or communications. To the extent that these expectancies are accurate, the individual has managed to form a set of veridical predictions regarding how

other participants evaluate specific actions. Unfortunately, social situations are not characterized
by an immutable structure; the way in which communications or gestures are evaluated is situationally
specific, or context dependent. In this sense, the
"realities" to which Hersen and Bellack (1977) refer
are the changing structures of social situations. A
major task facing an individual in social situations,
then, involves identifying relevant structural features upon which to base a set of expectancies, or
behavior-outcome relationships.

What might be some of these relevant structural
features? A look at how social psychologists have
defined social situations (an issue that has been of
major concern) may shed light on this question. The
Sherifs (1969) have discussed structure in social
situations in terms of ingredients related to the
location (with its cultural definitions and facil-
ities), the tasks to be performed, and the role and
status relations of the persons present (and accompanying norms). When people are members of a group
that conducts coordinated activities, they tend to
categorize (structure) situations in similar ways.
In consequence, they are likely to share a set of
expectancies regarding normative behavior. The
individual who wishes to function effectively in a
group must familiarize him/herself with the structure
of the group's activities and the normative expectations accompanying particular roles. An individual
not attuned to these social realities is likely to
behave in ways that violate normative expectations.
These same principles apply when an individual is
attempting to form a relationship with another for a
particular reason. To the extent that the two persons involved have categorized their social world in
different ways, they will act according to different
sets of norms. A satisfactory interaction requires
that they familiarize themselves with the relevant
categorical distinctions that each relies upon when
generating expectations of "appropriate" behavior in
various situations. Failure to do so may result in
continual surprise at the other's behavior. If the
perplexed participant fails to seek information that
would lend predictability to the other's behavior,
s/he may attempt to account for the unpredictable
actions in terms of global, dispositional features of
the other (e.g., "he's inconsiderate"). In addition
s/he is likely to burden the other's actions with
surplus, unintended meaning (e.g., "he must not care
about me").

The importance of these aspects of social interaction is underscored by developments in the treatment of dysfunctional relationships, which have pointed to information-seeking activity as essential to the amelioration of maladaptive interaction patterns (see, e.g., Watzlawick, Beavin, & Jackson, 1967). For example, some communication therapies teach participants to specify the referents of particular categories they use in day to day interaction. Rather than allowing participants to blame others' attributes for an unsatisfactory situation, each is trained to seek information about how the other interprets particular actions. For example, when an individual accuses another of not loving him/her, the respondent is encouraged to attempt to discern how that individual would know that s/he was loved; what sorts of things would the respondent have to do to make the other feel loved? In this manner, attention is refocused from explaining outcomes in terms of global dispositional attributes of the other to seeking specific information about how the other categorizes experience. By engaging in this process the parties can, over time, negotiate similar categorical distinctions that allow for effective communication, and that point to how they can behave so that mutual goals are realized.

To the extent that people are actively involved in attending to and categorizing information in a situation, they are engaging in a skillful exercise. Given that people are constantly confronted by novel social contexts, engagement in this process has no identifiable endpoint. To the extent that individuals do not engage in this process, they will not be attuned to situational "realities" (e.g., norms). That is, their expectancies are likely to be formed on the basis of irrelevant, inaccurate, or outdated information, and will therefore specify ineffective modes of social interaction.

Thus, an adequate definition of social skills should incorporate centrally the ongoing process of defining and categorizing relevant situational information. At this level of analysis, it becomes necessary to specify the cognitive mechanisms governing the acquisition of socially relevant information. In so doing, we can articulate clearly the ways in which people acquire and utilize information that leads to the formation of a set of expectancies which comprise the rules guiding behavior in a situation. In other words, we can specify how individuals become "attuned to the shifting realities of the situation".

Current approaches to social cognition have

generally assumed that individuals are actively processing information as they conduct their social
activities (see, e.g., Berkowitz, 1978). Recent research however, has suggested that a good deal of
social activity may be conducted in the absence of
any conscious information processing whatsoever; that
is, without awareness of the relevant details that
would seem necessary to accomplish these activities
(Langer, 1978). As we have proposed that a major
component of social skills is active identification
and categorization of relevant information in social
situations, this research has important implications
for the production of socially effective behavior.

We will proceed by describing a dichotomous concept - mindfulness/mindlessness - that has emerged
during the course of this research. This concept
characterizes qualitatively different ways in which
information available in a situation is utilized. We
will then discuss the implications of these two modes
of involvement with the environment, noting how one
represents a focus on situational outcomes, while the
other represents a process of defining the steps
involved in outcome attainment. These two orientations to social situations are likely to be associated with a host of different personal and
interpersonal consequences. In discussing these, we
will suggest ways in which clinicians may identify
and address some of the problems their clients are
experiencing when their complaints involve interpersonal difficulties.

THE MINDFULNESS/MINDLESSNESS DISTINCTION

The distinction between mindful and mindless human
activity is a qualitative, rather than quantitative
one. It is not captured adequately by stating that
an individual is paying more or less attention to
ongoing events (although that is certainly part of
it). Rather, a "mindless" state can be characterized
as one in which an individual relies on minimal information in a situation for executing (frequently
complex) sequences of behavior. Actions are carried
out routinely, accomplished by reduced levels of cognitive activity. To be mindless, in essence, is to
abstain from cognitively processing information - to
rely on previously constructed categories - available
in a situation. In the absence of any thoughtful
appraisal of the situation at hand, it does not occur
to the individual that alternative ways of engaging
oneself with the immediate environment are available.
Thus, intentional choices are not made regarding what

the best way to proceed might be. Rather, the individual responds to elements in the situation that
have been previously defined as relevant, and
executes well-learned sequences of behavior that are
specified by these cues. Mindlessness is characterized by the failure to make new distinctions based on
information available in a situation, and reliance on
previously made distinctions that dictate how to
proceed. In essence, the individual responds to that
which is familiar and well-defined in a situation,
and neglects that which is unfamiliar and undefined.
How is it that environments, or situations, can become so structured that they promote little thoughtful consideration; that they rigidly specify only one
way of behaving?

Mindlessness has been found to be engendered in
two ways. Both lead the individual to attend to
certain structural features of the environment that
have been previously defined as goal-relevant, and to
ignore other aspects of the situation. One way in
which this can be achieved is through repeated experience with a certain situation. Over time, a
structure of the situation is formed, and a defined
way of responding to the situation can be triggered
by the presence of familiar structural cues. This
mode of interacting with the environment is exemplified by research conducted by Langer, Blank and
Chanowitz (1978). In this series of studies, a
compliance paradigm was used to examine whether
people respond to the semantic sensibility or structural consistency of a communication. Specifically,
it was hypothesized that rates of compliance with a
request would be higher if the request was structured
in familiar ways (e.g., a reason for the request is
offered), even when these structural features did not
affect the semantic content of the communication
(e.g., "may I use the Xerox machine?" vs. "may I use
the Xerox machine because I have to make copies?").
The results of these studies supported this hypothesis; subjects responded to the structural aspects of
the communication rather than to its informational
content. However, this was the case only when the
request made did not require substantial effort on
the part of the subject. When it did, the informational content of the communication influenced the
subject's behavior, such that compliance was determined by whether or not the reason offered was a
legitimate one. This research suggests that when
people respond to structural familiarity in a
situation (i.e., behave mindlessly), they fail to
attend to information in the situation that may be

performance-relevant (see, e.g., Langer & Weinman, 1981). Thus, they proceed to behave in one well-defined way, when in principle other ways of responding would be available if the situation were thoughtfuly appraised.

The other way in which mindlessness can be achieved is via the appropriation of the structure of a situation from another source (Chanowitz & Langer, 1981). In this case, uncritical acceptance of categorical distinctions made by others is relied upon to specify the way in which one treats the categorical referents. For example, if one were to uncritically accept the distinction that "women are intellectually inferior to men" , then in situations where intellectual competence is relevant (e.g., hiring people to perform intellectual tasks), one would unthinkingly treat men and women differently, without regard to other potentially relevant information. Some of the conditions under which an individual is likely to accept an unconditional relationship between an element in the environment and the response it specifies have been explored by Chanowitz and Langer (1981). To date, these include when the information has little personal relevance, and when the individual is likely to behave according to these predetermined relationships, despite the fact that this may result in inferior performance.

Thus, whether mindlessness is achieved through repeated experience or uncritical acceptance of information, the consequences for how an individual uses information in a familiar situation are the same. When structural features of a situation are sufficiently similar to previous situations in which efficient (or unconditionally accepted) ways of behaving have already been defined, the individual is likely to respond to these structural cues and ignore other available information, although this may breed inefficient performances if new information (that is systematically ignored) becomes relevant to goal attainment (Chanowitz & Langer, 1981; Langer & Imber, 1979; Langer & Weinman, 1981). The critical features of mindlessness include: (1) Performance of sequences of behavior in a routine fashion, with respect to structured aspects of the environment that have been rigidly defined as relevant to the attainment of a particular goal; (2) the absence of active differentiation of the environment with respect to the activities the individual intends to accomplish, and, in the light of this; (3) a severely curtailed range of modes of interacting with the environment to produce desired outcomes.

Mindful activity, in contrast, can be character-ized as the process of actively differentiating the environment in the service of accomplishing certain goals. When one is operating mindfully, there is an appreciation that the character of the environment is unarticulated; distinctions relevant to attaining a goal remain to be created. It is not that the person acknowledges several particular possible ways of interacting with the environment that may produce different outcomes; rather, the person is aware that s/he has not yet grasped variations in the environ-ment that are and are not relevant to producing various outcomes. In this sense, the possibility of routine interaction with a well-structured environ-ment is precluded, and the individual must become in-volved in the process of choosing what do do, how to do it, and figure out what resources are available for manipulation. Consider, for example, the adoles-cent who is attending his first school dance. He is likely to be informed generally about what is and is not relevant to the conduct of this activity. How-ever, he is not likely to have yet defined the structure of the activity so that he can carry out specific steps in a routine manner. If he is mind-fully involved in the situation, he may be actively defining ways in which one can ask a girl to dance, differentiating approachable from unapproachable girls (e.g., does it matter if they are with another boy?), as well as attempting to define how one moves to produce particular dance steps. Involvement in this process can be characterized as an active search for frames of reference that specify relevant modes of interaction with the environment (with respect to intended outcomes). In fact, we can say that as long as one is mindfully involved in an activity, the way in which the situation is structured is up for con-tinual revision. A set of stable, categorical dis-tinctions has not been attained, and the possibility of viewing the environment from new, and different perspectives remains open. Different perspectives suggest different ways of treating elements of the situation to effect different outcomes. It is through this active involvement with the environment for certain purposes that people differentiate rel-evant from irrelevant features, and the environment begins to assume a manipulable structure. Thus, mindful activity represents the process of making new distinctions over the course of interaction with en-vironment (including, of course, other people). In sum, the mindful individual is (1) actively involved in the process of differentiating aspects of the environment, in relation to modes of interaction with them that are relevant to attaining desired outcomes, and (2) over time likely to exhibit change in the way s/he performs an activity in which s/he is mindfully engaged.

Mindless and mindful activity, then, represent quite different ways of utilizing information in a situation. It should be noted that these modes of involvement in activities are not stable states; a person who is performing mindlessly can be induced to be mindful under certain circumstances. These include (1) when significantly more effort is demanded by the situation than that required by the previously defined situation (as in the Langer, Blank, & Chanowitz study, 1978); (2) when external factors in the situation disrupt initiation of the mindless sequence; (3) when external factors prevent completion of the mindless sequence; or (4) when negative (cf. Wong & Weiner, 1981) or positive consequences are experienced that are sufficiently discrepant from the consequences of prior enactments of the same behavior (Langer, 1978). In principle, mindfulness is likely to be engendered when the structure of a situation is novel. However, an important feature of mindless activity is that one may enact a mindless sequence without attending to new, potentially relevant information and fail to realize that desired outcomes have not been attained. For example, if a familiar quotation that has been altered so that it is rendered non-sensical (but retains sufficient structural familiarity) is mindlessly read, the reader is likely to see (state) the original quote. Even though the person may have read quite inaccurately, s/he is likely to express great confidence that the quote was indeed read accurately (Langer & Weinman, 1979). Thus, unless there is clear specification that anticipated outcomes were not obtained, the mindlessly engaged individual may proceed as though s/he performed effectively, unaware of the fact that this was not the case. Should s/he be made aware of an ineffective performance, s/he may be left in the uncomfortable position of not knowing what information was neglected, nor how s/he failed to attend to relevant information to begin with. Because people are unaware of their own mindlessness, circumstances may render them vulnerable to negative self-evaluation, a point which we will return to later in the discussion. For the purposes of the present section, we will summarize by noting that when a task is performed mindlessly, the parts (or components) of the task are no longer the focus of attention. Rather, the steps are mindlessly executed in the service of attaining a given outcome. Let us return momentarily to our definition of social skills (as a process of identifying and categorizing relevant information in a social situation). We propose that the concept of mindfulness is of considerable utility in clarifying this definition. The processes that we have suggested underly the production of socially effective behavior and can be characterized in terms of mindful activity. The mindfully engaged individual will be actively attending to new information in a situation, distilling what is and is not relevant with respect to his/her goals in an interaction, and defining ways to proceed (or structure communications) that maximize the probability of goal attainment. Over the course of involvement in social situations, his/her social effectivenss is likely to increase, as behavior is generated according to an expanding, increasingly differentiated information base. The mindlessly involved individual may exhibit smooth, integrated performances in some social situations, but is likely to run into trouble when elements of situations change and critical information goes unnoticed. Thus, an examination of an individual's social behavior at a given point in time is unlikely to reflect the extent to which they are exercising skills, as we have conceptualized them. Rather, it is necessary to assess the way in which an individual is involved in social activities, since it is the nature of the experience they are having (how information is utilized) that will determine subsequent adaptive functioning in social situations. We will now address specifically the personal and interpersonal consequences of mindless and mindful involvement in social activities.

MINDFUL AND MINDLESS SOCIAL INVOLVEMENT: THE CONSEQUENCES OF PROCESS VS. OUTCOME ORIENTATION TO SOCIAL SITUATIONS

When an individual approaches an activity with an outcome orientation, s/he is likely to execute the activity mindlessly. Although we have noted that a focus on outcomes is engendered by mindlessness, we would also propose that when situational features (e.g., instructional sets) point to outcomes as the only critical feature of performance, such features will engender mindless enactment of the activity (Langer, Johnson, & Botwinick, 1981). Under these conditions, questions of "can I?" or "can't I do it?" are likely to be salient, directing the individual's attention to their capacities as problem-solver rather than to ways of performing the activity. To the extent that little attention is directed towards making new distinctions relevant to task performance, the individual can be said to be mindlessly involved in the activity; s/he is likely to rely on what is familiar and well-defined in the situation in the service of outcome attainment.

A focus on the process of task performance, conversely, is engendered by mindfulness. This orientation will be the preferred mode of involvement in an activity under conditions which occasion mindfulness, including when situational features emphasize the importance of process features of performance (Langer, Johnson, & Botwinick, 1981). Under these conditions, questions of "how do I do it?" are salient, directing attention towards defining the steps that are relevant to goal attainment. This orientation can be characterized in terms of the guiding principle, "there are no failures, only ineffective solutions". We have identified this mode of involvement in social activities as the mechanism underlying the production of socially effective behavior. In support of this proposition, we will now examine the consequences of an outcome vs. process orientation to social activities.

APPRAISAL OF CONTEXTUAL FEATURES OF SOCIAL SITUATIONS

We will begin by addressing research that shows how mindlessness may engender inaccurate social inferences. Such misperception of the attributes of others forms the basis of a set of inaccurate expectancies regarding how others are likely to respond in various situations. In consequence, the misinformed individual is likely to treat these others in inappropriate ways.

Langer and Abelson (1974) conducted a study in which they asked clinicians to view a videotape of a person who was labelled either "job applicant" or "patient", and then provide a description of the person. While the therapists' descriptions of the "job applicant" were neutral in character, they described the "patient" in terms that seemed to be quite independent of the actual person they viewed. This label invoked judgments of mental illness, and descriptions appeared to reflect attributes and evaluations specified by the predetermined category "patient". This study represents an example of how mindless reliance on previously defined categorical distinctions can generate an evaluation that is inconsistent with information present in a situation. Once such an evaluation is made a clinician is likely to structure interactions with the "patient" according to previously defined ways of dealing with members of this category (e.g., prescribing drugs, focusing on pathology, etc.). The implications of such treatment may be most unfortunate for the individual who may have been inaccurately evaluated.

Another study that shows how mindless acceptance of categorical distinctions can lead to misinformed inferences about others was conducted by Langer and Newman (1979). This study employed a variation of procedures used by Asch (1946) and Kelley (1950) to assess the centrality of traits such as warm/cold in person perception. In the original research, subjects were provided with a description of a speaker they were about to hear that characterized the person as "warm (cold), industrious, critical, practical and determined". They then heard the speaker lecture and evaluated him. The majority of subjects in these studies anchored their judgments of the speaker with reference to the warm/cold dimension; even if all other information was the same, variation of the warm/cold trait in the description generated very different perceptions of the speaker. The Langer and Newman (1979) study replicated these findings. However, an additional measure reflecting the amount of information subjects recalled about what the speaker actually said was taken. It was hypothesized that those subjects who were actively processing information about the speaker as she lectured would be less likely to respond to the warm/cold cue planted by the experimenter. The results revealed that those subjects who were behaving mindfully (as indicated by the amount of information processed) were indeed less likely to respond in the predictable manner than were those who processed minimal information (an indicant of mindlessness). The mindful subjects' evaluations did not vary as a function of the warm/cold manipulation in the description. These findings suggest that when people attend to well-defined cues in a familiar situation, they may proceed to mindlessly conduct their activities in the situation in ways specified by these cues. This phenomenon is likely to be a pervasive one, as the majority of situations people encounter during their daily routines are imbued with previously-defined cues. Situational familiarity may thus provoke premature evaluation based on well-defined categories, and trigger mindless enactment of well-learned scenarios indicated by these distinctions. If relevant information is not

processed, the ensuing behavior is likely to be situationally inappropriate, or ineffective. Consider,
for example, the man who has uncritically accepted
the distinction that "beautiful women have no
brains". When he encounters beautiful women, he may
mindlessly proceed to treat them according to a set
of normative expectations specified by the label "un-
intelligent". He, of course, should fail to solicit
their opinions on "serious" issues, assume their
interests and activities are trivial in nature, speak
"for" them if topics requiring "intelligent" conversation arise, generate most of the conversation, and
generally patronize them. Should he encounter a
beautiful woman at a party, who, unbeknownst to him,
happens to be a corporate executive, he may proceed
to interact in this mindless fashion. At some point
during the interaction (or after the party), it may
be made apparent to him that his behavior was quite
inappropriate. He may find himself in a most embarrassing situation if his categorization of beautiful
women specifies that they are easily manipulable by
intelligent men, and he proceeds to make overtures to
the corporate executive. Thus, mindless reliance on
a previously-defined categorical distinction may
trigger highly socially inappropriate treatment of
the categorical referent.

Mindless treatment of social situations can, via
failure to attend to potentially relevant (new) information, engender behavior that is based on inaccurate, or misinformed social inferences (and corres-
pondent expectancies). What are the consequences for
the individual who finds him/herself in the position
of suffering negative consequences resulting from a
mindless focus on outcome attainment? Since people
are typically unaware of their own mindlessness, they
tend to be unable to point to the situational features to which they responded when generating an "inappropriate" performance. Further, they are likely
to assume that they were actively thinking when they
were behaving and thus <u>should</u> know how they managed
to commit a social faux pas. In the absence of a
compelling situational account of their behavior,
people will tend to attribute the negative event to
some dispositional feature of themselves, or adopt a
negative label conferred upon them by others (Arkin &
Duval 1975; Jones & Davis, 1965). It is unlikely to
occur to the individual that they may have behaved
"stupidly" because they failed to attend to relevant
contextual features of the situation (after all, they
assume they were thinking). Thus, mindless misappraisal of a situation represents one way in which an

outcome orientation can lead to socially ineffective behavior and vulnerability to negative dispositional labels. Another example of this may be seen in some research conducted by Ross and his colleagues, which demonstrates how an outcome orientation may contribute to the maintenance of negative self-perceptions (Lau, Lepper, & Ross, 1976; Ross, Lepper, & Hubbard 1975). These researchers have found that self-perceptions and social judgments may persevere even when the data upon which they were based are completely discredited. For example, in the Ross et al. (1975) study, subjects performed a task upon which success-failure feedback was manipulated by the experimenter. These authors found that normal "outcome debriefing" procedures, in which subjects were made aware that the prior feedback manipulation had been a total deception, failed to eliminate inaccurate self-perceptions which subjects formed on the basis of the feedback. In contrast, a "process debriefing" procedure, in which subjects were additionally informed about attribution processes that might lead them to retain inaccurate self-perceptions, resulted in effective elimination of these beliefs. The therapeutic potential of informing clients of the concpepts of mindfulness and mindlessness, their relation to process/outcome orientations, and the personal and interpersonal consequences for individuals employing either orientation should be clear.

SOCIAL COMPARISON PROCESSES

Another way in which an outcome orientation can lead to pejorative self-evaluation is via mindless appraisal of social comparison information. People who experience social anxiety tend to engage in faulty social comparison. In fact, this may be the most pervasive problem for socially dysfunctional individuals. When they encounter another who has attained desired outcomes that they themselves have not achieved, they tend to judge themselves negatively. That is, they believe they should be able to generate personal attributes. Additionally, they tend to account for others' superior performances in terms of the actor's positive dispositional attributes.

Jones and Nisbett (1971) have discussed the tendency for observers to attribute actors' behavior to dispositions of the actor rather than to situational factors (with accounts of own behavior emphasizing situational influences). They provide an account of this phenomenon in terms of the different informational "perspectives" enjoyed by the actor and observer, with observers having less access to experiential factors controlling actors' behavior. In the absence of such information, accounts of actors' behavior are likely to be dispositional, rather than situational, in nature. To the extent that observers are outcome focused, we would propose that they will be more likely to generate these dispositional explanations for the behavior of self and other, and to explain discrepancies between their own and others' outcomes in terms of dispositional differences. This latter hypothesis futher differentiates Jones and Nisbett's (1971) proposition, and clarifies when actors are more likely to account for their own behavior in terms of situational determinants. Under circumstances where the process of outcome attainment receives little mindful consideration, there is likely to be a paucity of experiential data upon which to base a situational account of one's own performance. If one fails to attain a certain outcome attained by another and does not consider the respective ways in which different outcomes were achieved, attention is likely to be focused on self and other capabilities in accounting for the discrepancy. A consideration of the process involved in outcome attainment may lead an individual to conclude that s/he did not perform as well as another because s/he (1) never had or used previous opportunities to develop requisite skills; (2) failed to attend to relevant information during mindless enactment of the activity (provided this knowledge is available); or (3) was involved in developing other skills. (With this process orientation one would then discover s/he had not been idle. Consider, for instance, the individual who feels stupid for not having read a particular book that is being disucssed by his/her colleagues. The implication is that the individual had the choice of either reading or not reading the book, and is stupid for having made the wrong choice. However, the process oriented individual is likely to know that the choice was not the book or no book, but rather the book or some other activity. Obviously, then, an awareness of the real choice that was made reduces the likelihood that the individual will label him/herself pejoratively.)

Of course, a process orientation does not preclude faulty social comparison. For instance, one may be all too aware of the tedious process in which one engaged to achieve some end and mistakenly compare one's performance to another's outcome - as if the other's outcome had been achieved from the outset

in an effortless (mindless) fashion. Further, awareness of process features of one's activities may lead
an individual to be all too aware of what s/he could
have done but chose not to do. In this case, the
faulty comparison would be self with an idealized
version of self rather than the more appropriate comparison of e.g., self with other. A focus on process
features of another's performance is likely to involve seeking information about how the other achieved it, and enrich considerably the information base
upon which the observer relies when accounting for
the other's performance. Access to such information
is likely to engender situational, rather than dispositional accounts of the other's behavior, and thus
preclude maladaptive inferences about oneself which
may be drawn via failure to mindfully consider the
process in which another has engaged to attain an
outcome. This contention is supported by pilot work
conducted by Bashner and Langer, in which people were
asked to make judgments about how smart another person is when judges did or did not have information
about how the other person achieved an "impressive"
intellectual outcome. When the process of outcome
attainment was presented in terms of steps that the
judges could conceivably take, the judges perceived
the actor as less smart than when only outcome and
not process-relevant information was available. Research on attribution processes has revealed that
people are likely to account for events in terms of
what they focus their attention on in a situation
(Arkin & Duval, 1975; Duval & Wicklund, 1972). To
the extent that one attends to and seeks information
about the process of outcome attainment (own and
others'), attention will be directed towards ways of
treating situational elements that lead to an outcome. Thus, accounts of events are likely to take
the form of specific, conditional relationships between behavior and its consequences. When outcomes
are evaluated without reference to process-relevant
information, attention is focused upon aspects of the
self (or others) as causal in producing the outcomes,
and accounts of outcome attainment are likely to be
framed in terms of dispositional features of the
actor(s) involved (cf. Duval & Wicklund, 1972). This
latter form of evaluation thus predisposes individuals to assign enduring labels to themselves and
others, rendering an individual vulnerable to pejorative self-labelling. A focus on outcomes (and concomitant failure to attend to process features of
performance) may therefore engender faulty social
comparison.

Since goal comparison is so prevalent (cf. Albert, 1977; Festinger, 1954) it would seem best that individuals mindfully choose appropriate comparisons to make rather than mindlessly consider those that are immediately apparent. That is, people all too often mindlessly or, for that matter, mindfully consider the alternatives before them rather than mindfully generate what the alternatives should be in the first place. They should consider which self they want to compare with which other (e.g., ideal self, ideal other, present self, future self, present or future other, etc.), and for what purposes. These comparisons should, of course, specify the most constructive ways to proceed in the domain under consideration in light of one's goals.

A focus on outcomes when making comparative judgments may, for instance, lead people to make inadequate allowances for role-conferred advantages in self-presentation. For example, Ross, Amabile and Steinmetz (1977) conducted a study in which they assigned people roles that would, by definition, be associated with the production of different samples of information about the individuals involved. In this research, people were asked to play a quiz game in which one participant was assigned the role of questioner and the other the role of contestant, and provide feedback about the accuracy of the contestant's response to each question. Upon completion of the game, questioners and contestants were asked to rate both their own and their partner's general knowledge. Questioners rated their own general knowledge higher than that of contestants, a judgment that was endorsed by the contestants as well. As Ross et al. (1977) note, these judgments reflect a failure to account for situational features (specifically, role-conferred advantages and disadvantages) that lead to biased, unrepresentative samples of information about the participants. Were subjects considering the situational determinants of outcomes, they may have been more reluctant to assign differential ratings to themselves and their partners. However, when people are asked questions such as "how much (or little) of attribute X does one possess?" they may be likely to focus their attention on situational, or process-relevant determinants, rather than on dispositional attributes of the participants. Under these conditions, individuals will be less likely to make evaluative judgments of themselves and others, thus decreasing the probability that they will assign negative labels to themselves.

THE AVAILABILITY OF COMPETENCE-RELEVANT INFORMATION

We have outlined two ways in which an outcome orientation to social situations may engender ineffective social behavior and negative self-evaluation. These involve misappraisal of relevant contextual features in social situations, and faulty social comparison. A third, not entirely unrelated, way in which this focus may lead to disrupted performance and vulnerability to pejorative labels is associated with the effects of overpractice. In this case, the person who has achieved sufficient competence such that s/he can mindlessly perform an activity in the service of outcome attainment may find that s/he can no longer describe how the activity is accomplished (Langer & Imber, 1979). It is not that task components are unavailable for articulation, but they become obfuscated as a structure of the activity emerges that allows mindless enactment. Should circumstances arise in which competence is questioned, the individual may find s/he is unable to readily supply information about the solution process as evidence of competence, and erroneously draw an inference of incompetence. As is the case when people mindlessly misappraise social contexts and make faulty social comparisons, the overpracticed individual is in the position of having to encounter an ascription of incompetence without an adequate supply of process-relevant information upon which to draw. In the absence of such information, attention is likely to be focused on attributes of the self, and acceptance of a negative label conferred by another becomes likely.

A series of studies conducted by Avorn and Langer (1981), Langer and Benevento (1978), and Langer and Imber (1979) examined the debilitating effects of overlearning. These studies involved three phases. In the first phase, the amount of practice subjects were given on a new task was varied (either none, moderate, or overpractice). In phase two, subjects performed a second task in pairs, with one member of each pair instructed to act as the "boss" or the "assistant" (or no labels connoting relative status were assigned). In the third phase, subjects individually performed the original task. The results revealed that individuals who had no prior experience with the task and those for whom the task was overlearned showed performance decrements in this phase if they had received a label connoting inferiority ("assistant") in phase two of the study. Presumably, this label led them to question their competence during phase three, and since the components of the task were not available as evidence of competence, these subjects acted in the light of the previously assigned label. Subsequent work demonstrated that the no-practice and overpractice groups were less able to supply specific steps involved in the solution process than was the group receiving moderate practice. Thus, quite competent individuals may be particularly vulnerable to labels connoting relative inferiority, as specific task components may not be readily available for articulation when competence is questioned. Langer and Imber (1979) found that performance decrements displayed by the over-practiced subjects assigned inferior labels could be prevented by making subjects list task components prior to phase one of the experimental procedure. A comparison of their performance with a comparable group who listed task components following phase three (who showed performance decrements) revealed an interesting relationship between rules listed and rules followed during performance. The group that listed rules prior to performance adhered to them quite closely when conducting the task, while those who listed them after task performance in phase three showed no relationship between the components they generated and those they attended to while performing the task. These results suggest that those subjects generating task components prior to performing an overlearned task may, as a consequence, follow this new set of rules (thereby changing the task to a nonoverlearned one). These results suggest that a focus on the process of task performance (particularly on well-learned tasks) may inoculate people against the potentially debilitating effects of negative labels.

These studies suggest that people who have overlearned some or many social activities may be particularly susceptible to pejorative labels or, for that matter, to any other interpersonal contextual factor that engenders competence questioning (Langer & Benevento, 1978). Thus, the person who used to make friends with no trouble whatsoever but who now lacks confidence in his/her ability to do so (and experiences difficulty with this activity) may exemplify this phenomenon. An important feature of the re-research described is that the negative effects of these competence questioning factors (like labels) may generalize to other overlearned activities.

CONCLUSIONS

We have discussed how an outcome orientation to

social activites (engendered by or engendering mindlessness) is likely to result in (1) failure to attend to and categorize information relevant to
defining steps in outcome attainment; (2) lack of
accessibility to the solution process; and (3)
failure to consider the role of intentional choice in
the production of one's responses (that is, failure
to consider that the likelihood of any response leading to a given outcome is less than certain). In
consequence, individuals so oriented in social situations may be predisposed to misappriase contextual
features in social situations, engage in faulty
social comparison, and lack competence-relevant information. We have suggested that these processes
mediate negative dispositional attributions (to self)
and the production of socially ineffective behavior.
Thus, an outcome orientation to social activities may
lead individuals to develop, for example, perceptions
of low self-efficacy in social situations, and so
subsequently engage in negative self-referent thought
when performing social activities (Bandura, 1977;
Meichenbaum, 1977). Beliefs of incompetence with
respect to particular activities and negative self-
focused thought during performance have been related
to poor performance, avoidance of situations involving those activities, and rapid termination of involvement in the activity when difficulties are encountered. Our analysis suggests that this is
achieved through an outcome focus.

A process focus to social activities (engendered
by or engendering mindfulness), in contrast, is
likely to result in (1) definition and categorization
of information relevant to characterizing steps in
outcome attainment; and (2) appreciation of the role
of intentional choice in the production of one's
responses (that is, the probability of any response
leading to a given outcome is perceived as less than
certain). Thus, a process focus will tend to be associated with accurate appraisal of contextual
features of social situations, constructive use of
social comparative information, and the availability
of competence-relevant information. We have suggested that these processes mediate specific, conditional accounts of events and the production of
socially effective behavior. In particular, a process
focus represents an important cognitive mechanism
underlying adaptive social functioning in a non-
stable social world.

REFERENCES

Albert, S. Temporal comparison theory. Psychological
    Review, 1977, 84, 485-503
Arkin, R.M., & Duval, S. Focus of attention and cau-
    sal attributions of actors and observers. Jour-
    nal of Experimental Social Psychology, 1975, 11,
    427-438
Asch, S. Forming impressions of personality. Jour-
    nal of Abnormal and Social Psychology, 1946,
    41, 258-290
Avorn, J., & Langer, E. Induced disability in nurs-
    ing home patients: A controlled trial.
    Journal of the American Geriatrics Society,
    1982, 30, 397-400
Bandura, A. Self-efficacy: Towards a unifying the-
    ory of behavioral change. Psychological Review,
    1977, 84, 191-215
Beck, A.T. Cognitive therapy and emotional
    disorders. New York: International Universities
    Press, 1976
Berkowitz, L. (Ed.) Cognitive theories in social
    psychology. New York: Academic Press, 1978
Chanowitz, B., & Langer, E. Premature cognitive com-
    mitment. Journal of Personality and Social
    Psychology, 1981, 41, 1051-1063
Curran, J.P. Skills training as an approach to the
    treatment of heterosexual social anxiety: A
    review. Psychological Bulletin. 1977, 84,
    140-157
Duval, S., & Wicklund, R.A. A theory of objective
    self-awareness. New York: Academic Press, 1972
Festinger, L. A theory of social comparison proces-
    ses. Human Relations, 1954, 7, 117-140
Hersen, M., & Bellack, A.S. Assessment of social
    skills. In A.R. Ciminero, K.S. Calhoun, & H.E.
    Adams (eds.), Handbook of behavioral assess-
    ment. New York: Wiley, 1977
Jones, E.E., & Davis, K.E. From acts to dispos-
    itions: The attribution process in person per-
    ception. In L. Berkowitz (Ed.), Advances in
    experimental social psychology (Vol. 2). New
    York: Academic Press, 1965
Jones, E.E., & Nisbett, R.E. The actor and the ob-
    server- Divergent perceptions of the causes of
    behavior. In E.E. Jones, D.E. Kanouse, H.H.
    Kelley, R.E. Nisbett, S. Valins, & B. Weiner
    (Eds.), Attribution: Perceiving the causes of
    behavior. Morristown, N.J.: General Learning
    Press, 1971
Kelley, H.H. The warm-cold variables in first im-

pressions of persons. Journal of Personality, 1950, 18, 431-439

Lange, A., & Jakubowski, P. Responsible assertive behavior. Champaign, Ill.: Research Press, 1976

Langer, E. Rethinking the role of thought in social interaction. In J.Harvey, W.Ickes, & R.Kidd (Eds.), New directions in Attribution Research (Vol.2) Hillsdale, New Jersey: Lawrence Erlbaum Associates, 1978

Langer, E., & Abelson, R. A patient by any other name...: Clinician group differences in labelling bias. Journal of Consulting and Clinical Psychology, 1974, 42, 4-9

Langer, E., & Benevento, A. Self-induced dependence. Journal of Personality and Social Psychology, 1978, 36, 886-893

Langer, E., Blank, A., & Chanowitz, B. The mindlessness of ostensibly thoughtful action. Journal of Personality and Social Psychology, 1978, 36, 635-642

Langer, E., & Imber, L. When practice makes imperfect: The debilitating effects of overlearning. Journal of Personality and Social Psychology, 1979, 37, 2014-2025

Langer, E., Johnson, J., & Botwinick, H. Nothing succeeds like success, except... In E. Langer, (Ed.), The psychology of control. Beverly Hills, Calif.: Saage Publications, Inc., 1983

Langer, E., & Newman, H. The role of mindlessness in a typical social psychological experiment. Personality and Social Psychology Bulletin, 1979, 5, 295-298

Langer, E., & Weinman, C. When thinking disrupts intellectual performance: Mindfulness on an overlearned task. Personality and Social Psychology Bulletin, 1981, 7, 240-243

Lau, R., Lepper, M.R., & Ross, L. Persistence of inaccurate and discredited personal impressions: A field demonstration of attributional perseverance. Unpublished manuscript, 1976

Linehan, M.M. Structured cognitive-behavioral treatment of asserting problems. In P.C. Kendall & S.D. Hollon (Eds.), Cognitive-behavioral interventions: Theory, research and procedure. New York: Academic Press, 1979

Meichenbaum, D. Cognitive-behavior modification: An integrative approach. New York: Plenum, 1977

Ross, L., Amabile, T.M., & Steinmetz, J.L. Social roles, social control, and biases in social perception processes. Journal of Personality and Social Psychology, 1977, 35, 485-494

Ross, L., Lepper, M., & Hubbard, M. Perseverance
    in self-perception and social perception:
    Biased attributional processes in the debrief-
    ing paradigm. Journal of Personality and Social
    Psychology, 1975, 32, 880-892
Sherif, M., & Sherif, C.W. Social psychology. New
    York: Harper & Row, 1969
Watzlawick, P., Beavin, J.H., & Jackson, D.D.
    Pragmatics of human communication: A study of
    interactional patterns, pathologies, and
    paradoxes. New York: W.W. Norton, 1967
Wong, P., & Weiner, B. When people ask "why" ques-
    tions and the heuristics of attributional
    search. Journal of Personality and Social Psy-
    chology, 1981, 4, 650-663

Editorial Introduction, Chapter Seven

CONVERSATION ANALYSIS AND SOCIAL SKILLS TRAINING

Malcolm Coulthard

Much emphasis has so far been placed on the role of cognition (in structuring and generating social behaviour). In the previous chapter, Bandura et al. indicate how this cognitive work can be integrated with actual behavioural skills training. This chapter by Malcolm Coulthard (a linguist) focusses on the "behavioural" skills which need to be thus integrated. However, Coulthard's approach is embedded squarely in the agency approach, adopting a structural (i.e., linguistic) model rather than a parametric (i.e., behavioural) model which virtually all other approaches to social skills training have preferred. The structural model is highly germane to the cognitive approach because it shows how linguistic behaviour is generated by rules, which can be learned, and thus the behaviour generated in accordance with the rule, rather than in discrete elements.

Coulthard and his colleagues have developed a rank scale model for conversation. The model helps identify by rules the next act, move or higher unit that is required in the flow of conversation, and equally helps to identify failures of the speaker to supply appropriate speech units. In addition, the model specifies with precision the type of behavior (linguistic devices and intonation patterns) that the client might appropriately give at that point. This should help the client pinpoint conversation cues and make response choices in the mindful mode urged by Bandura et al.

Chapter Seven

CONVERSATION ANALYSIS AND SOCIAL SKILLS TRAINING

Malcolm Coulthard

INTRODUCTION

Arguments have been made in earlier chapters (e.g., chapter two) as to why a parametric approach to analyzing social skills, though almost universally adopted in that field, is in fact mistaken and should be replaced by a structural approach. It would seem obvious that linguistics is the natural heir to this particular throne, and it seems strange that social skills investigators have not turned to this long-established discipline. Linguistics, and in particular that branch of development termed discourse analysis, seems an obvious choice in that not only is it structural, thus befitting the nature of the subject, but speech has a much greater significance in social skills compared with other elements of behaviour (Marzillier & Lambert, 1976; Trower, 1980). Accordingly, in attempting to tackle the problem of abnormal social behaviour, it would seem we should incorporate assessment of and training in spoken interactions, using an applied linguistics approach. However, here, as in other areas of applied linguistics, progress has been hampered by the lack of an adequate linguistics. The authors of the most substantial piece of work on abnormal discourse so far reported (Rochester & Martin, 1979), admit that "the arguments for the study of dialogic patterns are very persuasive" and they "would like to study conversational behaviour in schizophrenic speaker-listeners"; nevertheless they in fact confined themselves to monologue on the grounds that the model they were using was reliable only for monologue.

In such a climate social skills training cannot make real progress - just as language teachers cannot construct a foreign language course without an adequate grammatical description of the language, so an interaction analysis is a sine qua non for a soundly-based social skills programme. Until it is possible to describe the target communicative behaviour in a reliable replicable way, the social skills trainer must work by intuition.

TOWARDS A DESCRIPTION OF INTERACTION

Work in Birmingham, by the English Language Research group has, in the past ten years gone a long way towards establishing a firm basis for the description of interaction, though there is still much development work to do. The description was initially developed for classroom interaction but has since been modified to cope with doctor-patient communication, committee meetings, foreign language classrooms and desultory conversation.

In setting out to produce a structural description of interaction one first needs a set of descriptive units - just as in describing the grammar of English we use the units sentence, clause, phrase, and word and the grammatical rules which tell us how the smaller ones combine together to form the bigger ones, and which combinations are unacceptable or "ungrammatical", so to describe interaction we need to postulate a similar set of units and discover the way they relate to and combine with each other. From the data we have studied we have derived empirically the following set of units, with each related to the one above in a "consists of" relationship: a move consists of one or more acts, an exchange of two or more moves ...

Interaction
|
Transaction
|
Exchange
|
Move
|
Act

Just as in grammar it is the structure of sentences and not paragraphs we set out to describe, so here it is interaction and not "days in the life of" that we concern ourselves with.

Interactions are described in terms of sequence of transactions, which are basically large topic units. In looking at lessons we noticed very early that teachers tended to mark the beginnings of new topics with one of five words <u>right</u>, <u>ok</u>, <u>well</u>, <u>good</u>, <u>now</u>, which, when so used, are strongly stressed, uttered with a high falling intonation and followed by a short pause. On such occasions their normal meaning is suppressed - <u>now</u> has no time reference, <u>right</u> or <u>good</u> no evaluative function - though at other places in the lessons these same items are used normally. We called these boundary marking items, <u>frames</u>.

Teachers very frequently follow a frame, which indicates to the pupils that one transaction has ended and another is beginning, with a <u>focus</u>, a meta-statement which tells them what the transaction is going to be about:

(1) frame: well..
    focus: today I thought we'd do three quizzes,

While a transaction often ends with a second meta-statement, a <u>conclusion</u>, which summarizes what the transaction was about or has achieved before the class moved on:

(2) conclusion: what we've just done, what we've
                just done is given some energy to
                this pen.
    frame: now..

Similar items occur in committee meetings, lectures and doctor-patient consultations. Our doctors invariably marked the end of the diagnostic transaction and the beginning of the prescribing one:

(3) right..   I'm going to give you these pills..

(4) now..   I want you to take this medicine...

Recently we have been looking in detail at intonation and can now see that although these words - and very similar ones are used in the major European languages with the same function - occur at boundaries, in fact the boundary is also indicated by a marked change in the pitch of the voice from low to high; indeed very frequently in ordinary conversation transaction boundaries are marked or "realized" <u>only</u> by this change in pitch between successive items.

Transactions in turn have a structure - they consist of a series of <u>exchanges</u>. To begin with a boundary exchange, which consists of a frame and/or focus followed by a succession of informing, directing or eliciting exchanges. Informing, directing and eliciting exchanges are concerned with what is more commonly known as "stating", "commanding" and "questioning" behaviour.

The structure of exchanges is expressed in turn in terms of <u>moves</u> and for illustrative purposes we will concentrate on eliciting exchanges. One might have expected an eliciting exchange in the classroom to consist typically of a teacher question followed by a pupil answer and a series of eliciting exchanges to produce the pattern T-P, T-P, T-P, but this in fact is not the case; the structure is rather T-P-T, T-P-T, T-P-T: the teacher asks a question, the pupil answers it and the teacher provides evaluative feedback before asking another question.

(5) T: Those letters have special names. Do you
         know what it is... What is one name that we
         give to these letters
      P: Vowels
      T: They're vowels, aren't they

      T: Do you think that you could say that sentence
         without having the vowels in

The three move eliciting structure is the norm within the classroom, for two reasons: firstly, answers directed to the teacher are difficult for others to hear and thus the repetition, when it occurs, may be the first chance some children have to hear what another child has said; secondly, because most teachers' questions are in some sense bizarre in that the questioner usually knows the answer already, while the answerer himself is often unsure and thus genuinely needs to be told whether the answer he has offered is the answer required. In many class-rooms this structure is so powerful that if there is no evaluative third party it is "noticeably absent", and its absence a clue that the answer is wrong:

(6) T: can you think why I changed "mat" to "rug"
      P: mat's got two vowels in it
      T: -

      T: which are they   what are they
      P: "a" and "t"
      T: -

      T: is "t" a vowel

```
P: no
T: no
```

While such three-part exchanges with evaluatory feedback are a marked feature of classroom discourse,
they do occur in other situations as well:

```
(7)  mother: have you brushed your teeth yet
     child:  yes
     mother: no you haven't
```

Though, as here, they normally presuppose an asymmetrical status relationship. For this reason occurrences in adult-adult interaction tend to be heard as
aggressive:

```
(8)  A: what time did you come in last night
     B: about midnight
     A: no you didn't
```

Those who have investigated other kinds of data have
in the main come up with structures which would be,
in our terms, two-move eliciting exchanges. Sacks
(passim) discusses two-part question-answer sequences
and Labov (1972, p.124) illustrates the category
request for information with the following sequence
of obviously two-part exchanges:

```
(9)  Therapist: oh so she told you
     Patient:   yes
     Therapist: she didn't say for you
     Patient:   no
     Therapist: and it never occurred to her to pre-
                pare dinner
     Patient:   no
     Therapist: but she does go to the store
     Patient:   yes
```

Nevertheless we want to argue that eliciting exchanges are always potentially three-part structures,
while accepting that a two-part realization may, and
in the case of requests for polar information often
does, occur. As we can see in the following extract
three-part exchanges are in fact by no means uncommon though obviously the third move is very
different in function from a third move in classroom
discourse:

```
(10) Doctor:  and what's been the matter recently
     Patient: well I've had pains around the heart
```

```
Doctor:   pains .. in your chest then
Patient:  yes

Doctor:   whereabouts in your chest
Patient:  on the .. heart side here
Doctor:   yes

Doctor:   and how long have you had these for
Patient:  well I had 'em a .. week last Wednesday
Doctor:   a week last Wednesday

Doctor:   how many. attacks have you had
Patient:  that's the first one

Doctor:   you've only had one in all
Patient:  well as far as I know .. there's only
          been one this severe like
Doctor:   yes
```

Exchanges consist minimally of two moves, an Initia-
ation (I) and a Response (R), with optionally a
third, Follow-up (F), move. An Initiation is inter-
actively prospective - it sets up constraints on what
can reasonably occur next by providing information
for acceptance or comment or requesting an action or
information from the addressee. A Response is in-
teractively retrospective in that it looks back to
the initiation and fulfils the constraint set
up by it.

The powerful structural relationship between I
and R means that any move occurring in the I slot
will be heard as setting up a prediction that there
will be an appropriate move in the R slot. The
result is that a speaker will make every effort to
hear what follows his initiation as an appropriate
response, and only in the last resort will he admit
that it may be an unrelated new initiation. Thus, to
take the simple case of an eliciting move in the I
slot looking for information about polarity, it will
classify whatever comes next as conveying polar
information, if this is at all possible:

(11) can you come   ⎧ no...
     round tonight   ⎨ I've got an essay to finish
                      ⎩ thanks

The joke in the following example from Labov (1972)
derives from the fact that Linus either fails to
interpret Violet's informing move as an adequate
response, or deliberately rejects the underlying
assumption that age is important:

(12) Linus: do you want to play with me Violet
     Violet: you're younger than me (shuts door)
     Linus: she didn't answer my question

The same interpretive strategy is used with wh-elic-
itations:

(13)

where's the
typewriter
$\left\{\begin{array}{l} \text{its in the cupboard} \\ \text{try the cupboard} \\ \text{isn't it in the cupboard} \\ \text{in the cupboard} \end{array}\right.$

Again all the items in the response slot are interpreted as attempts to provide the required
information.
    Following a Response in the classroom third
Follow-up items are typically evaluative: outside the
classroom as in example (10) they are typically an
indication of agreement or acceptance of the information.
    Moves combine to form exchanges; moves them-
selves consist of one or more acts. Acts are defined
principally by their function in the discourse, by
the way they serve to initiate succeeding discourse
activity or respond to earlier discourse activity.
The definition of the acts is very general, elicit-
ation for instance has as its function "to request a
linguistic response", directive "to request a non-
linguistic response". The analysis thus does not
attempt to distinguish for example between "request",
"ask", "entreat", "beg", "enquire" (a full list of
acts will be found in Sinclair & Coulthard, 1975,
p.40-44).
    Moves can consist of a single act, but often
consist of several. However, this is often related
to the status of the participants. Significantly, in
the classroom the second, responding move in an
exchange, typically the pupil's does not have a complex structure in terms of acts, while the third,
follow-up move, typically the teacher's and concerned
with fitting the reply into the ongoing discourse,
can consist of up to three acts - an accept, which
takes the information offered into the discourse, an
evaluation which assesses its worth and relevance,
and a comment which contributes new related information. A typical eliciting exchange could look like
this:

initiating move	can anyone have a shot a guess at that one Sally	(elicit) (nomination)
responding move	Cleopatra	(reply)
follow-up move	Cleopatra Good girl She was the most famous queen wasn't she	(accept) (evaluation) (comment)

Although in normal conversation the role of initiator passes readily and frequently from one speaker to another, the noticeable feature of asymmetrical interactions like teacher-pupil and doctor-patient communication is that the "dominant" participant does almost all the initiating; when the "inferior" does initiate s/he quickly loses the role:

(14) P: Miss, they showed you a Pharaoh's body
          on "Blue Peter"
      T: Did they

      T: When was this
      P: On Monday I think
      T: Good gracious me, that's fairly recent

      T: Do you remember which one it was
      P: No Miss

(15) P: Now then doctor could it be anything to do
          with erm constipation and kidney trouble
      D: I see

      P: Would that make me cold ... kidney trouble

      D: Have you been worried about having kidney
          trouble
      P: Well not really but I wonder if that would
          have caused it

Examples of this kind suggest that social skills training for hospitalized patients must be an uphill task - how can anyone in an odd hour each week combat the dominant hospital pattern which places the patient so often in the responding position?
A second insidious problem of this type of asymmetrical interaction is that almost always the topics are chosen for the patient and on an utterance

by utterance basis the range of relevant contributions is usually massively constrained. One of the fascinating things about ordinary conversation is the way control of topic passes from one participant to another and the way in which speakers produce coherent discourse with each successive utterance topically relevant to the one that preceded it (see Coulthard, 1977, p.75-84). However, in one video tape of a "conversational interview" between a consultant psychiatrist and a schizophrenic patient the over-riding impression left was that in many ways it was the psychiatrist who was deviant; whereas the patient picked up and responded to his utterances (the consultant's), he never followed on from anything she said - each of his contributions was an abrupt beginning of a new exchange.

Whereas one problem for patients in need of social skills training is knowing what is a relevant or useful thing to say at a particular point in a conversation, another major problem is how to get a turn to speak at the right moment. Turn-taking is one area in which a lot of work has been done (see Coulthard, ibid, p.52-62), and it is evident that ordinary speakers are very skilful. Most of the time there is "at least and not more than one party talking at a time" (Sacks ms) and speakers "have the technical capacity to select a precise spot to start (their) own talk no later than the exact appropriate moment" (Jefferson, 1973). We in Birmingham, are currently looking at non-verbal features of interaction to see how far we can produce an insightful description of their functioning both as surrogates for acts otherwise performed verbally and as ways of managing turn-taking (Gosling, 1982), but so far the most exciting work is that reported by De Long (1974). He examined a series of conversations between four and five-year-old pre-school children, and discovered a marked correlation between certain body movements and change of speaker. The transcription noted eight basic movements, including "up", "down", "left", "right", "forward" and "backward", for eight parts of the body, the head, the trunk and the left and right arms, hands and fingers. Analysis showed that two movements co-occurred, either simultaneously or in rapid succession to signal a termination. The first was a leftward movement of the head, the second a downward movement by the head, arms or hands individually or in a combination.

However, De Long stresses that to say that the intention to terminate verbalization (willingness to yield the floor), is signalled by downward and leftward movements does not mean that every time a left in the head is accompanied by a down in the head or in other parts of the body, the speaker intends to terminate.

In fact it is only when such signalling occurs at possible completions - points where utterances are grammatically and lexically complete - that termination is signalled.

Approaching the same question from a different viewpoint Kendon (1967) suggests that another important factor enabling the smooth change-over of speaker is gaze. He notes that, while listening, A typically looks at B with fairly long gazes broken by very brief away gazes, but while speaking A looks at and away from B for more equal periods. Focussing on the ends of utterances which lasted for more than five seconds, Kendon notes that

> usually the person who is bringing a
> long utterance to an end does so by
> assuming a characteristic head posture
> and by looking steadily at the auditor
> before he actually finishes speaking.
> (Kendon, 1967, p.60)

The auditor, who spends most of his time looking at the speaker, is able to pick up these signals and tends to respond by looking away just before or just as he begins to talk. By this time of course the initial speaker is looking at the auditor and can pick up the signal that he has accepted the offer of the floor.

> Such changes in behaviour which precede the
> utterance itself clearly make it possible
> for each participant to anticipate how the
> other is going to deal with the actual point
> of change of speaker role, perhaps facilit-
> ating the achievement of smoother...change-
> overs. (Kendon, 1967, p.60)

He notes that fewer than a third of the utterances which ended with an extended gaze were followed by silence or delayed response, as compared with almost three-quarters of those that ended without the speaker looking up.

In passing it is important to note that the chronically shy will obviously have added inter-actional problems because firstly they will not be comfortable enough to give the "normal" non-verbal signals themselves, and secondly they are unlikely to

215

be able to visually monitor their partners sufficiently to pick up many of the turn-taking signals
carried by the gaze.

In some ways, foreign postgraduate students have
problems analogous to those needing social skills
training; when they are participating in seminars
there are times when they have something to say but
do not have sufficient command of the language to
simultaneously encode their ideas and take over the
speaking role at the appropriate moment. Interesting
materials devised by T.F. Johns and discussed briefly
in Coulthard (ibid, p.143-46), to help foreign
students with turn-taking could very well be adapted
to social skills trainers.

INTONATION

Until recently analysts of interaction have ignored
the contribution of intonation because there was no
usable description. Following Brazil (1978a) we now
have an insightful description which was devised to
complement the structural description of interaction
presented above. Tests devised to measure subjects'
perception of the meaning carried by intonation and
discussed in Brazil (1978b) will enable us to test
whether any of the groups of social skills patients
have a productive or receptive problem with intonation and thus to decide how far such training needs
to include a component on intonation.

The description is expressed in terms of pitch
choices, though this is almost certainly a simplif-
ication - loudness and length regularly co-occur with
the pitch choices and it may well turn out that the
choices are being identified by hearers through associated intensity and durational phenomena. I propose to discuss here three systems of options, tone,
prominence, and key, each of which adds a different
kind of meaning to the tone unit.

Tone
Let us begin with tone, a major pitch movement. Although I could wax lyrical on the division of utterances into tone units, for our purposes here it is
sufficient to say that there is always and only one
tone in each tone unit and although we can distinguish five tones - falling, falling-rising, rising,
rising-falling and level - here we shall confine
ourselves to two, the falling ＼ and the falling-
rising ∨↗ . There is a good reason for this:
these two tones are by far the most frequent, precisely because they embody the basic meaning dis-

tinction carried by the tone; the other three choices
can usefully be seen as marked options, understood
and meaningful in contrast.

It is easiest to perceive the meanings of the
tones when they are presented in contrast as in the
following examples:

(16) // when I've finished Middlemarch // I shall
read Adam Bede//

(17) // when I've finished Middlemarch // I shall
read Adam Bede//

Whatever additional implications these readings
may have, we can confidently say that example (16) is
addressed to someone who is expected to know already
that the speaker is reading Middlemarch, but to whom
the speaker's future intentions are an item of news.
In example (17), on the other hand, the question of
the speaker's reading Adam Bede has already arisen in
some way and he is offering information about when he
will read it. Significantly the same comments hold
when the order of the grammatical constituents is
reversed:

(18) // I shall read Adam Bede // when I've finished
Middlemarch//

(19) // I shall read Adam Bede // when I've finished
Middlemarch//

To generalize from these examples, I want to
suggest that the function of the <u>fall-rise</u> tone is to
mark the experiential content of the tone unit, the
<u>matter</u>, as part of the shared, already registered
common ground, occupied by the participants at a
particular moment in an ongoing interaction; by contrast the <u>falling</u> tone marks the matter as new.

In the following examples we can see the effect
of altering the tone selections:

(20) // he'll be <u>TWEN</u>ty // in <u>AU</u>gust //

(21) // he'll be <u>TWEN</u>ty // in <u>AU</u>gust //

(The tonic syllable, the syllable on which the major
pitch movement begins is now underlined and capital-
ized.)

In lay terms, it may be said that in (20) a potential hearer is "told" when a mutual acquaintance
will have his twentieth birthday, while in (21) he is

"told" how old the acquaintance is (or will be). In either case, the tone unit having referring tone serves to match the assertion with an assumed focus of interest perhaps, though not necessarily, made explicit in the preceding dialogue either by a question from another participant or by being mentioned by the speaker himself. One could paraphrase (20) ponderously as: "What I assume you are interested in, because an intimation to that effect has already been exchanged between us, is when he will be twenty, and I hereby assert that it will be in August."

As we said above, decisions about what information to proclaim and what to refer to are a speaker's constant concern and are made in the light of his moment by moment assessment of the state of play.

Obviously, the larger and less familiar the audience the more difficult it is for the speaker to assess the area of common ground. Thus the news reader would have been likely to use referring tone for "Mr. Callaghan" but proclaiming tone for "M. Barre" in the following examples:

(22) // the prime MINister // mr CALlaghan // ...

(23) // the prime MINister // m. raymond BARRE //...

Indeed one of the skills necessary to be a good news reader or lecturer is the ability to assess the extent and boundaries of the group's common ground.

Prominence

A second meaningful choice to a speaker is to make a given word prominent. All words carrying tonic pitch movement are prominent by definition but other words can be more pitch prominent also. It is easiest to explain prominence by example. When we say Tom is the best boy in the class, we are emphasizing "is" by making it pitch prominent, and prominence is a linguistic choice available to a speaker independent of the grammatical structure of his utterance and the accent of the constituent words. Let us consider the following exchange:

(24) Q: What card did you play?
R: // the QUEEN of HEARTS //

It is easy to see that in the response the word "of" is the only word that could occupy the space between "queen" and "hearts". If we think of each word as representing a selection from a set of words available at successive places, then at the place filled by "of" there is a set of only one. In this respect it can be compared with the places filled by "queen" and "hearts". If we leave aside the slightly less straightforward case of "the", we can show the total range of possibilities thus:

(25)

(the)	ace two . . queen king	of	hearts clubs diamonds spades

The speaker has a limited choice of thirteen possibilities at the first place and of four at the third, but this time the limitation has nothing to do with the working of the language system: there is no <u>linguistic</u> reason why the response should not have been "the prince of forks" or "the seventeen of rubies", or any of an enormous number of combinations. What imposes the limitation is an extra-linguistic factor, the conventional composition of the pack of playing cards.

We shall use the term <u>existential paradigm</u> for that set of possibilities that a speaker can regard as actually available in a given situation. This will enable us to distinguish it from the <u>general paradigm</u> which is inherent in the language system. It is clear that at the place occupied by "of" the two paradigms coincide: there can be no possibility of selection in the existential paradigm because there is none in the general paradigm. We now want to argue that items marked as prominent indicate that the speaker is selecting from a set of oppositions in the existential paradigm. Thus we can invent a context in which "of" can be situationally selective - a correction of a foreigner's "the queen in hearts" would certainly be:

(26) // the queen OF hearts //

and there are also contexts in which "queen" and "hearts" would not be selective and therefore would be non-prominent:

(27) Q:What heart did you play? R: // the QUEEN of hearts//

(28) Q:Which queen did you play? R: // the queen of HEARTS //

In each of these examples the questioner sets up a context which effectively removes the possibility of choice for one of the items by indicating that he knows either the suit or the denomination of the card. Thus the answerer's use of "hearts" in (27) and "queen" in (28) are not the outcome of his making any kind of selection, a fact which would probably result, in many circumstances, in their being omitted altogether:

(27a) Q: What heart did you play? R: //the QUEEN//

(28a) Q: What queen did you play? R: // HEARTS //

Here again we see the existential paradigm reduced to a set of one by something outside the language system. It is because shared understanding with respect to one of the variables has already been acknowledged in the conversation that no selection is involved. However, all interaction proceeds, and can only proceed, on the basis of the existence of a great deal of common ground between the participants: that is what knowledge speakers (think they) share about the world, about each other's experience, attitudes and emotions, and common ground is not restricted to shared experience of a particular linguistic interaction up to the moment of utterance; rather it is a product of the interpenetrating biographies of the participants, of which common involvement in a particular ongoing interaction constitutes only a part.
Thus one can create a situation in which items are either contextually given, as in a game of cards when one person has, without saying anything put down the jack of hearts and a next player verbalizes:

(29) // QUEEN of hearts //

or available from past experience as in

(30) // CUP of coffee //

when the addressee is known to only drink coffee and the question is "cup or mug".

Key
In addition to making choices in the prominence system a speaker must also for each tone unit select relative pitch or key from a three term system high, mid and low. However, key choices are not absolutes, they are made and recognized with reference to the

Conversation Analysis and Social Skills Training

key of the immediately preceding tone unit. In other words there are no absolute values for high, mid and low key, even for a particular speaker; in fact a given high key tone unit may well be lower than an earlier mid key one.

The key choice is realized on the first prominent syllable of the tone unit and adds a meaning that can be glossed at the most general level as:

High Key	contrastive
Mid Key	additive
Low Key	equative

The way in which these intonational meanings combine with lexico-grammatical ones is discussed in detail in Brazil et al. (1980) but can be simply illustrated in the following invented examples where only key* is varied:

(31) he GAMbled//and <u>LOST</u>   CONTRASTIVE (contrary to expectations, i.e. there is an interaction-bound opposition between the two)

    he GAMbled//and <u>LOST</u>   ADDITIVE (he did both)

    he GAMbled//and _{<u>LOST</u>}   EQUATIVE (as you would expect; i.e. there is an interaction-bound equivalence between them)

In example (31) we see key being used to indicate particular relationships between successive tone units in a single utterance, but the same relationships can occur between successive utterances. If we begin wih the polar options "yes" and "no" we quickly realize that only when they co-occur with high key are they in opposition. In other words if he wishes to convey "yes not no" or "no not yes" a speaker must select high key:

(32) well you ^{WON'T} be <u>HOME</u> //^{before} <u>SEVen</u>

(i) ^{<u>YES</u>}//i <u>WILL</u>

(ii) ^{<u>NO</u>}//i <u>WON'T</u>//

---

* in all subsequent examples // marks the <u>mid</u> line; items that are in high or low key will be printed above or below this notional line.

Conversation Analysis and Social Skills Training

In (i) the speaker chooses contrastive high key* to
mark the choice of opposite polarity in his responses; in (ii) he chooses to highlight an agreed
polarity and this apparently unnecessary action is
usually interpreted as emphatic and then in a particular context as "surprised", "delighted", "annoyed"
and so on. Much more usual than (ii) is (iii):

(32a) well you WON'T BE HOME//before SEVen

(iii) NO//p i WON'T//

(iv) YES//p i WILL//

Example (iv) sounds odd because the speaker is heard
as simultaneously agreeing and contradicting or perhaps rather agreeing with something that hasn't been
said, and the normal interpretation would be that he
had misheard.
     Garfinkel (1967) emphasized that it is impos-
sible for speakers to "say in so many words" what
they actually mean and use of high key is one major
way in which speakers make appeal to and use of information which they assume their listener(s) have,
without actually verbalizing it. The following "mis-
reading" from a BBC newscast is amusing because of
the contrast which listeners were forced to derive
from the utterance to make sense of it:

(33) and tomorrow Mrs. Thatcher will make

       //a con SIDered statement//on immiGRAtion//

The previous day Mrs. Thatcher had made a speech including comments on immigration and the newscast was
supposed to be saying that in addition to other
things she was going to do, Mrs. Thatcher would make
a statement on immigration that would be "considered"
i.e., reasonable and well presented:

(33a) //a conSIDered STATEment on immiGRAtion//

The high key choice in (33) for "considered" marked
this statement as contrastive and the obvious contrast was with the previous day's statement which
must therefore be seen as not "considered" or even
"ill-considered".
     Whereas high key marks for the listener that an
item is to be heard as in contrast (while leaving him

* All items are assumed to have a falling tone.

Conversation Analysis and Social Skills Training

to fill out the existential paradigm), low key marks
an item as equative, or contextually synonymous.
Thus when the low key option is co-selected with
"yes" or a repetition the utterance does little more
than acknowledge receipt of the information:

(34)   D: whereabouts in your chest?
       P: on the heart side.
       D: //<u>YES</u>//

(35)   A: what's the time?
       B: ten o'clock.
       A: //ten o'<u>CLOCK</u>//

If a speaker reformulates in low key he is indicating
that he doesn't feel he is adding any new information, but simply verbalizing an agreement that the
two versions are situationally equivalent in meaning:

(36)   A: what's the time?
       B: ten o'clock.
       A: //<u>BED</u>time//

(37)   // HE'S <u>DEAD</u>//and <u>BUR</u>ied//

The choice of mid-key marks the matter of the tone
unit as additionally informing and thus (37a) is
slightly odd:

(37a) //HE'S <u>DEAD</u>//and <u>BUR</u>ied//

as in (38), from a newscast reporting how a Pales-
tinian terrorist organisation has tried to invade
Israel by balloon, but had met disaster when the
balloon

(38)   //<u>CRASHED</u>//and <u>BURNED</u>//

This listener, at least, expected a low key for
"burned" indicating "as you would have expected".
   Pitch is used in conversation to structure
content, a drop to low pitch marking the end of a
"mini-topic" in monologue or, in interactive chunks,
of an exchange or sequence of exchanges:

(39)   D: Whereabouts in your chest?
       P: On the heart side
       D: //<u>YES</u>//

(40)   D: And how long have you had those for?
       P: Well I had them a - week last Wednesday

223

D:// a WEEK last <u>WED</u>nesday//

While it is not unusual in certain types of interaction for an answer to end with low termination and
the following is unremarkable:

(41)   A: //have you GOT the <u>TIME</u>//

        B: //its THREE o'<u>CLOCK</u> //

usually second speakers keep the topic open by avoiding the drop to low pitch. However, one memorable
exception was an "interview" between a psychiatric
social worker and a depressive patient where all the
professional's initiations were answered by minimal
low pitch topic ending items, leaving him again and
again to search for a new beginning.

CONCLUDING REMARKS

In order for social skills training methodology to
advance further there seem to be two tasks that need
to be urgently undertaken: firstly a systematic
soundly based linguistic description of the target
behaviour, that is the kind of interactive competence, both productive and receptive, which patients
need to achieve; secondly an examination of work
currently going on in the area of English as a Foreign Language, to discover how far the techniques and
materials being developed there to teach non-native
learners to communicate effectively can be adapted
and adopted for those native speakers with a social
skills deficiency.

REFERENCES

Brazil, D. Discourse intonation. Unpublished Ph.D.
    dissertation, University of Birmingham,
    1978,(a)
Brazil, D. <u>An investigation of discourse inton-
    ation</u>. Final report to SSRC on research project
    HR 3316/1, 1978,(b)
Brazil, D., Coulthard, M., & Johns, C. <u>Discourse
    intonation and language teaching</u>, London:
    Longman, 1980
Coulthard, R.M. <u>An introduction to discourse anal-
    ysis</u>. London: Longman, 1977
Coulthard, R.M., & Brazil, D. <u>Exchange structure:
    Discourse analysis monographs No. 5</u>. Birmingham:
    English Language Research, University of
    Birmingham, 1979

Garfinkel, H. Studies in ethnomethodology. Englewood
    Cliffs, N.J.: Prentice-Hall, 1967
Gosling, J.G. Discourse kinesics. Birmingham:
    English Language Research, University of Bir-
    mingham, 1982
Jefferson, G. A case of precision - timing in ord-
    inary conversation. Semiotica, 1973, 9, 47-96
Kendon, A. Some functions of gaze direction in
    social interaction. Acta Psychologica, 1967,
    26, 22-63
Labov W. Rules for ritual insults. In D. Sudnow
    (Ed.), Studies in social interaction. New York:
    Free Press, 1972
de Long, A.J. Kinesic signals at utterance boundar-
    ies in pre-school children. Semiotica, 1974, 11,
    43-73
Marzillier, J.S., & Lambert, C. The components of
    conversational skills: Talking to a stranger.
    Unpublished, manuscript, 1976
Rochester, S., & Martin, J.R. Crazy talk: A study
    of the discourse of schizophrenia. New York:
    Plenum Press, 1979
Sacks, H. Mimeo lecture notes, 1967
Sinclair, J. McH., & Coulthard, R.M. Towards an an-
    alysis of discourse. Oxford: Oxford University
    Press, 1975
Trower, P. Situational analysis of the components
    and processes of behavior of socially skilled
    and unskilled patients. Journal of Consulting
    and Clinical Psychology, 1980, 48, 327-339
Trower, P. Towards a generative model of social
    skills: A critique and synthesis. In J.P.
    Curran & P.M. Monti (Eds.), Social skills
    training: A practical handbook for assessment
    and treatment. New York: Guilford Press, 1982

PART II

PRACTICE

Editorial Introduction, Chapter Eight

*COGNITION AND SOCIAL INADEQUACY: RELEVANCE
IN CLINICAL POPULATIONS*

Michael G. Dow and W. Edward Craighead

*Social skills training has become synonymous with
behavioural skills training, i.e., the training of
actual response components. The agency approach,
however, distinguishes between social skills training
of the behavioural type, and social skill training,
i.e., training in the process of generating skills,
and gives a central role to cognitions in this process. Because skill (or performance) training has
been largely neglected (for reasons argued in chapter
2), part II will be devoted to the assessment and
modification of processing deficiencies and mainly to
the cognitions that underlie these. It is planned at
a later date to publish an agency approach to social
skills training, using a structural paradigm, when
this field has developed further (see chapter seven).*

*If cognitions generate behaviour, and are in
turn modified by behavioural outcomes, then dysfunctional cognitions are likely to generate, or at least
exacerbate deficient behaviour, and to become increasingly dysfunctional following such feedback. We will
not easily produce beneficial change at either level
by neglecting to assess and influence cognitive processes. The first task, then, is to survey those
clients with social competence problems and examine
the extent and nature of their cognitive deficits.
Such a survey is here undertaken by Dow and Craighead
(both clinical psychologists). They begin with a
clarification of the meaning of cognitions as used in
the clinical literature, and then review six main
kinds of cognitive deficit which, from the literature
seem to be related to the problems of social inadequacy. These are negative thoughts, negative and/or
irrational beliefs, social perception, social problem
solving, attributional style and memory distortion.*

Chapter Eight

COGNITION AND SOCIAL INADEQUACY: RELEVANCE
IN CLINICAL POPULATIONS

Michael G. Dow and W. Edward Craighead

INTRODUCTION

In contrast to the phenomenal growth of research and
theory on social skills in the last decade (cf.
Arkowitz, 1981), it is now of some concern that several recent reviews have suggested serious inadequacies in current research and thinking about
social skills:

> We simply know much less about the assess-
> ment of social skill than we must.
> (Bellack, 1979a, p.173)

> The pace of social skills training over the
> past few years has hardly allowed for the
> orderly assimilation of scientific knowledge
> from social psychology and other disciplines.
> (Trower, 1979, p.3)

> In our research in the years to come, we must
> address the many methodological issues ...if
> social skills training is to remain a viable
> treatment alternative. (Curran, 1979, p.347)

> Everyone seems to know what good and poor
> social skills are but no one can define them
> adequately. (Curran, 1979, p.321)

> Nowhere is the contrast between conceptual
> rigor and applied convenience more apparent
> than in the assessment of social skills.
> (Bellack, 1979b, p.75)

It remains to be seen whether academic psychology will retain an interest in social skills during
this current period of collective soul-searching and

self-flagellation. The challenge is to improve methods, and become more sensitive to the complexity of social skills, while retaining interest in this area. Curran (1979) has expressed optimism that researchers are realizing the complexity of this area and addressing relevant issues. This shift in emphasis is exemplified by the increasing recognition that social skills may involve cognitive as well as motor components. This reflects the general trend in the field of behavior therapy, within which social skills research and treatment have developed (cf. Wilson, 1981).

Although strictly behavioral approaches to social skills training have been criticized as overly simplistic, it would be equally short-sighted to assume that social skills are not "skills" at all - but rather "cognitions". Instead, we endorse an individualized problem-specific approach to assessment and treatment which takes into account the environment, the person's overt skill level, physiological responses, and cognitions of their interactions.* Much of the early writing and research in the social skills area was focused on the non-cognitive factors; however, recent work has been more comprehensive and includes cognitive variables. Unfortunately, this development has been limited by an inadequate definition of cognition, in general, and the absence of a specific comprehensive model of social competence and social inadequacy which includes cognitive and other components (cf. Arkowitz, 1981).

RESEARCH, THEORY AND CONFUSED COGNITION

Part of the early reluctance to study cognitive factors in social skills research may have been due to the widespread disagreement over the meaning of cognition. At a broad semantic and conceptual level the term "cognition" has been used both to describe covert speech (which is an occurrent private event), and to describe other organizational and mental constructs (cf. Biglan & Dow, 1981). MacCorquodale and Meehl (1948) presented a finer distinction of organizational and mental constructs. They classified these phenomena as intervening variables which are semantic short-cuts that describe essentially

---

* Although the role of affect may be substantial in behavior therapy (cf. Wilson, 1981), the empirical data have not addressed that issue at this time, and the relationship between behavior, cognition physiological responses and affect have not been clarified.

empirical relationships in theoretical terms (they argued that even Skinner did this with his concept of reflex reserve), and <u>hypothetical constructs</u>, which are not reducible to known empirical relationships.

> It is suggested that the only rule for proper intervening variables is that of convenience, since they have no actual content surplus to the empirical functions they serve to summarize. In the case of hypothetical constructs, they have a cognitive, factual reference in addition to the empirical data which constitute their support.
> (MacCorquodale & Meehl, 1948, p.107)

Most behavior therapists, including those who employ an operant approach, have traditionally included the covert speech type of cognition within the realm of the experimental analysis of behavior (e.g., Biglan & Kass, 1977; Homme, 1965; Kanfer & Karoly, 1972; Skinner, 1974; Ullmann, 1981; Wolpe, 1978). Many behavior therapists have also employed constructs which can appropriately be considered intervening variables; for example, Kanfer and Karoly's (1972) theory of self-regulation employs terms such as alpha and beta variables, self-reinforcement, and self-control, but these have been carefully operationalized within a closed-loop learning model. They argued that their theory of self-regulation was consistent with a "basic behavioral analysis" (Skinner, 1953), and that it was <u>not</u> necessary "to go to 'cognitive' theory which postulates different mechanisms for private than for overt behaviors" (Kanfer & Karoly, 1972, p.412-413).

It may seem confusing that one of the classic papers on self-control theory, which has been fully adopted by cognitive-behavior modification, argued that self-control theory was not, in fact, cognitive. Resolution of the confusion may occur by considering the three levels of analysis for the term, cognition. Kanfer and Karoly (1972) have apparently eschewed the use of hypothetical constructs, while adopting intervening variables and covert speech in their self-regulatory model. Thus, their self-control model may be either "cognitive", or "not cognitive", depending on which definition of the term one accepts.

It should be apparent that much of the confusion surrounding the definition and utility of "cognitive" phenomena in behavior modification has resulted from failure to specify adequately which level of analysis is being discussed.

There seems to be fairly good agreement that covert speech is a relevant consideration for behavior therapists. Traditional behaviorists have varying degrees of "patience" with the intervening variables approach, while they characteristically reject hypothetical constructs. Many who have aligned themselves with cognitive-behavior modification have included all three levels of cognition by their insistence that there is "independence of the overt and covert" (Sarason, 1979, p.223). Hence, Beck (1967, 1976) can discuss the "silent assumptions" from which the depressed patient operates, and much more is meant than simply the frequency and content of covert self-talk.

Because of insufficient theory building and testing, to date, the usefulness of hypothetical constructs for behavior modification remains unsettled. In the following review of research on cognitive phenomena and social inadequacy we will summarize the results of the relevant empirical studies. Due to the nature of the research, the discussion will include covert speech and intervening variables; consequently, the findings are "cognitive" or "not cognitive" depending on one's orientation. The major focus of this review is on the functional implications of prior research for future research and clinical intervention. Perhaps future theoretical developments will provide an adequate integration of these findings and serve a heuristic purpose for cognitive-behavioral research and therapy.

THE ROLE OF COGNITION

The remainder of this chapter is a summary of research in six cognitive areas which may be related to the problems of social inadequacy: negative thoughts, negative and/or irrational beliefs, social perception, social problem-solving, attributional style and memeory distortion. In some instances, the research studies were directly concerned wih the issue of social inadequacy, while in other cases we have drawn the relationship ourselves. As will become apparent there has been limited research directly dealing with cognition and social inadequacy, despite indications of a possible relationship.

Most of the studies in this review are concerned with depression and anxiety. There are two reasons for stressing these target problems in our review. First, while fundamental sensorimotor deficits have been implicated in schizophrenia (Bourne, Dominowski, & Loftus, 1979, chap.11; Buss & Lang, 1965; Lang & Buss, 1965), theory and research relating cognition to depresssion or anxiety have tended to examine more specific cognitive processes and have implicated deficits that may be differentialy related to etiology and treatment. Thus, cognitive processes in depression and anxiety may be more amenable to the present analysis. Second, there is a plethora of research and theory relating problems of anxiety and depression to social inadequacy. "Social anxiety" is considered to be a kind of anxiety (e.g., Watson & Friend, 1969; Curran, 1977), often involving social avoidance; while depression has frequently been related to social inadequacy (Coyne, 1976; Libet & Lewinsohn, 1973; Weissman & Paykel, 1974).

Negative Thoughts

Negative thoughts are specific occurrent events. In keeping with the levels of analysis already discussed we make the distinction between negative thoughts and "beliefs", which are considered in a later section of this chapter. There may be a relevant clinical distinction between an individual who believes he is socially inadequate and rarely thinks about it (even in social situations), as compared to an individual who believes he is socially inadequate and frequently thinks about it. Negative thoughts are also more operationalizable - considered suitable even to a Skinnerian behavioral analysis (Biglan & Kass, 1977; Homme, 1965; Skinner, 1974), whereas beliefs can be conceptualized on many levels.

Failure to make the distinction between negative thoughts and beliefs can be very confusing. Consider the notion of "expectancy". Although of great importance to this area, we have intentionally omitted this specific category in our classification scheme because there are at least two very different ways of discussing the concept, each of which seems more appropriate in other categories we provide. The first use is to say that an individual thinks about (talks to herself or imagines) failures or personal inadequacies whenever she is about to be involved in a social situation. Hence, we consider this to be a negative thought. The other notion is more conceptual and less easily operationalized, suggesting that the individual has an expectancy - although this usage may be a semantic short cut (intervening variable) for learning history (including the effects of differential reinforcement on memory) or a theorized central organizational structure (hypothetical construct). We consider this use of expectancy to indicate a "belief", and discuss relevant studies in that section of the paper.

Research on negative thoughts. Beck (1963) has presented extensive anecdotal evidence that depressed and anxious patients exhibit negative thoughts. The thought content of depressed patients was characterized by, (1) low self-regard, (2) ideas of deprivation, (3) self-criticism and self-blame, (4) overwhelming problems and duties, (5) self-commands and injunctions (nagging or prodding to do certain things), and (6) escape and suicidal wishes. Anxious patients in this sample (with unspecified concerns) were characterized as often thinking of personal danger.

Lewinsohn, Munoz, and Larson (1978, as cited in Lewinsohn & Lee, 1981) found that depressed individuals reported more negative thoughts and fewer positive thoughts than nondepressed psychiatric controls or normal subjects. These data were collected using the Cognitive Events Schedule (Munoz & Lewinsohn, 1976a), which asks the respondent to report the frequency and emotional impact of 160 specific thoughts during the previous 30 days. The use of retrospective judgments can be questioned (cf. Jacobson, 1981), however, because differential rates may be influenced by current mood, and/or the tendency for selective recall of unpleasant events among depressed persons (see the section on memory distortion later in this paper).

Questionnaire measures of immediately preceding thoughts have been used in other investigations. This method presumably avoids some of the problems with retrospective judgments. Glass, Merluzzi, Biever, and Larsen (1982, as cited by Glass & Merluzzi, 1981) have developed the Social Interaction Self-Statement Test (SISST), which is a measure of self-statements in heterosocial situations. In their study, positive and negative self-statement scores on this questionnaire were significantly related to standardized measures of social anxiety and skill. Socially competent subjects demonstrated more positive and fewer negative thoughts. In addition, confederates' and judges' ratings of subject social skill and anxiety correlated significantly in the expected directions with the negative self-statement score, although they did not correlate significantly with the positive self-statement score.

Schwartz and Gottman (1976) compared low, medium and high assertive subjects on an assertion situations test. Subjects responded to a self-statement questionnaire after the situations test, which asked which of several positive and negative self-statements they were thinking about as they made their responses to the unreasonable requests. High assertive subjects reported significantly fewer negative self-statements than the moderate assertive subjects, who also reported significantly fewer negative self-statements than subjects in the low assertive group. High assertive subjects reported significantly more positive self-statements than the low assertive subjects, with the moderate assertive group being intermediate but not significantly diferent from the other groups. In an extended replication of this study, Bruch (1981) found essentially the same results for positive and negative self-statements.

Pitcher and Meikle (1980) assessed high, medium and low assertive subjects on a taped situations role play test for positive and negative assertion situations. Subjects completed a self-statement questionnaire for positive or negative assertion after each of these sets of situations. For negative assertive situations, the high and moderate assertive subjects used more positive, facilitating self-statements than the low assertive subjects. The high assertive subjects also had fewer negative, inhibitory self-statements. The moderate group was intermediate and not significantly different from either group. In positive assertion situations there were no differences between assertiveness groups for either kind of self-statement.

Self-monitoring of specific thoughts (or thought categories) is an additional assessment method which does not rely on retrospective estimates, although it could potentially be reactive. In the study by Vasta and Brockner (1979), the self-esteem of normal college students was measured by standardized inventories. Three weeks later, subjects began eight days of self-monitoring positive self-evaluations, negative self-evaluations, and physiological vocalizations such as coughing and sneezing. Physiological vocalizations were included to control for the possibility of a recording response bias. There was a significant negative correlation between self-esteem and self-monitored negative self-evaluations, while self-esteem did not correlate with positive self-evaluations or physiological vocalizations. Although this study was conducted on normal college students instead of clinical or analogue clinical groups, it indicates a relationship between thoughts and self-esteem, and it provides evidence that decreasing the frequency of negative self-evaluations may be of more clinical relevance than increasing positive self-evaluations.

Thought listing is another technique which can provide relevant information on a subject's thoughts. This procedure avoids many of the potential problems with retrospective judgments and reactivity of self-monitoring. It also has the advantage of an open-ended format. Subjects simply list or verbally report their thoughts in the assessment situation, and they are not forced to make judgments of positive/negative valence or restricted to a finite sample of thoughts which the experimenter provides. Using a written thought listing technique, Cacioppo, Glass, and Merluzzi (1979) investigated the spontaneous generation of thoughts in socially anxious and nonanxious males prior to a social conversation with a female student. Each item on the list of thoughts was rated by subjects and independent "blind" judges to be positive self-referent, negative self-referent, or neutral. Results of the judges' ratings indicated that socially anxious males generated more negative thoughts, but no differences occurred on the positive and neutral thoughts. Analyses of the subject ratings indicated no differences between the socially anxious and nonanxious students.

Results were interesting because if judges' standards were used, subjects differed on the frequency of negative thoughts. However, subjects in each group did not evaluate their thoughts differently. This result may call into question self-monitoring procedures which simply require subjects to report "positive" or "negative" thoughts. Subject groups may differ on their categorizations of these thoughts, confounding the analysis of thought frequencies. Correlational analyses in this study also indicated that the number of negative thoughts (as determined by either subjects or judges) correlated significantly with subjects' evaluative self-ratings of themselves (made after the thought listing technique).

Craighead, Kimball, and Rehak (1979, Experiment 1) selected high and low scorers on the importance of social approval scale from the Irrational Beliefs Test (Jones, 1968). Subjects imagined a social rejection scene and verbally answered four open-ended questions concerning their thoughts, feelings, and images in this situation. These statements were coded for positive self-referent statements, negative self-referent statements, positive task-referent statements and negative task-referent statements.

The high need for approval subjects made more negative self-referent statements than the low need for
approval subjects. There were no differences for the
three other kinds of statements.

Summary and comments. As a group, these studies seem
to implicate the relevance of negative thoughts to
depression and anxiety, and occasionally relationships were directly found with subjects who were selected to represent problems of social inadequacy.
The research in this area is clearly preliminary and
future research should investigate more carefuly (1)
distinctions between beliefs and thoughts, (2) distinctions between the frequency of negative thoughts
and amount of thinking in general (discriminant validity) (3) distinctions between types of negative
thoughts: social vs. nonsocial, and self-critical vs.
general pessimistic worries, and (4) the situational
specificity of particular thoughts. There may be
reason to speculate that self-critical thoughts relating to social interaction may characterize both
depressed and socially anxious individuals, while
more general self-criticism and negative worries may
be most relevant to depression.
If negative thoughts are found to characterize
the problems of social inadequacy in some clients,
there appear to be at least four ways that these
problems could be functionally related. First, there
is evidence from mood induction studies that negative
thoughts may directly contribute to depressed mood
(Coleman, 1975; Velten, 1968), less active speech
(Natale, 1977), and lower reported preferences for
social activity (Strickland, Hale, & Anderson, 1975).
Secondly, thoughts of negative consequences might
lead some individuals to avoid social situations by
making more apparent the possibility of negative
results. Thirdly, negative thoughts could subtly
interfere with active communication processes. Singer
(1975) has reviewed research which suggests that
active thought during a social situation can be detected by reduced eye movement, less eye contact, and
eyes slightly out of focus. If it is possible, in a
sense, to see another person thinking, then one may
speculate that this could partially account for the
negative social evaluations that some depressed or
socially anxious individuals elicit from others.
Fourthly, negative thoughts could produce more
obvious performance deficits in communication, although studies in social skill and anxiety have been
only moderately successful in isolating differences
in the behavior of socially inadequate and competent

individuals (Dow, Glaser, & Biglan, 1981).

Negative and/or Irrational Beliefs

Much research and theory has been concerned with the role of negative and irrational beliefs in depression (e.g., Beck, 1967). Recent emphasis has also been apparent in problems of anxiety, social withdrawal and assertiveness (cf. Glass & Merluzzi, 1981). However, there is a great deal of ambiguity in this area; few testable or operationalizable definitions of beliefs have been offered. Nor is it clear if such phrases as cognitive distortion, dysfunctional attitude, and irrational belief are referring to the same construct. The use of assessment measures with different names, for example, the Cognitive Bias Questionnaire (Krantz & Hammen, 1979) and the Irrational Beliefs Test (Jones, 1968), does not establish the existence of separate constructs. Without empirical or clear semantic distinctions at the present time, relevant research will be considered under the heading of "Negative and/or Irrational Beliefs".

General beliefs. Jones (1968) has developed the Irrational Beliefs Test, which is a measure of agreement with certain core beliefs described by Ellis (1962). The measure is concerned with an individual's degree of flexibility and autonomy. Using the IBT, irrational beliefs have been related to depression (LaPointe & Crandell, 1980; Nelson, 1977), low dating frequency (Gormally, Sipps, Raphael, Edwin, & Varvil-Weld, 1981), social anxiety (Goldfried & Sobocinski, 1975, Experiment 1; Sutton-Simon & Goldfried, 1979), and speech anxiety (Goldfried & Sobocinski, 1975, Experiment 1). A shortened measure of Ellis' Irrational beliefs was also related to problems of assertiveness (Alden & Cappe, 1981; Alden & Safran, 1978).

The Personal Belief Inventory (Munoz & Lewinsohn 1976b) is a somewhat heterogeneous measure of beliefs that are theoretically relevant to depression: guilt, contol over one's problems, failure, etc. Lewinsohn and Lee (1981) reported that the measure has discriminated between depressed and nondepressed controls.

The Subjective Probability Questionnaire (Munoz & Lewinsohn, 1976c) was designed to assess negative expectancies concerning the self, future, and surrounding world (cf. Beck, 1967). Lewinsohn and Lee (1981) reported that the SPQ has discriminated between depressed and nondepressed samples.

Krantz and Hammen (1979) developed a measure of cognitive distortion patterned after the typology of thinking errors formulated by Beck (1967) to be important in depression: selective abstraction, magnification/minimization, arbitrary inference and overgeneralization. Half of the situations involve interpersonal themes. Krantz and Hammen (1979) and Blaney, Behar, and Head (1980) found that higher depressed-distorted scores were significantly related with depression.

Beliefs regarding social performance. Questionnaire measures are typically used to classify individuals as socially competent or incompetent. Hence, it may be somewhat of a tautology that socially inadequate individuals have negative beliefs about their social performance and relationships. Depressed individuals have also reported problems of social inadequacy (Lunghi, 1977; Weissman & Paykel, 1974).

There are numerous studies which have compared the social interaction task performance and self-evaluations of socially anxious or depressed persons with normal controls. These studies have generally indicated that socially anxious or depressed subjects evaluate their social behavior more negatively than normal control subjects (e.g., Clark & Arkowitz, 1975; Lewinsohn, Mischel Chaplin, & Barton, 1980; Twentyman & McFall, 1975).

Summary and comments. Beliefs may be hypothetical constructs which are antecedent to clinical problems (Beck, 1967), or they may simply be semantic intervening variables which actually reflect learning history. Clinical problems and beliefs are usually assessed by self-report, which further confuses this issue because of common method variance. Depression or anxiety questionnaires could themselves be considered measures of negative beliefs about oneself. Discriminant validity is one approach that could be stressed in these studies to clarify these issues. Longitudinal studies could also be employed. One recent study by Lewinsohn, Steinmetz, Larson, and Franklin (1981) used a longitudinal design to investigate whether depression-related cognitions were antecedent, consequent, or concomitant with an episode of depression. The depressed differed from nondepressed on irrational beliefs and expectancies of positive and negative outcomes; however, these differences were considered to be concomitant with the experience of depression rather than causative.

Social Perception.
Social perception refers to the process of monitoring

events in social interaction, which is presumed to facilitate social interchange (Bellack, 1979b; Morrison & Bellack, 1981). A related concept of self-monitoring has been described by Snyder (1974, 1979) which stresses the selective self-presentation or impression management which can follow from perception of social situations. These appear to be overlapping processes, first concerned with perception of others and oneself, and then with regulation of one's own behavior. As such, they involve both cognitive and behavioral aspects of social competency. (A cybernetic model of attentional processes and behavioral consequences is discussed by Carver and Scheier, chapter five, this volume.)

Self-perception. The paradox in attempting to relate self-perception to problems of social inadequacy is that self-monitoring of one's behavior is seen to be facilitating in its self-regulatory role (Snyder, 1974, 1979), and interfering in the case of social anxiety. A curvilinear relationship is possible between the extent of self-awareness and its social utility. Degree of self-awareness may be beneficial up to a certain point, when it then becomes maladaptive. Further distinctions may also need to be made concerning types of self-awareness. For example, Scheier and Carver (1977) found only minimal correlations between the Self-Monitoring scale (Snyder, 1974) and the Self-Consciousness scale (Fenigstein, Scheier, & Buss, 1975).

Among depressed subjects, Harmon, Nelson and Hayes (1980) found that instructions to self-monitor mood or activity using temporal cueing on a variable-interval schedule (that averaged once per hour) improved mood and increased rate of activity. Hence, increased self-observation appeared to be therapeutically beneficial for these depressed subjects. It is possible that self-observation may have presented a more optimistic view of themselves than previously realized, thus improving mood and increasing activity. Bem (1972), and Schachter and Singer (1962), have stressed the role of self-observation in determining one's affective state. An alternative explanation offered by Harmon et al. (1980), is that self-monitoring may have cued the contingency between mood and activity - causing both to increase in a sequential fashion.

Hiebert and Fox (1981, Experiment 1) found that self-monitoring apparently decreased the self-reported anxiety of normal college students more than a no treatment control group. In a second study

238

(Hiebert & Fox, 1981, Experiment 2), self-reported anxiety and EMG were decreased significantly more among mildly anxious subjects who employed self-monitoring, as compared with no treatment. Self-monitoring subjects improved on these measures as much as another group of subjects doing biofeedback.

Somewhat in contrast with these two studies, Scheier and Carver (1977) showed that experimentally manipulated self-awareness (by the placement of mirrors) and dispositional tendencies for self-consciousness (as measured by self-report) may enhance the intensity of emotion (positive or negative affect) being experienced. Thus, it would be assumed from this perspective that anxiety or depression might be exacerbated by heightened awareness of physiological cues or behavior. Attention to negative thoughts was previously discussed as a possible mediator of social inadequacy, but more generally, heightened self-attention may be responsible for some of the problems of social inadequacy (cf. Carver, 1979).

While there appear to be theoretical reasons and some empirical evidence to suggest that either minimal or extensive self-monitoring could relate to problems of social inadequacy, little research has actually been conducted on the extent to which clinical groups or socially inadequate individuals are self-aware - apart from research on negative thoughts. As argued before, research discriminating self-attention and amount of thinking from negative thoughts may be quite valuable.

In one study by Borkovec, Fleischmann, and Caputo (1973), socially anxious males reported experiencing more signs of physiological arousal during a social interaction task than nonanxious males. However, on a related questionnaire, subject groups did not differ on their reported tendency to observe autonomic responses when anxious - perhaps questioning the role of heightened self-awareness of physiological cues for these subjects.

When little is known about the ongoing self-attention of clinical groups which relates to social inadequacy, numerous studies have asked socially anxious or depressed persons to evaluate their performance after being involved in a social interaction task. In a few of these studies, comparisons were made concerning the "accuracy" of these ratings and ratings made by observers. Lewinsohn, Mischel, Chaplin, and Barton (1980) found that clinically depressed individuals rated their performance similar to the way observers rated them, while nondepressed control subjects rated themselves higher. This suggests that the depressed are more accurate in their self-perception, while others have an "illusory glow". In the study by Curran, Wallander, and Fischetti (1980), high socially skilled subjects underestimated their performance in a social interacion task relative to judges' ratings (instead of an illusory glow), while the low skilled group was quite accurate. High assertive subjects overestimated their performance relative to judges on a role-play assertion test in the study by Alden and Cappe (1981), while low assertive subjects were more accurate in their self-perception. In a final study, Clark and Arkowitz (1975) found essentially no differences in the accuracy (absolute deviation from judges' ratings) of self-evaluation among socially anxious and nonanxious males, although the anxious tended to underestimate their social interaction task performance while the nonanxious tended to overestimate their performance.

Thus, in three of four studies, depressed, low assertive, or socially anxious subjects were more accurate in their self-perception than controls. This is consistent with the theorized effects of heightened self-attention (Carver, 1979; Pryor, Gibbons, Wicklund, Fazio, & Hood, 1977), although it is not clear that heightened self-attention was responsible for greater accuracy among the clinical subjects. Individual differences among subjects should also be considered.

Perception of others. Steffen and Lucas (1980, as cited by Glass & Merluzzi, 1981) found that socially competent males, as compared with low competent males, reported being more aware of the female confederate's appearance in a social interaction task, and were more aware of their thoughts about the social interaction, and of their feelings toward the female confederate.

In the study by Fischetti, Curran, and Wessberg (1977), socially competent and socially inadequate males listened to a videotape of a female speaking about her life, and pressed switches whenever they felt a verbal response or gesture would communicate understanding or rapport. The mean frequencies of responses were generally the same for socially competent and inadequate groups, while the distributions (timing) of responses were generally different. Socially competent subjects clustered their responses during certain popular intervals, which could be taken (among other possibilities) to indicate

superior discrimination of the other person's behavior compared to the socially inadequate subjects.
Peterson, Fischetti, Curran, and Arland (1981) generally replicated these results with female subjects
and a male speaker, although the results were not as
strong. Schrader, Craighead, and Schrader (1978)
used a similar procedure and found no differences in
the frequency or timing of responses between depressed and nondepressed subjects.

Prkachin, Craig, Papageorgis, and Reith (1977)
videotaped depressed psychiatric control, and normal
control subjects as they awaited an aversive auditory
stimulus, an interesting picture, or simply the termination of a trial. The same subjects viewed videotapes from other subjects in each group and based on
the subjects' reactions tried to guess the stimulus
which was presented. Subject groups generally did
not differ in their ability to infer correctly the
stimulus from subject reactions.

Gerson and Perlman (1979) found no differences
in the extent to which chronically lonely, currently
(but not chronically) lonely, or nonlonely subjects
could correctly ascertain, by observing videotapes,
which of five types of emotion-arousing slides were
being viewed by other subjects. Nor were there differences between groups in accuracy of estimating how
pleasant the subjects considered each slide.

Smith and Sarason (1975) investigated the evaluation of negatively-toned feedback among high, moderate, and low socially anxious subjects. High and
moderate anxiety groups rated the same hypothetical
feedback as significantly more negative than low
anxious subjects, and they indicated that it would
make them feel significantly worse. The high and
moderate anxious subjects did not differ from each
other on either measure. It should be noted that it
seems unclear whether this study involved social perception, per se, or was an indirect measure of irrational beliefs about the need for social acceptance.

While all of these studies seem related to perception of others, there appears to be a paucity of
research directly attempting to assess accuracy of
social perception. One promising assessment measure
has fairly recently been developed by Archer and
Akert (1977), but it has not yet been applied to
clinical problems. The Social Interpretations Test
is a videotape of 20 naturally occurring, spontaneous
sequences of behavior and a series of multiple choice
questions requiring the subject to make inferences
about the situation. An advantage of this measure is
that it provides a standardized opportunity to assess

real social interaction.

Summary and comments. Little research has been directly conducted on social perception. While certainly relevant to social perception, many of the studies reviewed in both sections were concerned with other cognitive factors or may also relate to overt skill deficits. Moreover, the results of these studies are somewhat unclear. In terms of self-perception, it tentatively appears that there is reason to believe that either excessive self-monitoring or infrequent self-monitoring might contribute to clinical problems. Situational specificity should also be considered, and differences between type and amount of self-awareness might be further delineated.

Research on perception of others in social situations is particularly scarce. Measures such as the Social Interpretations Test (Archer & Akert, 1977), previously described, would seem to assess more directly some of what is commonly meant by social perception, while other measures that have been used in research studies may be more tangential to social perception.

Morrison and Bellack (1981) argued that social perception may not be a generalized skill - but rather, situational variability may be important. Secondly, they argued that social perception is a complex process, and deficits could result from a number of different problems. "An adequate assessment must take into account both the situational variablity of perception skill and the specific nature of deficits manifested in diverse situations." (Morrison & Bellack, 1981, p.76)

A final concern is that self-perception and perceptions of others may interact in various ways. On a fairly basic level, it has been proposed that attention can be turned inward or outward (Duval & Wicklund, 1972). The relative amount of either focus may be relevant, and is probably related in a selective fashion to ongoing events. Borkovec and O'Brien (1977) found that speech anxious subjects who were instructed to attend to environmental events showed a rapid decline in self-reported fear during the speech situation, suggesting that shifts of attentional focus may mitigate the stressfulness of some anxiety-provoking situations.

Social Problem-Solving.
D'Zurilla and Goldfried (1971), defined problem-solving as:

> a behavioral process, whether overt or cognitive in nature, which (a) makes available a variety of potentially effective response alternatives for dealing with the problematic situation, and (b) increases the probability of selecting the most effective response from among these various alternatives. (D'Zurilla & Goldfried, 1971, p.108)

As such, problem-solving seems to be a mixture of what can be considered cognitive and behavioral processes. Five steps were outlined by D'Zurilla and Goldfried (1971) to describe effective problem-solving: (1) the adoption of a problem-solving orientation, (2) problem definition and formulation, (3) generation of alternatives, (4) decision making, and (5) verification.

Much of the theory and research on problem-solving has been concerned with interpersonal behavior - presumably because social behavior is valued in our culture, or because it is often problematic. Spivack, Platt, and Shure (1976) have presented a conceptualization of the interpersonal problem-solving process somewhat similar to the presentation by D'Zurilla and Goldfried (1971). They maintain that the following steps are involved in successful interpersonal problem solving: (1) an awareness of potential problems when human beings interact, (2) generation of alternative solutions to problems, (3) means-end thinking, which involves specifying necessary steps to carry out problem solutions, (4) consequential thinking, or understanding consequences of specific acts for self and others, and (5) cause-effect thinking, which involves the realization that social interchange may often be a reciprocal interactive process which is affected by the behavior and feelings of others.

Only a few studies have investigated the social problem-solving effectiveness of clinical groups. Platt and Spivack (1972) investigated the problem-solving ability of a mixed group of psychiatric inpatients as compared to a hospital employee control group. The specific dimension of means-ends thinking was analyzed by presenting subjects with the beginning and end of stories where a need was aroused in the protagonist and he or she successfully satisfied the need. Subjects were to provide the middle of the story. Most of the stories dealt with interpersonal themes. Normal subjects described more relevant means, a greater percentage of means that were relevant, and greater enumeration of means as compared to the psychiatric inpatients.

Gotlib and Asarnow (1979) used interpersonal situations based on the same format used by Platt and Spivack (1972) to compare the means-end problem-solving ability of mildly depressed and nondepressed analogue subjects, and depressed and nondepressed clients. The depressed analogue subjects, gave significantly fewer relevant means, elaborated on a significantly smaller percentage of the means, generated more irrelevant means, no-means, or no-response answers, and obtained significantly lower relevancy scores than the nondepressed analogue subjects. Among clients, the depressed subjects gave significantly fewer relevant means, gave more irrelevant means, no-means, or no-response answers, and obtained significantly lower relevancy scores than the nondepressed. Comparisons between client and analogue subjects were not presented. It is also noteworthy that depressed and nondepressed subjects did not differ on a nonsocial anagram problem-solving task.

Bruch (1981) compared high, moderate and low assertive subjects using the means-end problem-solving assessment format. No differences were found among assertive groups when American College Test verbal ability scores were used as a covariate.

Summary and comments. Little research has been conducted on social problem-solving among clinical or analogue clinical adult subjects. It seems important to distinguish social problem-solving ability from nonsocial problem-solving or general intellectual impairment (cf. Bruch, 1981). Another concern is whether manifest poor social problem-solving represents a cognitive/behavioral deficiency, or is the result of other performance or motivational factors.

Miller (1975) reviewed the literature on general cognitive-intellectual impairment among the depressed and found no evidence at that time for specific impairments unique to depression. Moreover, several studies which indicated impairment relative to nonclinical subjects found that "impairment" was reversed with improvement in depression. This, among other reasons, led Miller to conclude that cognitive-intellectual deficit, to the extent that it exists among depressives, may result from cognitive interference produced by intrusive thoughts and worries or because of motivational deficits. While certainly not proven, this alternative hypothesis remains equally viable for the social problem-solving literature. Compounding this problem is evidence from the study by Funabiki and Calhoun (1979) that mildly depressed subjects rated problematic social and academic situations as more difficult to cope with than nondepressed subjects. Hence, either deficient problem-solving or negative/irrational beliefs could be operative. The question in need of consideration seems to be whether social problem-solving is a relevant concern apart from (1) general intellectual deficit, and (2) performance deficit due to other cognitive factors such as negative thoughts and negative/irrational beliefs.

Attributional Style.
Attributional style refers to a particular manner of ascribing responsibility or making causal inferences for a behavior or event. Attributional processes have been employed as an explanatory construct in the development and etiology of depression by both the self-control (Rehm, 1977) and reformulated learned-helplessness models (Abramson, Seligman, & Teasdale, 1978). The reformulated learned-helplessness model posited a depressive attributional style in which depressed individuals attribute negative outcomes to internal, stable, and global factors. Although not suggested directly in the Abramson et al. (1978) paper, it appears logical to assume the opposite depressive attributional style for positive outcomes - external, unstable, and specific. Rehm (1977) had focused on the internal-external dimensions, suggesting that it is only when individuals make internal attributions for success and failure that events take on relevance for self-evaluation and consequent self-reinforcement and self-punishment.

No specific attributional style has been postulated for other specific types of psychopathology. As we shall see, however, this question has been addressed empirically in the use of psychopathological control groups in experimental studies of depression. As with other areas reviewed in this chapter the thorny issue of an attributional style which differentiates depression and anxiety remains unresolved.

Empirical investigations have evaluated the relationship between three types of attributions and depression (cf. Craighead, Kennedy, Raczynski, & Dow, 1984): (a) Subjects' attributions for experimenter-determined success or failure on laboratory tasks (e.g., Kuiper, 1978; Rizley, 1978); (b) retrospective attributions for recent significant life events (e.g., Gong-Guy, & Hammen, 1980; Hammen & Cochran, 1981; Harvey, 1981); and (c) attributions for hypothetical outcomes that subjects are asked to imagine themselves having experienced (e.g., Golin, Sweeney & Schaeffer, 1981; Janoff-Bulman, 1979; Seligman, Abramson, Semmel & von Baeyer, 1979). In the main, the results from these studies support the notion of a strong relationship between the style of internal, stable, and global attributions for negative events and mild to moderate depression in college student subjects. The data regarding positive events are less consistent, but some studies report data compatible with the Abramson et al. (1978) model (cf. Harvey, 1981; Rizley, 1978).

Most of the aforementioned studies have been conducted with college students, with the control group being limited to nondepressed or so-called "normal" college students. This raises at least two important questions: (1) will similar findings be obtained for clinically depressed subjects? (an evaluation of the continuity assumption), and (2) is the "depressive attributional style" specific to depression or does it also characterize other clinical problems? (an evaluation of the specificity assumption).

Raps, Reinhard, Peterson, Seligman, and Abramson (1981) investigated both questions by comparing the attributional styles of a group of unipolar clinically depressed patients with schizophrenic patients and a nondepressed medical control group of patients. The depressed patients made more internal, stable, and global attributions for negative outcomes and more external and unstable attributions for positive outcomes than did the nondepressed medical control patients. Furthermore, the pattern of the schizophrenic patients' attributions was almost identical to the nondepressed medical controls and different from those of the depressed patients. Lewinsohn, Steinmetz, Larson, and Franklin (1981), however, failed to obtain differences between clinically depressed female clients and women with no history of depression on measures of internality and stability of attributions for success or failure. These investigators used an attributional assessment instrument which has not been used in other studies of attributional style and depression. Consequently, because of subject differences (inpatient vs. outpatient), subjects' selection criteria, and the use of different studies, it is difficult to draw firm conclusions regarding the relationship between clinical depression and attributional style.

Metalsky and Abramson (1981) evaluated the specificity hypothesis by investigating the attributional

style of test-anxious college students. Test anxiety
was measured by the Test Anxiety Questionnaire
(Mandler & Sarason, 1952) and attributional style by
the Attributional Styles Scale (Seligman et al.,
1979). The test-anxious students reported the same
pattern of "depressive" attributions as outlined by
Abramson et al. (1978), which suggests it may not be
specific to depression. As just noted, however, Raps
et al. (1981) found that the depressive attributional
style characterized their depressive patients, but
not their psychopathological control group of schizophrenic patients.

The data from these studies leave both the continuity and specificity questions unsettled. This
research highlights the necessity of psychopathological control groups in depression research
(Lewinsohn, Biglan, & Zeiss, 1976) and especially the
need to control for anxiety in studies with mildly
and moderately depressed college students (Kennedy &
Craighead, 1981). Given the findings of Metalsky and
Abramson (1981) and the strong relationships between
anxiety and depression in college students, it is
possible that it is anxiety or some combination of
anxiety and depression instead of depression per se
which produced the results favoring a depressive
attributional style characteristic of mildly and moderately depressed college students. The same question
may be raised for clinically depressed patients, even
if they do differ from other psychopathological
control groups such as schizophrenia. As indicated
earlier, the relationship between anxiety and depression is a difficult unresolved problem in psychopathology, and its resolution has direct implications for
conceptual research in this area and the resultant
clinical assessment and treatment.

Another major issue has to do with the causal
role of attributional style in the etiology of depression. Abramson et al. (1978) hypothesized that
the depressive attributional style is causative. The
data to date, however, have been primarily correlational in nature. Future research should seek to
determine if the depressive attributional style plays
a causative role in the development of depression or
if it is merely an associated characteristic. It
seems likely that the depressive attributional style
is characteristic of some (but not all) depressed individuals, and for some (but not all) of these depressed people it may be a causal factor.

Summary and comments. Research in this area has focused on the depressive attributional style posited by

Abramson et al. (1978), and the data have been consistent with that model. However, whether this depressive attributional style is specific to depression and whether it is as characteristic of clinically depressed as of more mildly depressed college students (with whom most of the research has been conducted) remains to be demonstrated. The "depressive" attributional style is associated with or plays a causal role in the development of social inadequacy among depressed clients. Certainly the current data warrant further research regarding attributional style as it relates to social interactions, and clients with social competency problems should be assessed on the attributions they make regarding their social problems. Whether specific attributional therapies are warranted must await further investigation.

Are the findings regarding a characteristic attributional style in anxiety and depression relevant to social skills? Since none of the reviewed studies have been specific to attributions regarding social interactions, either imagined or in the laboratory, an empirically based answer is not possible. However, the format of the Attributional Styles Scale allows each subject to determine the situation about which the attributions are reported. In completing the questionnaire, many college students employ social situations, which suggests that the findings may be replicated in investigations of the social interactions and attributional style.

Memory Distortion

Beck's (1976) cognitive model of psychopathology and therapy posits that depressed individuals have and maintain a negative view of themselves, the world, and the future by engaging in a number of cognitive distortions such as magnification, selective abstraction, arbitrary inference, dichotomous thinking, and overgeneralization. Because of the clinical observation that depressed people focus on their past, negative memory distortion has evolved as a major topic in the psychopathology of depression.

As early as 1932, Bartlett had suggested that individuals may reconstruct their experiences in memory so as to make them consistent with their beliefs or views of the world. He, like Beck (1976), labelled these beliefs schemata. Subsequent research on "constructive" memory in cognitive psychology reported data consistent with their view that individuals will interpret experiences to make them fit their schemata better (cf. Abramson & Martin, 1981).

Because depressed people have a negative view, they both screen-out information and distort their memories of events in a negative direction. Several studies have reported that depressed subjects show a negative bias or distortion in their recall of high rates of positive feedback on a laboratory task (Wener & Rehm, 1975; Buchwald, 1977; Nelson & Craighead, 1977). This finding was replicated by DeMonbreun and Craighead (1977) with depressed psychiatric patients. This study included a nondepressed psychiatric patient control group and a normal control group and indicated that the memory distortion of positive feedback may be specific to depression. The data for distortion of moderate rates (about 50% of the time) of positive feedback are ambiguous with Kuiper (1978) reporting data indicating distortion in a negative direction and Craighead, Hickey, and DeMonbreun (1979) reporting no differences between depressed-anxious, nondepressed-anxious and nondepressed-nonanxious subjects.

The findings for distortion of negative feedback however, have not been consistent with Beck's (1976) predictions. Nelson and Craighead (1977) found significant differences between depressed and nondepressed subjects in their recall of low-rate (30%) of negative feedback, but the differences were due to the nondepressed subjects' inaccurately low recall of negative feedback; the depressed subjects were extremely accurate in their recall of low rates of negative feedback. This finding has been recently replicated by Kennedy and Craighead (1981).

This area of research has been extended to social situations in a recent study by Lewinsohn et al. (1980). They asked depressed clients, nondepressed psychopathological controls, and normal controls to rate themselves on a combined positive and negative measure of social competence following a social interaction task. They were also rated by independent, objective observers. The depressed clients were more accurate (compared to the independent observers' ratings) than either of the control groups both of whom rated themselves more positively than the observers had. Because of the nature of the task and the absence of information regarding whether it was perceived as positive or negative by the subjects it is difficult to fit the findings with the other laboratory studies on distortion of memory in depression. However, there appears to be little doubt that a negative bias is associated with depression and that a slight positive bias or "illusory glow" (Mischel, 1979) is adaptive. Of course, an extreme

249

positive bias may be maladaptive and even characteristic of sociopathy.

As with other areas of research, there have been
only minimal attempts to control for the strong
positive relationship between anxiety and depression.
Kennedy and Craighead (1981) in two recent studies
with college females replicated the Nelson and
Craighead (1977) findings that depressed subjects
were accurate in their recall of low rates of negative feedback but that nondepressed subjects underestimated the number of errors they had made. However, Kennedy and Craighead also found that the
accurate recall of negative feedback is not specific
to depressed subjects but occurs among anxious-nondepressed subjects as well. Additional specificity
studies with anxious control groups and clinically
depressed patients are needed to clarify this issue.

Summary and comments. Data on memory distortion generally indicate that depressed subjects show a negative bias when recalling high rates of positive
feedback. However, they are accurate in the recall
of low rates of negative feedback, and it is
"normals" who distort their recall in a positive
direction. Although the data indicate this problem
to be specific to depression relative to general psychopathological control groups, it may also characterize anxious-nondepressed individuals. The
findings suggest that the cognitive component of
social skills therapy should be geared toward teaching clients a slight positive bias in their interpretation and memory of social experiences. Depressed
clients' memory distortions may weaken the effects of
therapeutic approaches which focus only on increasing
the skill and frequency of social interactions.

SUMMARY

This chapter reviewed research regarding cognition
and social inadequacy. The focus was on the relevance of these findings for clinical problems, particularly anxiety and depression. Relevant methodological considerations and the need for specificity
when discussing cognition were stressed. Because the
reviewed research dealt with operationalized measures
of cognitive phenomena, cognitions were considered at
the levels of covert speech and intervening variables. Perhaps future development of clinical cognitive theory will clarify the role of cognitions as
hypothetical constructs.

We identified six areas of cognitive deficits

which may be relevant to social inadequacy. They included negative thoughts, negative/irrational beliefs,
social perception (self and others), social problem-
solving, attributional style and memory distortion.
In general, it was found that each of these cognitive
deficits was associated with social inadequacy in
various problem areas. Further research is needed to
determine whether: (1) the cognitive factors are
causative or merely associated with clinical problems; and (2) whether the data collected mostly with
college populations will be replicated with clinical
populations (the preliminary findings suggest they
will). This research also highlights the need to
study the interrelationships between anxiety, depression and social inadequacy; to a certain degree these
are three overlapping constructs. Such controlled,
conceptually related research should clarify the
relevance of cognition in social inadequacy for psychopathology, assessment and treatment. It appears
that the most effective clinical interventions will
follow from an individualized assessment of the
various components of social competence.

REFERENCES

Abramson, L.Y., & Martin, D.J. Depression and the
    causal inference process. In J. Harvey, W.
    Ickes, & R. Kidd (Eds.), New directions in
    attribution research (Vol.III). Hillsdale,
    N.J.: Erlbaum, 1981
Abramson, L.Y., Seligman, M.E.P., & Teasdale, J.D.
    Learned helplessness in humans: Critique and
    reformulation. Journal of Abnormal Psychology,
    1978, 87, 49-74
Alden, L., & Cappe, R. Nonassertiveness: Skill def-
    icit or selective self-evaluation? Behavior
    Therapy, 1981, 12, 107-114
Alden, L., & Safran, J. Irrational beliefs and non-
    assertive behavior. Cognitive Therapy and Re-
    search, 1978, 2, 357-364
Archer, D., & Akert, R.M. Words and everything else:
    Verbal and nonverbal cues in social interpret-
    ation. Journal of Personality and Social Psy-
    chology, 1977, 35, 443-449
Arkowitz, H. The assessment of social skills. In M.
    Hersen & A. Bellack (Eds.), Behavioral assess-
    ment: A practical handbook. New York: Pergamon,
    1981
Bartlett, F.C. Remembering. Cambridge: Cambridge
    University Press, 1932
Beck, A.T. Thinking and depression. I. Idiosyncratic

content and cognitive distortions. *Archives of General Psychiatry*, 1963, 9, 324-333

Beck, A.T. *Depression: Causes and treatment*. Philadelphia: University of Pennsylvania Press, 1967

Beck, A.T. *Cognitive therapy and the emotional disorders*. New York: International Universities Press, 1976

Bellack, A.S. A critical appraisal of strategies for assessing social skill. *Behavioral Assessment*, 1979, 1, 157-176 (a)

Bellack, A.S. Behavioral assessment of social skills. In A.S. Bellack & M. Hersen (Eds.), *Research and practice in social skills training*. New York: Plenum Press, 1979 (b)

Bem, D.J. Self-perception theory. In L. Berkowitz (Ed.), *Advances in experimental social psycholgy* (Vol.6). New York: Academic Press, 1972

Biglan, A., & Dow, M.G. Toward a second-generation model: A problem-specific approach. In L. Rehm (Ed.), *Behavior therapy for depression: Present status and future directions*. New York: Academic Press, 1981

Biglan, A., & Kass, D.J. The empirical nature of behavior therapies. *Behaviorism*, 1977, 5, 1-15

Blaney, P.H., Behar, V., & Head, R. Two measures of depressive cognitions: Their association with depression and with each other. *Journal of Abnormal Psychology*, 1980, 89, 678-682

Borkovec, T.D., Fleischmann, D.J., & Caputo, J.A. The measurement of anxiety in an analogue social situation. *Journal of Consulting and Clinical Psychology*, 1973, 41, 157-161

Borkovec, T.D., & O'Brien, G.T. Relation of autonomic perception and its manipulation to the maintenance and reduction of fear. *Journal of Abnormal Psychology*, 1977, 86, 163-171

Bourne, L.E., Jr., Dominowski, R.L., & Loftus, E.F. *Cognitive processes*. Englewood Cliffs, N.J.: Prentice-Hall, 1979

Bruch, M.A. A task analysis of assertive behavior revisited: Replication and extension. *Behavior Therapy*, 1981, 12, 217-230

Buchwald, A.M. Depressive mood and estimates of reinforcement frequency. *Journal of Abnormal Psychology*, 1977, 86, 443-446

Buss, A.H., & Lang, P.J. Psychological deficit in schizophrenia: I. Affect, reinforcement and concept attainment. *Journal of Abnormal Psychology*, 1965, 70, 2-24

Cacioppo, J.T., Glass, C.R., & Merluzzi, T.V. Self-statements and self-evaluations: A cognitive-response analysis of heterosocial anxiety. Cognitive Therapy and Research, 1979, 3, 249-262

Carver, C.S. A cybernetic model of self-attention processes. Journal of Personality and Social Psychology, 1979, 37, 1251-1281

Clark, J.V., & Arkowitz, H. Social anxiety and self-evaluation of interpersonal performance. Psychological Reports, 1975, 36, 211-221

Coleman, R.E. Manipulation of self-esteem as a determinant of mood of elated and depressed women. Journal of Abnormal Psychology, 1975, 84, 693-700

Coyne, J.C. Toward an interactional description of depression. Psychiatry, 1976, 39, 28-40

Craighead, W.E. Away from a unitary model of depression. Behavior Therapy, 1980, 11, 123-129

Craighead, W.E., Hickey, K.S., & DeMonbreun, B.G. Distortion of perception and recall of neutral feedback in depression. Cognitive Therapy and Research, 1979, 3, 291-298

Craighead, W.E., Kimball, W.H., & Rehak, P.J. Mood changes, physiological responses, and self-statements during social rejection imagery. Journal of Consulting and Clinical Psychology, 1979, 47, 385-396

Craighead, W.E., Kennedy, R.E., Raczynski, J.M. & Dow, M.G. Affective disorders - unipolar. In S.M. Turner & M. Hersen (Eds.), Adult psychopathology: A behavioral perspective. New York: Wiley, 1984

Curran, J.P., Wallander, J.L., & Fischetti, M. The importance of behavioral and cognitive factors in heterosexual-social anxiety. Journal of Personality, 1980, 48, 285-292

Curran, J.P. Skills training as an approach to the treatment of heterosexual-social anxiety: A review. Psychological Bulletin, 1977, 84, 140-157

Curran, J.P. Social skills: Methodological issues and future directions. In A.S. Bellack & M. Hersen (Eds.), Research and practice in social skills training. New York: Plenum Press, 1979

DeMonbreun, B.G., & Craighead, W.E. Distortion of perception and recall of positive and neutral feedback in depression. Cognitive Therapy and Research, 1977, 1, 311-330

Dow, M.G., Glaser, S.R., & Biglan, A. The relevance of specific conversational behaviors to ratings of social skill: An experimental analysis. Journal of Behavioral Assessment, 1981, 3, 233-242

Cognition and Social Inadequacy

Duval, S., & Wicklund, R.A. A theory of objective
    self-awareness. New York: Academic Press, 1972
D'Zurilla, T.J., & Goldfried, M.R. Problem-solving
    and behavior modification. Journal of Abnormal
    Psychology, 1971, 78, 107-126
Ellis, A. Reason and emotion in psychotherapy. New
    York: Stuart, 1962
Fenigstein, A., Scheier, M.F., & Buss, A.H. Public
    and private self-consciousness: Assessment and
    theory. Journal of Consulting and Clinical
    Psychology, 1975, 43, 522-527
Fischetti, M., Curran, J.P., & Wessberg, H.W. Sense
    of timing: A skill deficit in heterosexual-
    socially anxious males. Behavior Modification,
    1977, 1, 179-194
Funabiki, D., & Calhoun, J.F. Use of a behavioral-
    analytic procedure in evaluating two models of
    depression. Journal of Consulting and Clinical
    Psychology, 1979, 47, 183-185
Gerson, A.C., & Perlman, D. Loneliness and expressive
    communication. Journal of Abnormal Psychology,
    1979, 88, 258-261
Glass, C.R., & Merluzzi, T.V. Cognitive assessment
    of social-evaluative anxiety. In T.V. Merluzzi,
    C.R. Glass, & M. Genest (Eds.), Cognitive ass-
    essment. New York: Guilford, 1981
Glass, C.R., Merluzzi, T.V., Biever, J.L., & Larsen,
    K.H. Cognitive assessment of social anxiety:
    Development and validation of a self-statement
    questionnaire. Cognitive Therapy and Research,
    1982, 37-56,
Goldfried, M.R., & Sobocinski, D. Effect of irr-
    ational beliefs on emotional arousal. Journal
    of Consulting and Clinical Psychology, 1975,
    43, 504-510
Golin, S., Sweeney, P.D., & Shaeffer, D.E. The caus-
    ality of causal attributions in depression: A
    cross-lagged panel correlational analysis. Jo-
    urnal of Abnormal Psychology, 1981, 90, 14-22
Gong-Guy, E., & Hammen, C. Causal perceptions of
    stressful events in depressed and nondepressed
    outpatients. Journal of Abnormal Psychology,
    1980, 89, 662-669
Gormally, J., Sipps, G., Raphael, R., Edwin, D., &
    Varvil-Weld, D. The relationship between mal-
    adaptive cognitions and social anxiety. Jour-
    nal of Consulting and Clinical Psychology, 1981,
    49, 300-301
Gotlib, I.H., & Asarnow, R.F. Interpersonal and
    impersonal problem-solving skills in mildly and
    clinically depressed university students.

Journal of Consulting and Clinical Psychology, 1979, 47, 86-95

Hammen, C.L., & Cochran, S.D. Cognitive correlates of life stress and depression in college students. Journal of Abnormal Psychology, 1981, 90, 23-27

Harmon, T.M., Nelson, R.O., & Hayes, S.C. Self-monitoring of mood versus activity by depressed clients. Journal of Consulting and Clinical Psychology, 1980, 48, 30-38

Harvey, D.M. Depression and attributional style: Interpretations of important personal events. Journal of Abnormal Psychology, 1981, 90, 134-142

Hiebert, B., & Fox, E.E. Reactive effects of self-monitoring anxiety. Journal of Consulting Psychology, 1981, 28, 187-193

Homme, L.E. Perspectives in psychology: XXIV, control of coverants, the operants of the mind. The Psychological Record, 1965, 15, 501-511

Jacobson, N.S. The assessment of overt behavior. In L. Rehm (Ed.), Behavior therapy for depression: Present status and future directions. New York: Academic Press, 1981

Janoff-Bulman, R. Characterological versus behavioral self-blame: Inquiries into depression and rape. Journal of Personality and Social Psychology, 1979, 37, 1798-1809

Jones, R.G. A factored measure of Ellis' irrational belief systems with personality and maladjustment correlated. Wichita, Kansas: Test Systems, 1968

Kanfer, F.H., & Karoly, P. Self-control: A behavioristic excursion into the lion's den. Behavior Therapy, 1972, 3, 398-416

Kennedy, R.E., & Craighead, W.E. Recall of positive and negative feedback by depressed and nondepressed-anxious university students. Unpublished manuscript, 1981

Krantz, S., & Hammen, C. The assessment of cognitive bias in depression. Journal of Abnormal Psychology, 1979, 88, 611-619

Kuiper, N.A. Depression and causal attributions for success and failure. Journal of Personality and Social Psychology, 1978, 36, 236-246

Lang, P.J., & Buss, A.H. Psychological deficit in schizophrenia: II. Interference and activation. Journal of Abnormal Psychology, 1965, 70, 77-106

LaPointe, K.A., & Crandell, C.J. Relationship of irrational beliefs to self-reported depression. Cognitive Therapy and Research, 1980, 4, 247-

250

Lewinsohn, P.M., Biglan, A., & Zeiss, A.M. Behavioral treatment of depression. In P.O. Davidson (Ed.), The behavioral management of anxiety, depression and pain. New York: Brunner-Mazel, 1976

Lewinsohn, P.M., & Lee, W.M.L. Assessment of affective disorders. In D.H. Barlow (Ed.), Behavioral assessment of adult disorders. New York: Guilford Press, 1981

Lewinsohn, P.M., Mischel, W., Chaplin, W., & Barton, R. Social competence and depression: The role of illusory self-perceptions. Journal of Abnormal Psychology, 1980, 89, 203-212

Lewinsohn, P.M., Munoz, R.F., & Larson, D.W. The measurement of expectancies and other cognitions in depressed individuals. Paper presented at the meeting of the Association for the Advancement of Behavior Therapy, Chicago, November, 1978

Lewinsohn, P.M., Steinmetz, J.L., Larson, D.W., & Franklin, J. Depression-related cognitions: Antecedent or consequence? Journal of Abnormal Psychology, 1981, 90, 213-219

Libet, J.M., & Lewinsohn, P.M. Concept of social skill with special reference to the behavior of depressed persons. Journal of Consulting and Clinical Psychology, 1973, 40, 304-312

Locke, E.A. Is "behavior therapy" behavioristic? (An analysis of Wolpe's psychotherapeutic methods). Psychological Bulletin, 1971, 76, 318-327

Lunghi, M.E. The stability of mood and social perception measures in a sample of depressive inpatients. British Journal of Psychiatry, 1977, 130, 598-604

MacCorquodale, K., & Meehl, P.E. On a distinction between hypothetical constructs and intervening variables. Psychological Review, 1948, 55, 95-107

Mandler, G.M., & Sarason, S. A study of anxiety and learning. Journal of Abnormal Social Psychology, 1952, 47, 166-173

Metalsky, G.I., & Abramson, L.Y. Unpublished data, 1981.

Miller, W.R. Psychological deficit in depression. Psychological Bulletin, 1975, 82, 238-260

Mischel, W. On the interface of cognition and personality: Beyond the person-situation debate. American Psychologist, 1979, 34, 740-754

Morrison, R.L., & Bellack, A.S. The role of social perception in social skill. Behavior Therapy, 1981, 12, 69-79

Munoz, R.F., & Lewinsohn, P.M. The Cognitive Events Schedule. Unpublished mimeo, University of Oregon, 1976 (a)

Munoz, R.F., & Lewinsohn, P.M. The Personal Belief Inventory. Unpublished mimeo, University of Oregon, 1976 (b)

Munoz, R.F., & Lewinsohn, P.M. The Subjective Probability Questionnaire. Unpublished mimeo, University of Oregon, 1976 (c)

Natale, M. Effects of induced elation-depression on speech in the initial interview. Journal of Consulting and Clinical Psychology, 1977, 45, 45-52

Nelson, R.E. Irrational beliefs and depression. Journal of Consulting and Clinical Psychology, 1977, 45, 1190-1191

Nelson, R.E., & Craighead, W.E. Selective recall of positive and negative feedback, self-control behaviors, and depression. Journal of Abnormal Psychology, 1977, 86, 379-388

O'Banion, K., & Arkowitz, H. Social anxiety and selective memory for affective information about the self. Social Behavior and Personality, 1977, 5, 321-328

Peterson, J., Fischetti, M., Curran, J.P., & Arland, S. Sense of timing: A skill deficit in heterosocially anxious women. Behavior Therapy, 1981, 12, 195-201

Pitcher, S.W., & Meikle, S. The topography of assertive behavior in positive and negative situations. Behavior Therapy, 1980, 11, 532-547

Platt, J.J., & Spivack, G. Problem-solving thinking of psychiatric patients. Journal of Consulting and Clinical Psychology, 1972, 39, 148-151

Prkachin, K.M., Craig, K.D., Papageorgis, D., & Reith, G. Nonverbal communication deficits and response to performance feedback in depression. Journal of Abnormal Psychology, 1977, 86, 224-234

Pryor, J.B., Gibbons, F.X., Wicklund, R.A., Fazio, R.H., & Hood, R. Self-focused attention and self-report validity. Journal of Personality, 1977, 45, 513-527

Raps, C.S., Reinhard, K.E., Peterson, C.R., Seligman, M.E.P., & Abramson, L.Y. Attributional style among depressed patients. Journal of Abnormal Psychology, 1982, 91, 102-108

Rehm, L.P. A self-control model of depression. Behavior Therapy, 1977, 8, 787-804

Rizley, R. Depression and distortion in the attribution of causality. Journal of Abnormal Psychology, 1978, 87, 32-48

Sarason, I.G. Three lacunae of cognitive therapy, Cognitive Therapy and Research, 1979, 3, 223-235

Schachter, S., & Singer, J.E. Cognitive, social, and physiological determinants of emotional state. Psychological Review, 1962, 69, 379-399

Scheier, M.F., & Carver, C.S. Self-focused attention and the experience of emotion: Attraction, repulsion, elation, and depression. Journal of Personality and Social Psychology, 1977, 35, 625-636

Schrader, S.L., Craighead, W.E., & Schrader, R.M. Reinforcement patterns in depression. Behaviour Therapy, 1978, 9, 1-14

Schwartz, R.M., & Gottman, J. Toward a task analysis of assertive behavior. Journal of Consulting and Clinical Psychology, 1976, 44, 910-920

Seligman, M.E.P., Abramson, L.Y., Semmel, A., & von Baeyer, C. Depressive attributional style. Journal of Abnormal Psychology, 1979, 88, 242-247

Singer, J.L. Navigating the stream of consciousness: Research in daydreaming and related inner experience. American Psychologist, 1975, 30, 727-738

Skinner, B.F. Science and human behavior. Macmillan, 1953

Skinner, B.F. About behaviorism. New York: Knopf, 1974

Smith, R.E., & Sarason, I.G. Social anxiety and the evaluation of negative interpersonal feedback. Journal of Consulting and Clinical Psychology, 1975, 43, 429

Snyder, M. Self-monitoring of expressive behavior. Journal of Personality and Social Psychology, 1974, 30, 526-537

Snyder, M. Cognitive, behavioral, and interpersonal consequences of self-monitoring. In P. Pliner, K.R. Blankstein, & I.M. Spigel (Eds.), Perception of emotion in self and others (Advances in the study of communication and affect, Vol.5). New York: Plenum Press, 1979

Spivack, G., Platt, J.J., & Shure, M.B. The problem solving approach to adjustment. San Francisco: Jossey-Bass, 1976

Steffen, J.J., & Lucas, J. Social strategies and expectations as components of social competence. Unpublished manuscript, 1980

Strickland, B.R., Hale, W.D., & Anderson, L.K. Effect of induced mood states on activity and self-

Cognition and Social Inadequacy

reported affect. Journal of Consulting and
Clinical Psychology, 1975, 43, 587
Sutton-Simon, K., & Goldfried, M.R. Faulty thinking
patterns in two types of anxiety. Cognitive
Therapy and Research, 1979, 3, 193-203
Trower, P. Fundamentals of interpersonal behavior: A
social psychological perspective. In A.S.
Bellack & M. Hersen (Eds.), Research and
practice in social skills training. New York:
Plenum Press, 1979
Trower, P. Towards a generative model of social
skills: A critique and synthesis. In J. Curran
& P. Monti (Eds.), Social skills training:
A practical handbook for assessment and treatment. New York: Guilford Press, 1981
Twentyman, C.T., & McFall, R.M. Behavioral training
of social skills in shy males. Journal of Consulting and Clinical Psychology, 1975, 43, 384-
395
Ullmann, L.P. Cognitions: Help or hindrance? Journal of Behavior Therapy and Experimental Psychiatry, 1981, 12, 19-23
Vasta, R., & Brockner, J. Self-esteem and self-evaluative covert statements. Journal of Consulting
and Clinical Psychology, 1979, 47, 776-777
Velten, E., Jr. A laboratory task for induction of
mood states. Behaviour Research and Therapy,
1968, 6, 473-482
Watson, D., & Friend, R. Measurement of social-eval-
uative anxiety. Journal of Consulting and
Clinical Psychology, 1969, 33, 448-457
Wener, A.E., & Rehm, L.P. Depressive affect: A test
of behavioral hypotheses. Journal of Abnormal
Psychology, 1975, 84, 221-227
Weissman, M.M., & Paykel, E.S. The depressed woman:
A study of social relationships. Chicago:
University of Chicago Press, 1974
Wilson, G.T. Psychotherapy process and procedure:
The behavioral mandate. Paper presented at the
meetings of the Association for Advancement of
Behavior Therapy, Toronto, November,1981
Wolpe, J. Cognition and causation in human behavior
and its therapy. American Psychologist, 1978,
33, 437-446

Editorial Introduction, Chapter Nine

ASSESSMENT OF COGNITIONS IN SOCIAL SKILLS TRAINING

Geoff Shepherd

After broadly surveying the types of dysfunctional cognitions which are associated with and hypothesized to produce deficient social behaviour, we next turn to the cognitive assessment of the individual - a prerequisite to effective therapy - as Dow and Craighead suggest.

In this chapter, Shepherd (who is a clinical psychologist) takes up the challenge by Bellack (1979) that no empirically sound techniques exist for the assessment of cognitive variables in social skills. He critically reviews the range of assessment techniques and spells out the pros and cons for each. He goes into considerable practical detail on one of these - the Personal Questionnaire - with guidance on its administration. This questionnaire fulfils many of our requirements. It is a specific, individualized approach to scaling self-reports and has good psychometric properties. Shepherd confesses, however, that the nature of the problem - measuring cognitions - leaves all instruments with unresolved difficulties, though the reader may find solutions suggested elsewhere in this volume (e.g., Harre, Bandura et al.).

Chapter Nine

ASSESSMENT OF COGNITIONS IN SOCIAL SKILLS TRAINING

Geoff Shepherd

INTRODUCTION

Future historians of psychology may find a certain
irony in the fact that behaviour therapy which began
partly as a reaction to traditional psychotherapies
and their preoccupation with unobservable and un-
measurable thoughts and feelings, should find itself
twenty years later grappling with those same thoughts
and feelings that it was at first at such pains to
avoid. Behaviour therapy has gradually gone "cognitive" (Mahoney, 1974; 1977) and social skills is no
exception to this general trend. Nearly every current writer in the field is now careful to stress the
importance of cognitions and subjective processes
(Trower, 1979; Bellack, 1979; Yardley, 1979; Wallace
et al., 1980; Eisler & Frederiksen, 1980). The question that is immediately raised by this shift in
emphasis is: how are such cognitive processes to be
measured? Bellack (1979) suggests that, "despite the
importance of assessing the various social perception
skills and associated cognitive parameters, no empirically sound assessment techniques exist" (p.99,
op. cit.). What would constitute "empirically sound
assessment techniques"? What are the alternatives,
and how might we set about investigating the relationship of cognitions to other aspects of difficulties in social functioning? These are the issues
to be addressed in this chapter. Let us begin by
reviewing briefly why cognitive processes are important and make it clear what sort of cognitions we are
talking about.

WHY COGNITIONS?

This is not a rhetorical question. There is a distinct body of opinion which has argued that a

concern with cognitive processes may eventually weaken the effectiveness of behavioural treatments (Ledwidge, 1978). However, in relation to social skills training there also seems to be a compelling feeling that descriptions which are based only on behaviour are simply inadequate for the task. This feeling is most clearly expressed by Yardley (1979) where she states that, "the social skills model of social interaction was found wanting in explanatory power, particularly in the area of understanding and establishment of meaningful behaviour... It is in the area of 'meaning' that the social skills model has produced greatest problems" (p.61). This concern with the subjective meaning of social events is supported by theoretical social psychologists such as Harre and Secord (1972) and Gauld and Shotter (1977). But, what is meant by "meaning" in this context? Can we give it a clearer operational definition?

Essentially, meaning appears to refer to the expectancies that each participant in the interaction holds with regard to the likelihood that particular outcomes will occur. These expectancies are concerned with the outcomes of one's own actions, or the reactions of others. Those individuals who experience social difficulties may appear to have distorted expectancies about the effects of their own behaviour. For example, a tendency to expect negative outcomes to accrue (Eisler et al., 1978), or a generalized feeling of being helpless and "out of control" (Seligman, 1975; Bandura, 1977). Alternatively, they may expect negative consequences, e.g., disapproval, criticism, etc., from others (Nichols, 1974) and have a low opinion of their own ability to bring about positive and rewarding outcomes (Rotter, 1966; Fielder & Beach, 1978). Trower (1981) has suggested that stereotype expectations of this kind may lead to self-fulfilling prophecies and he shows how, through the processes of selective attention and recall, such self-defeating mechanisms can maintain themselves and may interfere with progress during treatment.

Apart from the need to provide an adequate explanation, there are also empirical reasons why it is clear that cognitive processes must be taken into account. These stem from the difficulty of discriminating between socially adequate and inadequate groups on the basis of behaviour alone. Admittedly there are sometimes extreme behavioural differences. For example, socially inadequate patients tend not to talk very much (Gillingham et al., 1977; Trower, 1980) and there may also be some specific social

situations, e.g., assertive encounters, where behavioural skills are crucial (Eisler et al., 1973;
1975). Nevertheless, in general social interaction
specific behavioural differences between skilled and
unskilled groups are difficult to demonstrate
(Arkowitz et al., 1975; Glasgow & Arkowitz, 1975).
There is certainly no evidence for a correlation in
the strict, statistical sense of a continuous relationship between rated skill and behavioural performance. Judgments of skill seem to be based on
more subtle criteria. For example, the timing of the
behavioural inputs (Fischetti et al., 1977), or the
sensitivity of each interactant to changes in the
other's behaviour (Trower, 1980). There are certainly many instances where the criteria that are
being used are rather mysterious. As Curran (1979)
has commented somewhat wryly, "everyone seems to know
what good and poor social skills are but no-one can
define them adequately" (p.321, op. cit.). In these
instances the adequacy of the social skills seems to
lie more in the minds of the interactants, rather
than in their behaviour. It then becomes particularly important to develop satisfactory methods for
assessing these cognitive events. As Argyle (1969)
himself noted, the social skills model was only meant
to be "a starting point" (p.186), and "the full role
of cognitive processes .... has yet to be delineated"
(p.431, op. cit.). So, let us consider the alternative assessment approaches.

QUESTIONNAIRES

Standardized questionnaires have been a traditional
tool for psychological research almost ever since our
discipline began. Questionnaires have been developed
for investigating the cognitive aspects of social
difficulties by Wolpe and Lazarus (1966), Watson and
Friend (1969), Rathus (1973), and Richardson and
Tasto (1976) among others. Their use has been reviewed previously by Hersen and Bellack (1977),
Bellack (1979), and Galassi and Galassi (1979). These
instruments are all generally well standardized, they
have good internal consistency, and high test-retest
reliability. Questionnaires provide a rapid and con-
venient method for collecting data but as previous
reviewers have noted, despite their apparently satisfactory conventional psychometric properties, they
still have a number of inherent disadvantages.
    Firstly, the usual pitfalls of questionnaire
constructuion are waiting to trap the unwary. There
is the familiar problem of response "sets" (Anastasi,

1968). These are global biases which influence response choice irrespective of item content. Category sets may lead subjects to consistently choose one type of response, e.g., a moderate or an extreme one, a "yes" as opposed to a "no". Positional sets may lead subjects to repeatedly choose the left, or the right-hand, alternative. Social desirability sets may lead the subject to give what he perceives to be the "expected" answer. He/she may even consciously (or unconsciously) fake their score to be high or low depending on the perceived consequences. All these effects are well-known and to a certain extent they can be controlled for by careful scale construction, e.g., the randomization of scoring direction, etc. However, some response sets, particularly social desirability and "faking", are difficult to eradicate. They require a more sensitive method of data collection, e.g., interviewing, to be detected.

There are other problems with standard questionnaires. They are often very general, thus, they ask questions like, "I have no particular desire to avoid people - TRUE/FALSE?" "I find social occasions upsetting - TRUE/FALSE?" (Watson & Friend, 1969, Items 4 and 5, emphasis added). Which "people"? What kinds of "social occasions"? Since Mischel's classic review (Mischel, 1968) we now recognize the specificity that is common in behaviour. Many patients with social difficulties have cognitions which are highly specific and, depending on their interpretation of such general items, they may or may not give valid replies. Subjects may also not understand the terms that are being used. For example, Leff (1978) has shown that patients understand such concepts as "fear" and "anger" in ways that are quite different from therapists. If subjects use language and conceptual schema which are subtly different from the experimenter's, then, on examining the relationship between subjective report and behaviour, apparent discrepancies may arise. Bem and Allen (1974) have argued that these inconsistencies often disappear if the subject is allowed to define the appropriate behavioural referent, rather than having to use the experimenter's. Harre and Secord (1972) put forward a similar argument from a more philosophical point of view. Given the possibility of specific and idiosyncratic interpretations of item content, it thus becomes important to have some estimate not only of the internal reliability of the total scale, but also the internal reliability of each specific item. We need to know if an individual's response to a particular item is reliable, or is it just a random response, an error? Unless we know this, summing and averaging across items, with the assumption of some kind of underlying homogeneous trait, is a very dubious procedure.

There is one final reason why standard questionnaires are of limited value in the investigation of social cognitions: this is due to their generally high test-retest reliability. Although high test-retest reliability is usually seen as a desirable psychometric property, it is only useful if it is thought that the underlying variable being measured is stable over time. If the variable being measured is thought to change - as cognitions presumably do, for example during treatment - then a measure with high test-retest reliability will not be suitable for assessing it. What constitutes desirable reliability characteristics is therefore determined by what you think you are measuring and what use the measure is to be put to (Levy, 1973). To measure cognitions in social skills training we ideally need an instrument with high internal consistency (and specificity) but low test-retest reliability.

Given all these problems, it is perhaps not surprising that standard questionnaires do not generally yield very high correlations with behaviour (Mischel, 1968; Hersen et al., 1979). Of course it does not necessarily follow that no such relationship exists. It is quite possible that specific, reliable self-reports may correlate very well with specific, individually-defined, behavioural referents. Indeed evidence reviewed by Ajzen and Fishbein (1977) and Schwab et al. (1979) suggests very strongly that this is the case. If specific intentions and expectancies are taken into account then the relationship between self-reports and behaviour may be quite strong. It is also worth emphasizing that correlating self-reports and behaviour across a group may obscure important relationships within individuals. Alker (1972) has suggested that the correlation between self-report and behaviour may itself be an individual difference and therefore perhaps should be examined on an individual basis. So, let us now look at some simple, more individual-centred methods.

Simple Individual-Centred Methods.

The simplest form of individual-centred assessment is to generate a number of cognitive statements, for example "I expect to be anxious when in the company of women of my own age", or "I often find it difficult to put my point of view across" and then ask

the subject to agree/disagree, or indicate the frequency of occurrence, using simple Likert-type rating
scales. Examples of these methods are to be found in
Eisler et al. (1978) and Schwartz and Gottman (1976).
These methods have some advantages over standard
questionnaires in that the items can be made quite
specific. However, they often do not use the subject's own language in formulating the items and in
this sense they are not truly individualized. They
are also psychometrically rather crude and in particular the reliability of the subject's responses to
each item is unknown. A similar criticism can be
made of in vivo "thought-sampling" (Kendall &
Korgeski, 1979). Here the subject simply records the
occurrence of specific thoughts directly using a
wrist counter or similar device. Once again the
reliability of the recording is unknown and, as
Bellack (1979) notes, such procedures have a tendency
to be "reactive", i.e., they affect the phenomena
that they are trying to observe. This is not
necessarily an inconvenience in practical terms as
the reactivity tends to operate in the direction of
reducing the problem. However, it is a difficulty in
methodological terms as an unreliable, reactive
variable hardly seems a suitable starting point to
tackle fundamental problems about the relationship
between cognitions and behaviour. The problem of
reactivity will be discussed again later, but let us
now go on to consider some rather more sophisticated
individual-centred methods.

Grids
Grid techniques are a generalized method by which any
object (or person) is rated according to a number of
dimensions. The commonest grid method is probably
Osgood's Semantic Differential (Osgood et al., 1957).
However, one of the most interesting methods for
clinical purposes is the Repertory Grid derived from
Kelly's Theory of Personal Constructs (Kelly, 1955).
According to Kelly, we use constructs as classific-
atory concepts in trying to understand the world and
the various situations - social and otherwise - in
which we find ourselves. Constructs can thus be seen
as a body of expectations about our own and others'
behaviour. They provide the means by which we structure our experience, encode it, and reflect upon it.
Constructs arise from experience and they can be
changed by it. They are idiosyncratic, highly per-
sonalized, private "goggles" through which we view
the world (Bannister, 1962). Repertory grids have
been used quite extensively to investigate patients'

Assessment of Cognitions in Social Skills Training

cognitive structures (Bannister & Fransella, 1971; Fransella & Bannister, 1977), but they have received little attention in relation to the assessment of cognitions in social skills training. In order to understand how they might be applied we need to describe the method in a little more detail.

Constructs may be defined operationally as bipolar dimensions through which two or more objects ("elements" as they are known) can be classified as similar and thereby different from a third object, or objects. Repertory grids are the procedures by which these elements are "mapped" in semantic space. The information from a grid is usually presented in the form of the relationship between specific elements and constructs. For example, the "distances" between elements, or the strength of the association between constructs. The statistical analysis of the grid can be fairly simple, e.g., using factor analysis. The method of analysis chosen largely depends on whether a ranking or a rating procedure is used to determine the relationship between the constructs and elements. The administration of a grid consists of three stages: first, the selection of elements and constructs; second, the rating or ranking of elements using the constructs; and third, the scoring and interpretation of results.

The choice of elements and constructs depends on whether they are to be supplied or elicited. Fransella and Bannister (1977) supply a list of possible elements organized under a number of headings (Self-Concept, Family, Intimates, Authority Figures, etc.). For clinical purposes it is probably advisable to elicit the elements by careful interviewing. This will ensure that they have the maximum personal relevance for each individual. Elements can be people, but they can also be situations or even relationships, e.g., "starting a conversation with an attractive woman"; "asking for a date"; "my relationship with a close friend". Constructs may also be supplied, e.g., "makes me feel anxious - doesn't make me feel anxious"; "is important to me - is not important to me". Alternatively, and again this is probably preferable, they may be elicited. There are a number of methods for doing this, the most common being the technique of triadic presentation. In this procedure triads of elements are presented and the subject is asked to specify some important way in which two of them are alike and thereby different from the third. For example, "how I would like to be" and "my best friend" (elements) might both be seen as "confident" (construct) and thereby different from "myself as I

267

am now". The dimension of mutual similarity defines the "emergent" pole of the construct. The subject is then asked, if they have not already made it clear, how the third element differs, e.g., "myself as I am now" may be seen as "not confident". This defines the "contrast" pole. Constructs are thus always bi-polar.

There are various restrictions on the selection of constructs. For example, they should not be sit-uational ("Lives in London - doesn't live in London"); or too precise ("is a postman - is not a postman"); or too vague ("is O.K. - is not O.K."); or too superficial ("is tall - is short"). Elements must also fall within the "range of convenience" of the constucts to be used, i.e., they must be applic-able to them. For example, the construct of "is intelligent - is not intelligent" would be difficult to apply to an element which was a relationship rather than a person. One must also decide how many constructs to use. Experience with the triadic pres-entation method suggests that most people's con-structs are exhausted after about 15-20 presen-tations and this seems a suitable number to work with.

When the elements and the constructs have been selected, the subject is asked to rank or rate each element using each construct. For example, a ranked grid might look like this:

	CONSTRUCTS	
ELEMENTS	1. Makes me feel anxious/does not make me feel anxious	2. Is success-ful/is not successful
1. Girls my age	Rank 8	Rank 4
2. My flatmate	Rank 3	Rank 1
3. My mother	Rank 2	Rank 2
.	.	.
.	.	.
.	°	.
.	.	.

Assessment of Cognitions in Social Skills Training

A rated grid might look like this:

<u>ELEMENT 1</u>
<u>Starting a conversation with an attractive female</u>

<u>CONSTRUCTS</u>	<u>EMERGENT POLE</u>	<u>RATING</u>	<u>CONTRAST POLE</u>
1.	Makes me feel terrible	- x - - -	Doesn't make me feel terrible
2.	Makes me want to run away	x - - - -	Doesn't make me want to run away
3.	Makes me scared I'll blush	x - - - -	Doesn't make me scared I'll blush
.	.		
.	.		
.	.		

Depending on whether the ranking or the rating method is used, different statistical procedures may be employed to analyse the data. The rating method allows for factor analytic methods to be applied and commonalities between the constructs may then be identified. This may lead to the elucidation of central or "core" dimensions of personal meaning. As treatment progresses it is then possible to examine how the position of the elements changes in relation to these major dimensions of personal meaning. Similarly, the "distance" between elements ("self", "ideal-self", "close friend") may be considered either as part of a pre-treatment "diagnosis", or during the course of treatment.

It is not possible in the space available here to do justice to the range and flexibility of grid methods and interested readers are referred to texts such as Landfield and Leitner (1980). Grids are highly specific and individualized and since they are constructed on the basis of interviews they do not suffer many of the problems of traditional questionnaires. Personal construct therapy also bears a striking resemblance to some "cognitive" therapies, e.g., Beck's therapy of depression (Beck et al., 1979). In both cases the subject is encouraged to test out "hypotheses" about the relationship between constructs and elements. For example, is it true that "I" (element) "am a failure in making friends" (construct)? If the hypothesis is falsified by experience, then the relationship between the element and the construct should change. Grids are therefore suitable for exploring the cognitive changes during treatment, however, they still have some disadvantages.

Firstly, the statistical analysis involves assumptions about the equivalence of the underlying scales for each element and such assumptions may not be justified. Summing and averaging, or subjecting the data to a multivariate analysis, then confounds the problem. Secondly, the "maps" of semantic space that are generated may be difficult to understand. What do these "distances" and "relationships" between constructs mean psychologically? What do they mean in relation to behaviour? Finally, and perhaps most importantly, there is no estimate of the reliability of individual ratings or rankings. Without this information it is impossible to know if the relationships between elements or constructs are meaningful, or if they are produced by errors. We shall now turn to a method which is individual-centred, based on interview, and also contains a built-in procedure for estimating the reliability (internal consistency) of each item.

Shapiro's Personal Questionnaire

The Personal Questionnaire (PQ) approach was developed by Shapiro (1961; 1970; 1975) as a method for scaling changes in pyschological symptoms over time. It was developed primarily as a clinical tool and with no particular theory of personality or behaviour underlying it. The construction of a PQ involves: firstly, an interview to elicit symptom statements; secondly, a scaling of these statements; thirdly, the construction and administration of the questionnaire; and fourthly, its scoring and interpretation.

Shapiro attaches considerable importance to the process of assessment interviewing (Shapiro, 1979). He, like Bellack (1979), emphasizes the superiority of human beings as data-gatherers, if not data-processors. Shapiro has developed a standardized, semi-structured, interview schedule which attempts to comprehensively cover the complete range of possible psychological dysfunctions, but for social skills training a more restricted interview focusing on the common dimensions of subjective distress, e.g., feelings of failure, anticipations of criticism, etc., would be more suitable. We have found that the dimensions identified by Richardson and Tasto (1976) in their factor analysis of social anxiety questionnaires provide a very useful basis for structuring such an interview. The aim of the interview is thus to elicit from the subject a number of symptom statements. These may be highly specific and are expressed in the subject's own words, e.g., "I feel trembly when older men are angry with me"; "I worry that attractive women think my nose looks funny", etc. Statements may be "Referential", i.e., with a very specific content - for example, "my flatmate", "my friend", "my mother"; or "Non-Referential", i.e., general; for example, "I feel panicky with people of my own age"; "I don't like going into shops". Once a number of symptom statements have been chosen (about 4-8 seems a manageable number) three variants are constructed to reflect different degrees of symptom intensity. Thus,

(1)   "I feel very nervous talking to attractive women" ("illness" statement)

(2)   "I feel quite nervous talking to attractive women" ("improvement" statement)

(3)   "I don't feel at all nervous talking to attractive women" ("recovery" statement)

These three variants are presented to the subject and he is asked to rate them in terms of their unpleasantness using a modified version of Singer and Young's (1941) affective rating scale. "Illness" statements should be rated towards the unpleasant end of the scale, "improvement" statements towards the middle and "recovery" statements towards the pleasant end. If the subject does not scale the statements consistently, then they are re-worded and re-presented until a consistent scale is produced. This individually-centred scaling procedure is part of the built-in internal reliability check and is an important feature of the procedure. It should be repeated periodically to ensure that the subject's scaling of the items does not alter.

The PQ itself is constructed by preparing three cards each one bearing a pair of symptom statements, i.e., 1/2, 2/3, 1/3. This set of three cards constitutes an item and the final questionnaire consists of all the items prepared from the original symptom statements. The questionnaire is administered by presenting each card in random order and asking the subject to indicate which of the two statements comes closer to describing how he feels "right now". His responses may be recorded in a matrix as illustrated in Figure. 1.

Figure 1: Consistent and Inconsistent Response Patterns for Shapiro's PQ.

Consistent

(a)	1	2	3		(b)	1	2	3
1	-	0	0		1	-	x	0
2		-	0		2		-	0
3			-		3			-

Score = 1   Score = 2

(c)	1	2	3		(d)	1	2	3
1	-	x	x		1	-	x	x
2		-	0		2		-	x
3			-		3			-

Score = 3   Score = 4

Inconsistent

(e)	1	2	3		(f)	1	2	3
1	-	0	0		1	-	0	x
2		-	x		2		-	0
3			-		3			-

Key: x = Column preferred to row
      0 = Row preferred to column

    Patterns (a)-(d) represent the four possible consistent response patterns of gradually increasing intensity; they may be assigned scores from 1-4 respectively. Patterns (e) and (f) are examples of inconsistent responses. In (e) both the "illness" and the "recovery" statement are preferred to "improvement". In (f) the "illness" statement is preferred to "improvement", which itself is preferred to "recovery", but "recovery" is preferred to "illness". In both cases, these patterns are not logically consistent, provided that the subject's original scaling of the items has not been altered. If unreliable sorts of this kind do occur, they should be investigated. They may be due to simple lapses of concentration, ambiguities in the wording of the items, changes in subjective scaling, thought disorder, obsessional slowness, low IQ, or a number of other reasons. In practice, inconsistent sorts are fairly rare (usually between 5 and 10% of the total) and they often disappear if the item is immediately re-presented. This suggests that they are commonly simple errors. However, if a subject persists in producing inconsistent sorts and they cannot be eradicated, then the data must be accepted as unreliable.

Shapiro's method thus provides a specific, individualized approach to scaling self-reports. It uses an interview to elicit the statements and formulates cognitions in the subject's own words. It also provides a check on the internal reliability of each item for each administration. It has high test-retest reliability, and the method is simple and direct. It is suitable for investigating the relationship between cognitions and specific behavioural events over time e.g., during the course of treatment (see Shapiro et al., 1973; Shapiro & Hobson, 1972).

The approach has been developed by several other workers. For example, Phillips (1977) has shown that a whole "family" of Personal Questionnaires may be constructed which differ only in terms of underlying scaling of the items. Depending on the initial scaling procedure and the method of item presentation it is possible to construct PQs with ratio, ordinal, or even logarithmic scales. (Shapiro's original is actually based on a partially ordered metric scale). Phillips discusses the advantages and disadvantages of each and notes that they share in common their individualization, and the built-in internal reliability check. Mulhall (1976) has also refined Shapiro's work and produced a rapid method for constructing and administering PQs based on an easy-to-use booklet. We have been working with an extension of Shapiro's method specifically for patients with social difficulties (Shepherd & Bilsbury, 1979) and this method will now be illustrated with a case example.

Case illustration. We decided to investigate the possibility of a four point version of Shapiro's PQ. We reasoned that a larger range of scale points would enhance the sensitivity of the measure to changes over time. Since we were primarily interested in using it to evaluate the effects of treatment interventions this seemed a significant possible advantage. A four point version means that there are six cards per item (1/2, 1/3, 1/4, 2/3, 2/4, and 3/4). It can be shown that there are only eight logically consistent response patterns which can be derived from these pairs. These patterns can then be ordered on a seven point scale, with two patterns "tying" on one scale point. (A full description of the scoring rationale and the development of the measure are available from the author on request.)

The case to be described is of a 29-year-old, single man - Paul. He was referred because of "social anxiety in a paranoid personality". At the time of referral he was almost completely unable to leave his flat and to enter any social situation for fear of being attacked. He lived alone, but still saw quite a lot of his widowed mother with whom he was rather over-involved. He had had two long in-patient admissions of seven months and six months when aged 23 and 25 and he had also attended a day hospital for nearly fifteen months, aged 26. In the past he had received major and minor tranquillizers, group and family therapy, all to little effect. He had never felt very comfortable with people and has always been rather lonely and isolated. Now he almost never went out socially and was even beginning to be reluctant to do the shopping. He supported himself by doing some clerical work at home but because of his difficulties in going out this was also in jeopardy. He did live in a rather troubled part of the city and had actually been attacked about a year previously. Although he recognized his present fears as being irrational he "just couldn't get them into perspective".

Paul was interviewed carefully and four key cognitions were identified. These were formulated in his own words and reflected his anticipated feelings and expectations when in public places with other people about. The four cognitions were:

1. I am feeling - <u>very / moderately / slightly /
    not at all</u> - frightened to go out.

2. I am feeling - <u>very / moderately / slightly /
    not at all</u> - weak and inadequate as a person.

3. I believe it is - <u>virtually certain / fairly
    likely / not at all likely</u> - that someone will
    come up and threaten me if I go out.

4. I think I would - <u>cope very well / cope fairly
    well / just cope a bit / not cope at all</u> - if
    someone did come up and threaten me.

The four variants for each cognition were produced as indicated and these were presented to him

Assessment of Cognitions in Social Skills Training

for scaling. When he was confident that each set
comprised a consistent dimension from "very" to "not
at all", the variants were compiled into the six
paired comparisons for each cognition. These were
then presented to him and he was asked to indicate
for each pair which statement corresponded most
closely to how he was feeling at that time. The
pattern of choices was recorded and a score assigned
for each cognition of the seven point scale. After a
baseline period, Paul was treated with a mixture of
cognitive therapy (modified from Beck et al., 1979)
and in vivo exposure with graded task assignment. At
the beginning of each treatment session he sorted the
items and the ratings for each cognition were
recorded. These data are presented in Figure 2.

Figure 2: Changes in Key Cognitions During Treatment Using a Modified Version of Shapiro's Personal
Questionnaire.

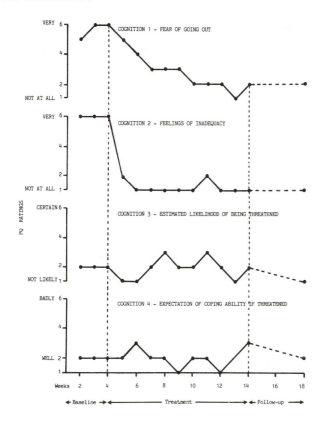

Paul never produced an inconsistent sort. This is rather unusual, but he was an intelligent, careful man and he took considerable trouble over his decisions. The results can therefore be taken as a reliable estimate of the strength of his cognitions on each occasion of testing. It can be seen that the fear of going out decreased steadily during the course of treatment and this was mirrored by changes in his behaviour. His feelings of inadequacy also dropped dramatically and stayed low throughout the follow-up period. Surprisingly, his estimated likelihood of being threatened was never very high and showed little change during the course of treatment. His expected degree of coping showed a similar course. Perhaps the most striking feature of these results is the degree of independence between the four cognitions. Although they are all conceptually related, they are clearly not empirically correlated. This is an important point and emphasizes the possibility of high specific and subtle relationships between cognitive and behavioural events. The PQ provides a sensitive and reliable method of monitoring these cognitive changes during the course of treatment.

DISCUSSION AND CONCLUSIONS

We have reviewed the various alternative methods for assessing social cognitions. They all have advantages and disadvantages and the final choice of which instrument to use will obviously be determined by the use to which it is to be put. Standard questionnaires and simple rating scales may be useful for group-based studies, Repertory Grids are suited to exploring the relationship between cognitive constructs, and Personal Questionnaires provide a simple and direct way of scaling self-reports and monitoring them during treatment.

In the first place they assumed that what can be measured is explicit, rational and amenable to conscious access. By contrast, Nisbett and Wilson's (1977) influential review suggested that many of the higher order cognitive processes which govern decision-making and action are not themselves open to conscious access. Whatever the general truth of Nisbett and Wilson's assertion, it is beyond doubt that there are many instances where individuals cannot verbalize the cognitive processes underlying their actions. In these cases attempts to measure cognitions are literally impossible and we may have to rely on "non-scientific" intuitions and theories (e.g. psychoanalytic ones). The usefulness of these kinds of theories can only be evaluated by their plausibility, rather than their empirical correctness. The problem of unconscious, or pre-conscious processes, also brings us back to the problem of reactive measurements. The attempt to measure cognitions may itself bring them into consciousness and thereby alter them. This seemed to occur in Paul's case and Nairne (1980) has reported how during a single-case study, using an ordinal PQ, there was evidence of considerable changes during the baseline period. Cognitions are not fixed in this sense and the process of assessment often causes the patients to reflect upon feelings and expectations that they had not examined closely before. They may then "change their mind", or want to change the content of the cognitions that are being assessed, feeling that the originals are no longer relevant. These problems of reactivity may either be viewed as a methodological nuisance, or as an illustration of how the processes of assessment and treatment cannot always be easily separated.

In considering the process of measurement we can also ask what exactly is it that is being measured? Cognitions are not directly observable, so how can we be sure that we have a valid assessment? The answer, of course, is that we cannot. We can demand that the measurement is reliable, hence the importance of the internal reliability check which is a feature of Shapiro's method, but validity is another question. Phillips (1977) suggests that perhaps we should not even use the term "measurement". He suggests that all we can do is to try to ensure that the subject communicates with the experimenter in a logical and internally consistent manner. What he is actually communicating about, may remain something of a mystery.

If at least this minimum criterion of internal reliability is met, then either we can avoid the question of validity altogether, accepting as Shapiro (1975) argues that symptom statements are criterion variables in their own right, or we can invoke the concept of "construct validity" (Cronbach & Meehl, 1955). The question then becomes not "is this a valid measure?", but "how does this measure relate to other measures which are thought to reflect different aspects of the same construct?". Social difficulties can be viewed as a construct with behavioural, cognitive and performance components, in exactly the same way as fear (cf. Rachman & Hodgson, 1974; Hodgson & Rachman, 1974). Just like fear, there may be synchrony and desynchrony among the various elements, depending on external pressures. Using this notion of construct validity, we can then assess the relationship between cognitions and behaviour by simultaneously monitoring the progress of both over time. Studies of this kind are currently under way (Shepherd, 1981).

This brings us to the final difficulty. Although we can see how such methods might enable us to investigate the relationship between cognitions and behaviour and to attempt an unravelling of the causal mysteries of why people behave as they do, nevertheless we come up against a philosophical problem. This arises from the apparent conflict between "autonomy" and "determinism" (Davidson, 1970). Scientists are determinists and scientific psychologists believe in a deterministic and lawful relationship between psychological and physical events. However, it also seems that mental events are themselves "anomalous", i.e., not lawful, hence the notion of "free will". So, how can a subjective sense of autonomy be reconciled with a deterministic belief in causal relationships between mental events and actions? Davidson argues that the implied contradiction here is more real than apparent and he concludes that although there may be lawful causal relationships between mental and physical events, there are no strict laws on the basis of which we can predict and explain purely mental phenomena. If Davidson is correct then this would seem to place a limit on the boundaries of scientific enquiry within psychology. Psychologists may be perfectly correct to wish to apply scientific methods to investigate the relationship between psychological and behavioural events (say the synchrony and desynchrony between cognitive and behavioural elements in the construct of social functioning). However, they may find it impossible to apply the same methods to the investigation of the relationship between purely psychological phenomena. The mind may thus turn out to be a place for physiologists and philosophers, but not for psychologists after all.

Whatever the validity of such speculations, the attempt to assess cognitions and to examine their relationship to other variables remains an intriguing challenge. The central problem is still the choice of a suitable measure. Unless this problem is solved, then behaviourally-oriented therapists — social skills trainers included - may appear to have gone on a very long detour and not look very much wiser for having made the trip.

REFERENCES

Ajzen, I., & Fishbein, M. Attitude-behavior rel-
    ations: A theoretical analysis and review of
    empirical research. Psychological Bulletin,
    1977, 84, 888-918
Alker, H.A. Is personality situationally specific
    or intrapsychically consistent? Journal of
    Personality, 1972, 40, 1-17
Anastasi, A. Psychological testing. London:
    Macmillan, 1968
Argyle, M. Social interaction. London: Methuen,
    1969
Arkowitz, H., Lichtenstein, E., McGovern, K. & Hines,
    P. The behavioral assessment of social com-
    petence in males. Behavior Therapy, 1975, 6,
    3-13
Bandura, A. Self-efficacy: Toward a unifying theory
    of behavioral change. Psychological Review,
    1977, 84, 191-215
Bannister, D. Personal construct theory: A summary
    and experimental paradigm. Acta Psychologica,
    1962, 20, 104-120
Bannister, D., & Fransella, F. Inquiring man: The
    theory of personal constructs. London: Penguin,
    1971
Beck, A.T., Rush, A.J., Shaw, B.F., & Emery, G.
    Cognitive therapy of depression. New York:
    Guilford Press, 1979
Bellack, A. Behavioral assessment of social skills.
    In A.S. Bellack and M. Hersen (Eds.), Research
    and practice in social skills training. New
    York: Plenum Press, 1979
Bem, D.J., & Allen, A. On predicting some of the
    people some of the time: The search for cross-
    situational consistencies in behavior. Psych-
    ological Review, 1974, 81, 506-520
Cronbach, L.J., & Meehl, P.E. Construct validity in
    psychological tests. Psychological Bulletin,
    1955, 52, 281-302
Curran, J. Social skills: Methodological issues and
    future directions. In A.S. Bellack & M. Hersen
    (Eds.), Research and practice in social skills
    training. New York: Plenum Press, 1979
Davidson, D. Mental Events. In L. Foster & J.W.
    Swanson (Eds.), Experience and theory. London:
    Duckworths, 1970
Eisler, R.M., Miller, P.M., & Hersen, M. Components
    of assertive behavior. Journal of Clinical
    Psychology, 1973, 29, 295-299
Eisler, R.M., Hersen, M., Miller, P.M., & Blanchard,

E.B. Situational determinants of assertive behavior. Journal of Consulting and Clinical Psychology, 1975, 43, 330-340

Eisler, R.M., Frederiksen, L.W., & Peterson, G.L. The relationship of cognitive variables to the expression of assertiveness. Behavior Therapy, 1978, 9, 419-427

Eisler, R.M., & Frederiksen, L.W. Perfecting social skills. New York: Plenum Press, 1980

Fielder, D., & Beach, L.R. On the decision to be assertive. Journal of Consulting and Clinical Psychology, 1978, 46, 537-546

Fischetti, M., Curran, J.P., & Wessberg, H.W. Sense of timing: A skill deficit in heterosexual socially anxious males. Behavior Modification, 1977, 1, 179-194

Fransella, F., & Bannister, D. A manual for repertory grid technique. London: Academic Press, 1977

Galassi, J.P., & Galassi, M.D. Modification of heterosexual skills deficits. In A.S. Bellack & M. Hersen (Eds.), Research and practice in social skills training. New York: Plenum Press, 1979

Gauld, A., & Shotter, J. Human action and its psychological investigation. London: Routledge & Kegan Paul, 1977

Gillingham, P.R., Griffiths, R.D.P., & Care, D. Direct assessment of social behaviour from videotape recordings. British Journal of Social and Clinical Psychology, 1977, 16, 181-187

Glasgow, R.E., & Arkowitz, H. The behavioral assessment of male and female social competence in dyadic heterosexual interactions. Behavior Therapy, 1975, 6, 488-498

Harre, R., & Secord, P.F. The explanation of social behavior. Oxford: Blackwells, 1972

Hersen, M., & Bellack, A.S. Assessment of social skills. In A.R. Ciminero, K.S. Calhoun & H.E. Adams (Eds.), Handbook for behavioral assessment. New York: Wiley, 1977

Hersen, M., Bellack, A.S., Turner, S.M., Williams, M.T., Harper, K., & Watts, J.G. Psychometric properties of the Wolpe-Lazarus assertiveness scale. Behaviour Research and Therapy, 1979, 17, 63-69

Hodgson, R., & Rachman, S.J. II. Desynchrony in measures of fear. Behaviour Research and Therapy, 1974, 12, 319-326

Kelly, G.A. The psychology of personal constructs (Vols. 1 & 2). New York: Norton, 1955

Kendall, P.C., & Korgeski, G.P. Assessment and cog-
    nitive behavioral interventions. Cognitive
    Therapy and Research, 1979, 3, 1-21
Landfield, A.W., & Leitner, L.M. Personal construct
    psychology. New York: Wiley, 1980
Ledwidge, B. Cognitive behavior modification: A
    step in the wrong direction? Psychological Bul-
    letin, 1978, 85, 353-375
Leff, J.P. Psychiatrists versus patients' concepts
    of unpleasant emotions. British Journal of
    Psychiatry, 1978, 133, 306-313
Levy, P. On the relation between test theory and
    psychology. In P. Kline (Ed.), New approaches
    in psychological measurement. London: Wiley,
    1973
Mahoney, M.J. Cognition and behavior modification.
    Cambridge, Mass.: Ballinger Press, 1974
Mahoney, M.J. Reflections on the cognitive learning
    trend in psychotherapy. American Psychologist,
    1977, 32, 5-13
Mischel, W. Personality and assessment. New York:
    Wiley, 1968
Mulhall, D.J. Systematic self-assessment by P.Q.R.
    S.T. (Personal questionnaire rapid scaling tech-
    nique). Psychological Medicine, 1976, 6, 591-597
Nairne, K.D. An investigation of the use of a per-
    sonal questionnaire method for monitoring att-
    itudes in a single case. Unpublished study,
    Department of Psychology, Institute of Psy-
    chiatry, Camberwell, London, 1980
Nichols, K.A. Severe social anxiety. British Jour-
    nal of Medical Psychology, 1974, 47, 301-306
Nisbett, R.E., & Wilson, T.D. Telling more than we
    can know: Verbal reports on mental processes.
    Psychological Review, 1977, 84, 231-259
Osgood, C.E., Suci, G.J., & Tannenbaum, P.M. The
    measurement of meaning. Urbana: University of
    Illinois Press, 1957
Phillips, J.P.N. Generalised personal questionnaire
    techniques. In P. Slater (Ed.), The measurement
    of intrapersonal space grid techniques (Vol.2).
    London: Wiley, 1977
Rachman, S.J., & Hodgson, R. 1. Synchrony and desyn-
    chrony in fear and avoidance. Behaviour Re-
    search and Therapy, 1974, 12, 311-318
Rathus, S.A. A 30-item schedule for assessing ass-
    ertive behavior. Behavior Therapy, 1973, 4, 398-
    406
Richardson, P.C., & Tasto, D.L. Development and fac-
    tor analysis of a social anxiety inventory.
    Behavior Therapy, 1976, 7, 453-462

Rotter, J.B. Generalized expectancies for internal
    v. external control of reinforcement. Psychol-
    ogical Monographs Supplement, 1966, 80, 609
Schwab, D.P., Olian-Gottlieb, J.D., & Heneman, H.G.
    Between-subjects expectancy theory and research:
    A statistical review of studies predicting eff-
    ort and performance. Psychological Bulletin,
    1979, 86, 139-147
Schwartz, R.M., & Gottman, J.M. Toward a task anal-
    ysis of assertive behavior. Journal of Consul-
    ting and Clinical Psychology, 1976, 44, 910-920
Seligman, M.E.P. Learned helplessness. San Fran-
    cisco: Freeman Press, 1975
Shapiro, M.B. The single case in fundamental clin-
    ical psychological research. British Journal of
    Medical Psychology, 1961, 34, 285-298
Shapiro, M.B. Intensive assessment of the single
    case. In P. Mittler (Ed.), The psychological
    assessment of mental and physical handicaps.
    London: Methuen, 1970
Shapiro, M.B. The assessment of self-reported dys-
    functions: A manual with its rationale and ap-
    plications. Parts I & II. Unpublished man-
    uscript, Department of Psychology, Institute of
    Psychiatry, Camberwell, London, 1975
Shapiro, M.B. Assessment interviewing in clinical
    psychology. British Journal of Psychology,
    1979, 18, 211-218
Shapiro, D.A., & Hobson, R.F. Change in psycho-
    therapy: A single case example. Psychological
    Medicine, 1972, 2, 312-317
Shapiro, M.B., Litman, G.K., & Henndry, E. The
    effects of context upon the frequency of short-
    term changes in affective states. British Jour-
    nal of Social and Clinical Psychology, 1973, 12,
    295-302
Shepherd, G. Social skills training: The way back-
    wards? Paper presented at the Annual Conference
    of British Association for Behavioural Psycho-
    therapy, Bristol, July, 1981
Shepherd, G., & Bilsbury, C. The assessment of
    social cognitions. Paper presented at the
    Annual Conference of the British Association
    for Behavioural Psychotherapy, Bangor, North
    Wales, July, 1979
Singer, W.B., & Young, P.J. Studies in affective
    reaction.I. A new affective rating scale.
    Journal of Genetic Psychology, 1941, 24, 281-301
Trower, P. Fundamentals of interpersonal behavior -
    A social psychological perspective. In A.S.
    Bellack & M. Hersen (Eds.), Research and prac-

tice in social skills training. New York: Plenum Press, 1979

Trower, P. Situational analysis of the components and processes of the behavior of socially skilled and unskilled patients. Journal of Consulting and Clinical Psychology, 1980, 48, 327-339

Trower, P. Social skill disorder: Mechanisms of failure. In S. Duck & R. Gilmour (Eds.), Personal relationships.3: Personal relationships in disorder. London: Academic Press, 1981

Wallace, C.J., Nelson, C.J., Liberman, R.P., Aitchison, R.A., Lukoff, D., Elder, J.P., & Ferris, C. A review and critique of social skills training with schizophrenic patients. Schizophrenia Bulletin, 1980, 6, 42-62

Watson, D., & Friend, R. Measurement of social-evaluative anxiety. Journal of Consulting and Clinical Psychology, 1969, 33, 448-457

Wolpe, J. & Lazarus, A.A. Behavior therapy techniques. New York:Pergamon Press, 1966

Yardley, K. Social skills training: a critique. British Journal of Medical Psychology, 1979, 52, 55-62

Editorial Introduction, Chapters Ten and Eleven

SOCIAL SKILLS ASSESSMENT AND TRAINING FROM A
RATIONAL-EMOTIVE PERSPECTIVE

W. Dryden

The next two chapters by Dryden (who is a counsel-
ling psychologist) form a unit - the use of rational-
emotive therapy and other cognitive methods in both
assessment and training. RET is of course an explan-
atory theory of emotional and social dysfunction as
well as a practical procedure, and is conceptually
the closest "cognitive" therapy to the agency
approach, hence the extensive utilization of it here.
Dryden's aim is to provide guidlines for helping the
client to generate his own social skills - in other
words, to put the agency back into the organism.
*   One of the main roles of RET in social skills*
assessment and training is to help the client over-
come faulty cognitions that block his capacity to
acquire and generate social skills. For example,
distorted inferences, biased data-gathering and
attributions, negative expectancies of self-efficacy,
intolerance of discomfort, self-condemnation, and,
above all, thinking like an organism, are all pot-
ential "blockers" to skill learning.
*   We have already seen, in chapter eight, the*
characteristic cognitions of clients with social
problems. In the first of his chapters, Dryden
begins by laying down an explanatory framework for
understanding the function of such cognitions. It
can be seen from this just what the cognitions
reported actually do (i.e., inferences or eval-
uations) and how they function in producing emotional
distress, and behavioural disturbance and withdrawal
(see chapter five). Dryden goes on to suggest asses-
sment strategies for eliciting disturbing cognitions
which often lie outside the awareness of the client
(in the "mindless" realm, along with overlearned
behavioural programmes - see chapter six). These
techniques will often unearth deeply buried beliefs
where questionnaires and traditional interviews will

fail.

In the second chapter Dryden describes how to establish the working alliance essential for social skills training before outlining treatment strategies and the many techniques available to help clients modify dysfunctional thoughts and so facilitate the learning, implementation and continual use of new skills, and consequent further modification of beliefs.

Chapter Ten

SOCIAL SKILLS ASSESSMENT FROM A RATIONAL-EMOTIVE
PERSPECTIVE

W. Dryden

INTRODUCTION

A comprehensive approach to helping clients with
social skills problems involves therapists paying
attention not only to the behavioural skills present
or absent in the client's social repertoire but also
to other modalities which may be implicated (Lazarus,
1976). The concern of the present chapter is to
detail the contribution of rational-emotive therapy
(RET) and to a lesser extent other cognitive therapies which take such a multi-modal, comprehensive
stance to the assessment of clients' interpersonal
problems. The goals of the present chapter are as
follows:

(1) To introduce and to describe the "emotional
     episode" framework.

(2) To detail the cognitive components of the major
     dysfunctional emotions experienced by clients
     with social problems.

(3) To review various interview-based cognitive ass-
     essment strategies.

(4) To detail stages of social skills training to
     which such assessment strategies can be applied.

APPLICATIONS OF RATIONAL-EMOTIVE THERAPY TO SOCIAL
SKILLS TRAINING

Overview of RET
RET was founded in 1955 by Albert Ellis. It is a
system of psychotherapy which has from its very in-
ception aimed to effect changes in philosophies or
"world views" of clients, and thus has always been

one of the "cognitive" therapies.

The popularity of RET increased in the mid 1970's when the so-called "cognitive" revolution in behaviour therapy took place. The major tenet of RET is that humans create and sustain their emotional experiences by the way they view events in their lives. Another important tenet of RET theory is that humans have a strong biological tendency towards illogical and irrational thinking and yet have the ability to work against such a tendency, in that they can work at correcting such thinking styles. The major task of rational-emotive therapists is to help clients to identify and dispute faulty inferences and irrational evaluations that they make of events in their lives. The therapist in doing so uses a wide variety of cognitive, emotive and behavioural methods.

The tasks of clients in RET are (a) to similarly identify and dispute such thinking processes which are leading to dysfunctional emotions, (b) to continually work at correcting their faulty thinking and irrational evaluating, and (c) to put into practice the newly acquired more accurate inferences and rational evaluations of events in their lives by acting differently.

The process of RET is best characterized as the therapist and client working together in a collaborative fashion to identify, dispute and change faulty cognitions.

The "Emotional Episode"

The model of human functioning and dysfunctioning that rational-emotive therapists employ in their therapeutic practice can be best described by the ABC model of human disturbance for which RET is well-known. Such a model stresses that humans' emotional experiences at point C are not determined by events in their lives at point A, but by their evaluations of such events at point B.

Recently however, Wessler and Wessler (1980) have expanded the ABC model and have described the "emotional episode" (see Figure 1), which constitutes a more helpful framework for the analysis of clients' social problems.

The "emotional episode" is best described with reference to a clinical example. Consider John, a socially anxious student, who relates the following episode to his therapist.

John: "I got drunk at a discotheque after the girl I wanted to dance with turned away from me as I approached her."

Using the emotional episode framework the therapist makes sense of the various processes involved in the episode.

Figure 1.   The "Emotional Episode" (Wessler & Wessler, 1980)

STEP 1 STIMULUS (EXTERNAL OR INTERNAL)

STEP 2 DETECTION OF STIMULUS   A*

STEP 3 DESCRIPTION OF STIMULUS

STEP 4 INFERENCES

STEP 5 EVALUATIONS   B*

STEP 6 EMOTIONAL CONSEQUENCES

STEP 7 BEHAVIOURAL CONSEQUENCES   C*

STEP 8 REINFORCING CONSEQUENCES

* Corresponds to the ABC theory of emotional disturbance

A: STEP 1 - STIMULUS (EXTERNAL OR INTERNAL).   A stimulus configuration begins the emotional episode. The stimulus might be external to the person (such as the actions of other people) or internal (such as thoughts and bodily sensations).   Thus, many different stimuli were potentially available to John that night at the discotheque.   External stimuli included the ashtrays on the table where John was sitting, the lights attached to the ceiling, and each of the people that were present.   Internal stimuli that were available to John included the sensations that he was experiencing in various parts of his body.

B: STEP 2 - DETECTION OF STIMULUS.   Here, a particular part of the stimulus configuration is attended by the person (in this case, John).   As John scanned the many different stimuli in his perceptual field, both external and internal, one figure stood out from the ground.   In other words, John focussed on a

288

portion of the total stimulus configuration and a particular stimulus pattern was detected.

C: STEP 3 - DESCRIPTION OF STIMULUS. At this step the particular stimulus pattern that was detected at step 2 is described. Such a description is, of course, made at a covert-automatic level. In the present example, that part of the total field which was detected was a blonde girl standing alone at the edge of the dance floor looking in John's general direction. As he approached her with the intention of asking her to dance, the girl looked away.

D: STEP 4 - INFERENCES. At this stage, inferences and interpretations are made of the covertly described stimulus. This step is crucial in the assessment of clients' social problems in that the personal meanings that are created to account for events outlined in stage 2 and 3 are featured. John linked the fact that the girl turned away at the time of his approach with his approach. He further concluded: "She thinks I'm ugly; she wants nothing to do with me".
        Wessler and Wessler (1980) have stressed such a specific inference may represent a special case of a more generalized and enduring inference such as "I'm ugly, no women will find me attractive".

E: STEP 5 - EVALUATIONS. At this step the judgments that are made of the inferences formed at step 4 are featured. Evaluative thinking involves some variant of value appraisal of the inference. Evaluations may be made about the self, another person, persons or world conditions in general. In the provided example John evaluated himself thus: "Because she thinks I'm ugly and wants nothing to do with me, that means I am worthless". Here the judgment is "I am worthless". It needs to be stressed that such evaluations are often made automatically and are not immediately available to the person's awareness.

F: STEP 6 - EMOTIONAL CONSEQUENCES. According to the emotional episode model, the feelings a person experiences depends on the evaluations made at step 5 and not the inferences at step 4. In the example provided, John became depressed because he evaluated himself as "worthless" as a result of inferring rejection. Thus, it is important to stress that it was not the rejection which was inferred at step 4 which led to John's depression but his evaluation of such rejection.

G: STEP 7 - BEHAVIOURAL CONSEQUENCES. Step 7 features the behavioural consequences of the evaluations made at step 5. It is this step that indicates how a person copes with the emotional consequences of the judged event. In this case, John went to the bar at the discotheque and proceeded to drink heavily and became drunk. Other behavioural consequences of similar judgments made by clients are drug taking and withdrawal.

H: STEP 8 - REINFORCING CONSEQUENCES. Wessler and Wessler (1980) point out that although this step is not strictly part of the emotional episode but a result of it, it is included in their model to stress the fact that rewards or penalties occur as a result of behaviour which thereby has an effect on future behaviour. In this case, John went home and was berated by his angry mother for getting drunk. Such a consequence has different reinforcing properties than the consequence of John being comforted and listened to by his mother.

As can be seen from Figure 1 Wessler and Wessler (1980) consider steps 1 - 4 to be part of "A" in the traditional ABC model of human disturbance according to RET theory. They consider step 5 alone, that is evaluation, to be equivalent to "B", and equate steps 6 and 7 to "C" in the model.

In the remainder of the chapter the focus will be on the assessment of inferences and evaluations that clients make. In doing so the present writer does not deny the importance of the assessment procedures at the other steps, in particular steps 7 and 8.

Inferences
As noted, inferences refer to the interpretations made of stimuli that have been covertly described. In assessing clients' inferences, it is important to distinguish between specific inferences, i.e., interpretations made of discrete events, from generalized inferences or inferential styles, i.e., habitual styles of information processing. Clinicians begin to build up a picture of clients' inferential style, as the latter relate their interpretations of a wide variety of events. Here clinicians should guard against a tendency to attribute a particular inferential style to clients based on minimal data.

Beck et al. (1979) have described a number of faulty modes of information processing which are relevant here.

Arbitary inferences. Here a conclusion is drawn in the absence of data to support such a conclusion, or indeed where the data is contrary to the drawing of the conclusion. For example, Jane, a member of a social skills group, related an incident where a man she had just met kept on avoiding her eye gaze. She concluded that this meant that he did not like her. However, as she related the event, a fellow member identified the man in question and informed Jane that the man was extremely nervous and found it difficult to look females in the eye.

Selective abstraction. This occurs when the person focusses on an event which is taken out of context and where more important aspects of the situation have been ignored. The entire experience is then conceptualized on the basis of this detail. For example, Jim, another member of a social skills group, related an event where two acquaintances smiled at one another as Jim was relating a serious story. Jim, in relating this to the group, conceptualized his entire evening with his two friends as one where they were laughing at him. However, when pressed to relate the other events of the evening, Jim told the group that indeed his two friends had paid him serious attention for most of the evening. He had, in conceptualizing the evening's experience, edited out the remaining data.

Overgeneralization. Here a general rule or conclusion is made on the basis of single or isolated incidents, the conclusion then being applied to other related and unrelated contexts. Thus Ahmed in an individual therapy session related an incident when the night before he asked an English girl to dance and was refused. He told the therapist that this proved that all English girls do not like Pakistanis.

Magnification. Here the situation is exaggerated beyond realistic bounds. When Judy, a withdrawn university student, on being asked why she did not attend discotheques even though she liked to dance, replied "I don't go because as soon as I would walk in the door everybody would turn round and laugh at me".

Minimization. Here a situation is interpreted as less important or having less impact than it has. For example, Stan, another social skills group member, had received warm appreciation from his group for asking a girl out and being accepted for a date. He told the group that "It is no big deal really". This, despite the fact than Stan had not asked a girl for a date for over four years and avoided virtually all contact with the opposite sex.

Personalization. Here the person tends to relate external events to himself when there is no apparent basis for such a connection being made. For example, Stan related an incident where he saw Jane, a fellow group member, leave a coffee social as soon as he arrived at the event. He concluded that Jane left as soon as she saw him. However, Jane was astounded at such a disclosure and assured Stan that she had not seen him and generally left social events at 10 pm (when Stan arrived) in order to catch her last train home.

All or nothing thinking. This occurs when a person tends to place all experiences in one of two opposing categories, e.g., brilliant or stupid, popular or un-popular, witty or dull. In such thinking there is no tolerance for ambiguity and no apparent realization that a person can be, for example, reasonably popular or reasonably witty.

Another related sub-class is prediction-making. It has been the author's experience that such clients form overly negative predictions concerning their own progress in response to treatment, and other people's reactions to their attempts to form social alliances. In particular clinicians had better be alert for such statements as: "It's hopeless; I'll never be able to make friends". Such a prediction is often made early on in treatment when clients experience set-backs in trying to put into practice their newly acquired social skills.

Another important class of inferences is "attri-butional style". Clients in social skills groups tend to attribute negative social experiences to defects in their own character as opposed to skills deficits or variations in situations. However, when they do achieve positive outcomes as a result of their own endeavours, they tend to attribute such outcomes to luck or to the fact that the other person in question only responded in a positive way out of pity.

Evaluations. As noted earlier, evaluations concern judgments or appraisals of inferred events. Trad-itionally, rational-emotive therapists have been con-cerned with helping clients to make discriminations between rational and irrational beliefs. There have been a number of attempts to distinguish between these two classes of beliefs. Ellis and Harper (1975), for example, consider rational beliefs to involve evaluations that promote the survival and happiness of the individual, whereas irrational beliefs are deemed to be founded on evaluations that block, inhibit or defeat the individual from surviving or achieving happiness.

Another way of distinguishing rational from irrational beliefs is one preferred by Wessler and Wessler (1980). They argue that "by far the most useful definition of rational in counselling and clinical situations centers on empirical proofs about the basis of one's evaluations of A" (p.33). Thus, rational beliefs are characterized by evaluations that pertain to a person's preferences, desires, wants or wishes. For example, if I say that I like something then I can easily find evidence for this statement since my preference exists. Irrational beliefs, however, consist of "evaluations derived from non-empirical premises stated in absolutistic language" (Wessler & Wessler, 1980, p.33). Irrational evaluations exist when reality is ignored in favour of what the evaluation demands should exist. Thus, irrational beliefs can often be detected in phrases concerning such words as "should", "must", "have to", "got to", "ought" and "need" where such words imply absolutistic demands that elements of reality should be different from what they are. In virtually all instances there is no empirical basis for such statements.

It is sometimes helpful in distinguishing irrational from rational beliefs to use the framework presented in Figure 2. Here the format of a syllogism is used. The premise of the irrational belief concerns a demand on self, other(s), and/or the world. When the demand is not met evaluative conclusions are made of the self, other(s), and/or the world. The same format is used in the rational belief column. It can be seen by looking at the three conclusions stemming from the irrational beliefs that such conclusions deny human complexity, human choice and human fallibility. Furthermore the assertion that the world should be a certain way implies that the person making the demand is "special" and it is this specialness that is a prerequisite for the world being a certain way.

The conclusions that stem from rational beliefs, in contrast, assert human complexity, human fallibility and human choice and there is no "special" person assertion made. The world is considered a place which follows laws of the universe which are often

Figure 2: Distinctions Between Irrational and Rational Beliefs

	IRRATIONAL BELIEF	RATIONAL BELIEF
Premise:	DEMAND on self, other(s), the world	PREFERENCE for self, other(s), the world
Event:	DEMAND NOT MET	PREFERENCE NOT MET
Conclusion:	(a) I'm no good (global negative rating of my personhood, denial of human complexity and human fallibility)	(a) I'm a fallible human person (acceptance of self, recognition of human complexity and human fallibility)
	(b) You are no good (global negative rating of your personhood – denial of human complexity and human choice)	(b) You are a fallible human person (recognition and acceptance of human complexity and human choice)
	(c) The world is no good (global negative evaluation of the world – denial of the complexity of life and assertion of "special person")	(c) The world is neither bad nor good but a place where desirable and undesirable things happen (recognition of the complexity of life, no assertion of "special person" syndrome)
	I CAN'T STAND IT	I DON'T LIKE IT BUT I CAN STAND IT

independent of the person expressing the preference.

In Figure 3 a similar format is used in considering an irrational belief expressed by John, a member of a social skills group, and its rational alternative.

Special consideration needs to be given to the self-evaluative portion of the irrational conclusion. An important tenet of rational-emotive theory is that a human being is an on-going, ever-changing complexity, i.e., an organism which defies a single global rating. The rational-emotive alternative to self-evaluation is self-acceptance, i.e., acceptance of oneself as a fallible human person, an organism of great complexity, having an ever-changing ongoingness which defies rating. While it is nonsense to make a global rating on one's "self", it does make sense to make evaluations of aspects of one's "self".

Clients tend to make a variety of self-denigrating global evaluations. Distinction needs to be made amongst four major sub-classes of self-ratings (Young, 1980).

(a) "Bad me" - Here clients make statements about self, based on concepts of moral worth, e.g., "I am a wicked person", "I am a bad person".

(b) "Less me" - Here clients, while not concluding that they have no worth, conclude that they are less worthy or less deserving as a result of failure to live up to self-imposed demands.

(c) "Weak me" - Here clients conclude that they are weak persons or weaker persons for failing to live up to self-imposed demands. One related aspect of "weak me" thinking is self-pity which is based on the concept of "poor me". Here clients consider themselves helpless victims of malevolent forces.

(d) "Poor me" - Here clients believe that they are undeserving of their fate.

Thus, it is important not to consider negative self-evaluations as uni-dimensional but as multi-dimensional phenomena.

Emotions
Central to an accurate assessment of clients' social problems is a clear understanding of their emotional experiences and the cognitive components of these experiences. In this section, the major dysfunc-

Figure 3: John's Irrational Belief and Rational Alternative

	IRRATIONAL BELIEF	RATIONAL BELIEF
Premise:	I must have Judy like me	I want Judy to like me
Event:	If what I demand does not happen	If what I want does not happen
Conclusion:	(a) I'm no good and/or	(a) She may have rejected me because I have some flaw or she may be exercising her personal tastes. If I do have a flaw I can accept myself as a human being with a flaw and work to eliminate the flaw
	(b) Judy is no good and/or	(b) Judy is a person who has every right to exercise her choices, express her preferences
	(c) The world is no good for depriving me	(c) The world is a complex place where I won't often get what I want. That's unfortunate but I can stand it.
	i.e., I can't stand it, it's awful	

tional emotional states that clients in social skills group training experience will be outlined and linked to their cognitive counterparts.

Anxiety. According to RET theory there are two forms of anxiety. The first is termed Ego anxiety. This is based on a prediction that future events will occur which will result in clients making global self-evaluations. Often associated with such negative self-evaluations are predictions of future events based on magnification and personalization. Typically clients in social skills groups predict harsh negative responses from others, distorted in terms of the intensity of and duration of the responses. For example, Sue experienced anxiety whenever she thought of going to a discotheque and dancing. She imagined that other people would stop what they were doing to focus on her and laugh for an extended period of time. It is important to be clear that such predictions are inferences and do not themselves imply any evaluation. In order for anxiety to occur, Sue would have to make the judgment that such an experience would be "awful" and prove that she was no good.

The second type is called Discomfort anxiety which stems from the belief that (1) I must be comfortable, and (2) the experience of anxiety is intolerable. As a result the person seeks a guarantee of comfort and in doing so often adds to his ego anxiety. It should be made clear that ego and discomfort anxiety often interact and are present in clients' problems. Thus, in the above example, it emerged that Sue also experienced discomfort anxiety in that she became anxious whenever she thought that the images that she experienced might occur. Thus, she would say to herself "I must not get these horrible images!". As a result of making such demands she, as one might expect, experienced the images more often.

Anger. In RET theory anger is distinguished from annoyance. Both these emotions stem from the frustration where some personally valued rule is transgressed. Annoyance stems from the rational preference that other people follow my personally valued rule and when such transgression occurs, the following conclusions are typically made: (1) it's annoying that this person has acted in such a way, and (2) I really do not like his behaviour. Anger results from the irrational demands that the other person should not break my rule and that that person is damnable as a result of breaking my rule.

It is important to realize that some forms of anger are defensive in nature in that they serve to protect clients from self condemnation (Grieger, 1977; Wessler, 1981). Thus some clients get angry when other people mock them or make fun of them. The anger serves to attempt to destroy the stimulus which if not destroyed would lead to the angry persons condemning themselves.

One emotion which clients often express is "hurt". Hurt is typically experienced when some perceived injustice to self happens, such as being badly treated or not being appreciated. The evaluation of such an inference is based on beliefs that "I am a deserving person (a subtle form of positive self-rating) and I don't deserve to be treated in this manner. I must get what I think I deserve". Hurt may be expressed by behaviours such as sulking and pouting.

Depression. Inferences that commonly lead to clients becoming depressed include negative interpretations of events and negative interpretations of the client's ongoing and future experiences (Beck et al., 1979). Evaluations which are made of these negative interpretations include negative self-ratings (e.g., I am no good), and evaluations of the world (e.g., life is rotten for letting this thing happen). In addition, judgments that "I am helpless" (to effect change), and "it is hopeless" (i.e., life events cannot be changed) are added to the resultant evaluation that "I can't stand it".

Another form of depression results from self-pity, the cognitive dynamics of which are similar to that of the emotion "hurt". Where self-pitying depression exists, the person believes that life is rotten for allowing the negative event to occur particularly when the person did not deserve to experience the event. Whereas hurt has a greater anger component since the perpetrator of the "hurt" is an identifiable individual, the perpetrator of the negative event which leads to self-pitying depression is the more amorphous "life conditions".

Shame. Shame is experienced when some weakness or undesirable trait is revealed in public which has incurred or might incur the disappointment or disapproval of other people. The evaluation which is added to such an inference so that shame is experienced is that "I must have their approval, I am worthless if they disapprove of me". Clients who are involved in social skills training groups are particularly concerned about the public display of such weaknesses. Again they often imagine extremely harsh reactions to such a display. Here it is important for the clinician to make the fine distinctions between exaggerated inferences and irrational evaluations.

Guilt   Guilt is distinguished from shame by the fact that the emotion is experienced both in public and in private whereas shame tends to be experienced only in public situations. Guilt is based on the inference that I have done something bad, stupid or wrong, i.e., something which has violated my moral code. However, guilt is experienced when the judgment I am a bad person for violating my code is added to the inference. Consider the case of Steven, a socially anxious, unskilled client. One important aspect of his moral code was that he should not gossip about other people. As he started to improve his social skills he found himself getting drawn into a conversation with some newly made acquaintances, where they were gossiping about another mutual acquaintance. Steven became guilty when he joined in such a conversation and violated his own moral code and made a negative evaluation of himself that he was a bad person for doing such a bad thing.
     To contrast this emotion from shame, a similar client might experience shame when another person criticizes him for gossiping. He would experience shame only in the public domain because he is evaluating himself negatively for revealing a presumed weakness. However, such an emotion would disappear and not be replaced by guilt since in this situation the person had not violated a personally held moral code.

Problems about Problems
One important issue in RET concerns the fact that clients often experience problems about their original problems. Thus, clients may become anxious about feeling angry or experiencing shame, depressed about being depressed, anxious about being anxious, depressed about feeling angry, etc. Consider the case of Joanne, a socially withdrawn student with bulimia who became extremely anxious when she was invited out on a date. The original anxiety was based on ego anxiety, namely that "I must make a good impression on my date; if I don't it will prove what a dim person I am". This anxiety, which can be considered to be step 7 in the first emotional episode, served to act as step 1 in a second emotional

episode. In the second emotional episode, Joanne became anxious about her anxiety in that she was demanding that she had to be at ease on her date. The only way that she knew of controlling anxiety when it reached such proportions was for her to go on an eating binge and then vomit her food. Such a behavioural consequence, step 7 in the second emotional episode, served to be step 1 in a third emotional episode in which Joanne became very depressed. The depression was based on her negative self-evaluations for having gone on a binge and vomiting.

To reiterate, the crucial aspect of rational-emotive assessment concerns making clear distinctions between initial problems and secondary or even, as in the above example, tertiary problems.

ASSESSMENT STRATEGIES

The goal of this section is to outline a variety of different methods of assessing clients' cognitions. It is essential for clinicians at the outset of their assessment procedure to educate their clients as to the relationship between thoughts, feelings and behaviours.

As a rule rational-emotive therapists teach the traditional ABC framework in some form to clients. In this simple version of the emotional episode, clients are shown that "A" stands for the person's perceptions of the event, i.e., their inferences, "B" stands for the belief about the inferred event and "C" stands for the emotional and behavioural consequences of "B".

Clinicians will find that their initial enquiries concerning clients' cognitions will yield inferences rather than evaluations. A thorough assessment of clients' cognitions should reveal both types of cognitions prior to interventions.

Overall Strategy

The traditional way of assessing cognitions in RET is first to assess the client's emotional experiences or behavioural acts at point "C" in the ABC framework. With regard to assessing emotional experiences, therapists need to clearly distinguish between such negative functional emotions as concern, sadness, disappointment, annoyance, feelings of responsibility, etc., from such dysfunctional negative emotions as anxiety, depression, anger, guilt, etc. This distinction is important in that it orients clinicians to look for the existence of inaccurate inferences and rational beliefs in cases where

dysfunctional negative emotions are present. Thus
RET clinicians are influenced by rational-emotive
theory which posits that such negative dysfunctional
emotions as have been outlined stem from irrational
beliefs, whereas negative functional emotions stem
from rational beliefs. The next step is to assess
inferences at "A".

Assessing Inferences

Inferences are non-evaluative interpretations of
actual events. Inferences may be revealed if clinicians ask clients what situations triggered off
their emotional upset. Thus, for example, Sally, a
recent client, reported that she became depressed
when one of her lecturers criticized her. On further
exploration, it transpired that the lecturer cor-
rected one of her statements which she made in class.
However, she interpreted such a correction as
criticism.

It often transpires that inferences are hierarchically organized in a client's cognitive structure. Since rational-emotive therapists are
primarily concerned with evaluations, it is crucial
for them to identify the most relevant inference,
i.e., the inference which forms the basis for the irrational evaluation.

One method which is often used to identify
levels of inferences is called inference chaining.
In inference chaining, clinicians begin with the
first inference that clients express and then
continue by asking detailed questions which reveal
more deeply embedded inferences. The clinicians'
purpose is to work down the ladder of inferences
until an evaluation is provided by clients. For
example, in a recent interview with Charles, a
socially withdrawn client, the following dialogue
ensued:

Therapist: I understand, Charles, that you have
             been avoiding attending evening classes,
             is that right?

Client: Yes, that's right.

Therapist: Do you want to go to your evening class
             or would you rather not?

Client: I would rather go.

Therapist: Then what stops you?

Client: I am scared.

Therapist: Scared of what?

Client: I am scared that I might say something
            stupid in class.
(This is a first level inference)

Therapist: Well, let's suppose you do. Let's sup-
            pose you do say something stupid in
            class, what would that mean?
(This question is designed to elicit more deeply embedded inferences)

Client: Well, then the people in the class would
            laugh at me.
(second level inference)

Therapist: Well again, let's suppose that that hap-
            pens. Let's suppose that you say some-
            thing stupid and people laugh at you.
            What would that mean?
(Another enquiry designed to elicit more deeply embedded inferences)

Client: Well that would prove that I was stupid
            if they laughed at me.
(Here the therapist suspects that he has elicited a
client self-evaluation, but he still tests whether
there are more deeply embedded inferences)

Therapist: So if I understand you then, if the
            people in your class laughed at you that
            would mean that you would consider your-
            self stupid, is that right?

Client: Yes.

Therapist: What's so bad about being stupid?

Client: I couldn't stand it if I was stupid. I
            would hate myself.

     This example illustrates that the therapist, by
asking such open-ended questions, such as "what would
that mean" elicited increasingly deeper inferences
until the client stated an evaluation.   In this
example, the client shows his vulnerability, inferring that the laughter of his classmates means
that they consider him stupid, and if so that this
would prove that he was stupid.

302

Therapists often suggest that clients participate in the assessment of inferences outside therapy sessions. The general rule here is that the closer in time that clients record their thoughts, the better. As a result therapists often suggest to clients that they keep a written record of thoughts that were going through their mind in particular situations. For clients who have pocket tape recorders, a suggestion might be made that they keep a verbatim on-going record of such thoughts provided that this can be done in an unobtrusive manner.

Sometimes clients report difficulty in identifying their thoughts or claim that no thoughts were going through their mind at the time. Here clinicians need to be creative in using a variety of methods to aid the assessment process. The following list of strategies is employed by therapists to aid them in the assessment of inferences.

Imagery. Here clients are encouraged to, for example, picture a TV screen where a re-run of the event in question is to be shown. Clients are given instructions that they pay particular attention to whatever thoughts were going through their mind at the time of the event. A second imagery procedure involves therapists addressing themselves to the images that clients may experience rather than the thoughts that might be going through their mind. Sometimes clients are more influenced by visual images than by particular thoughts. Thus, for example, one client expressed anxiety about meeting gay men. This client was not aware of any thoughts, but on further exploration reported an image of himself as a gorilla-like figure walking into a club with his arms drooping down near his knees and with his body hunched up.

Another imagery procedure which is designed to elicit both thoughts and images is the simple one of asking clients to close their eyes and to experience the relevant event as if it were happening right now. Here therapists may have to facilitate the execution of this task by eliciting a detailed description of the relevant context and incorporating this description in the imagery procedure.

Role-play technique. Clients are asked to describe the relevant situation and attempt to re-create the situation using themselves, or if working in a group situation, the fellow group members to play the role of significant other(s). As the role-play unfolds clients are often helped to experience feelings and thoughts that were not immediately available to their awareness.

Two-chair dialogue. Clients are encouraged to play both self and the role of significant other. Chairs are used to facilitate the movement from one role to the other. For example, consider the following dialogue. Jenny, who expressed a lot of anxiety about making a 'phone call to a man whose name she received from a dating agency was asked to make the 'phone call from one chair and move to the other chair where she would play the role of the man.

Jenny (as Jenny):   Hello, is that Pete? I was given your name from the dating agency that I imagine you also approach- ed. How are you?

Jenny (as the   I am sorry, I don't have much time man):   to talk now as I'm just going out on another date. Perhaps you would like to call me back in a month's time.

Jenny (as Jenny):   Yes, OK, I will do that.

As a result of this procedure, Jenny was able to specify what response she feared from the man and was later helped to identify through the inference chain procedure what such a response meant to her.

Problem-simulation. This technique has to be em- ployed with accurate timing and tact. In problem- simulation therapists adopt a role which they suspect will help clients to identify in the here-and-now of the therapy situation, dysfunctional thoughts and feelings. Thus, while working with a client who was trying to identify what thoughts were preventing him from refusing requests, without great success, the author took the following role.

Therapist: OK. So it seems that you have trouble refusing requests but are not quite sure why, is that right?

Client: Yes.

Therapist: I see. Oh wait a minute before we con- tinue I find that I'm out of cigars right now. Would you like to go down the road and get me some cigars? It's only about

> 1/4 of a mile and if you run you may be able to get back before our session ends but I can't really continue without a cigar. Will you go?

Client: Well. . . .um . . .well, I suppose so.

Therapist: (Handing client some money)
            I'd like five slim panatellas please.

Client: (Again hesitantly)
            Are you sure it can't wait?

Therapist: No, I have a heavy day before me and I would appreciate your help in this matter.

Client: OK then.

As the client opened the door and was rather reluctantly about to do what the therapist asked, the therapist asked him to return to his seat and a very fruitful exploration of the client's thoughts and feelings ensued.

In-vivo assessment. This assessment procedure has been suggested by Sacco (1981). Here the therapists actually enter anxiety-producing situations with clients and help them to identify thoughts or images going through their minds at the time. Sacco (1981) reports a situation where he went out with a client to a singles bar and helped him to identify negative thoughts which the client was unable to identify in his report of similar situations in the therapist's office. Another in-vivo assessment procedure that has proven valuable in working with a social-skills population is having clients view video-recordings of themselves while interacting with other members of the group. This often aids clients' recall of thoughts and feelings of which they were minimally aware at the time of the recording. Lastly, just watching others in a social skills group situation and hearing others express dysfunctional inferences often aids clients in recalling similar thoughts relevant to their own situations.

Assessing Beliefs
As noted earlier the major task of therapists is to assess the irrational evaluations that clients make. This is often a difficult procedure since clients will rarely spontaneously report such evaluations.

The major thrusts of such therapists' approaches are to teach the client the differences between inferences and evaluations and between rational and irrational evaluations, and to employ such distinctions as guides when they attempt to identify the existence of such beliefs in their own experiences. Thus, for example, Ellis often urges his clients to "look for the should",and "look for the must" when they attempt to identify the cognitive underpinnings of their negative dysfunctional emotions. This is done on the assumption that much emotional disturbance stems from the making of such a demand on self, others and/or the world. Sometimes rational-emotive therapists use the model to show clients that while they claim to be merely saying, for example, "I want this person to like me but I don't need them to", such a rational evaluation often obscures the irrational evaluation: "I must have this person like me" since the anxiety and not just concern was the expressed emotion. Therapists had better not force their viewpoint on clients even though they are convinced that they are correct. They might, however, urge clients who resist such interpretations to reconsider and to report back later on their deliberations. The author has found that such a strategy often helps clients who are concerned not to be "controlled" by the therapist, to say such things as: "Well now I've had a chance to think about what you suggested to me and having had a chance to think about it and to test it out in my daily experience, I have decided that you are right".

In assessing beliefs, it is important that clinicians periodically review the rational-emotive theory of human disturbance with clients and avoid assuming that because the model has been explained once it is now remembered and accepted. Therapists may find the following framework useful with their clients (see Figures 4 and 5). This framework is one that clients could be encouraged to use in assessing their own beliefs between sessions and one that therapists could employ in the initial analysis of beliefs in the therapy sessions themselves. Such a framework is best used in conjunction with other methods of assessing beliefs, such as the inference chain procedure rather than used as a sole assessment strategy.

Some clinicians employ psychometric instruments to detect irrational beliefs. Thus, for example, Jones' Irrational Beliefs Test (Jones, 1968) has been used in the clinical assessment of clients' belief systems. The author cautions that if such inventories

Figure 4:

FRAMEWORK FOR IDENTIFYING IRRATIONAL BELIEFS

1. DESCRIBE THE SITUATION THAT CONTRIBUTED TO
    YOUR UPSET.

2. DESCRIBE HOW YOU FELT.

    IF YOU EXPERIENCED ANY OF THE FOLLOWING
    EMOTIONS, GO ON TO QUESTIONS 3 AND 4 –
    ANXIETY, DEPRESSION, ANGER, GUILT, SHAME.

3. LIST ANY DEMANDS YOU MADE OR MIGHT MAKE OF
    YOURSELF, OTHER(S), OR ON THE SITUATION
    (SHOULD(S), OUGHT(S), HAVE TO('s), GOT TO('s)).

    SELF:

    OTHER(S):

    SITUATION:

4. LIST ANY EVALUATIONS YOU MADE OF YOURSELF,
    OTHER(S), OR ON THE SITUATION

    SELF:

    OTHER(S):

    SITUATION:

Figure 5:

FRAMEWORK FOR IDENTIFYING IRRATIONAL BELIEFS(example)

1. DESCRIBE THE SITUATION THAT CONTRIBUTED TO
   YOUR UPSET

   THINKING ABOUT GOING TO
   JILL'S PARTY

2. DESCRIBE HOW YOU FELT

   ANXIOUS

   IF YOU EXPERIENCED ANY OF THE FOLLOWING
   EMOTIONS, GO ON TO QUESTIONS 3 AND 4 -
   ANXIETY, DEPRESSION, ANGER, GUILT, SHAME

3. LIST ANY DEMANDS YOU MADE OR MIGHT MAKE OF
   YOURSELF, OTHER(S), OR ON THE SITUATION
   (SHOULD(S), OUGHT(S), MUST(S), HAVE TO('s), GOT
   TO('s)).

   SELF: I MUST NOT MAKE A FOOL OF MYSELF

   OTHER(S):   OTHER PEOPLE MUST LIKE ME

   SITUATION: THE PARTY MUST GO WELL

4. LIST ANY EVALUATIONS YOU MADE OF YOURSELF,
   OTHER(S), OR ON THE SITUATION

   SELF: I WOULD BE A FOOL AND UNPOPULAR

   OTHER(S):

   SITUATION:

are to be used they are employed only as a guide since a number of problems concerning the use of such inventories in clinical practice exist. One of these problems concerns the unsupported assumption that if individuals endorse irrational belief items on the inventories, they in fact hold those beliefs in practice. Secondly, the manner in which the items on these scales are phrased is problematic since the items are too general and not constructed for clients' own situations. Lastly, the content of such items is not situation specific. Thus, for example, clients may adhere to an irrational philosophy in one area but not in another area of their lives. In conclusion such scales should be used with due caution.

Application of Assessment Procedures to Stages of Social Skills Training

How can such assessment procedures be employed at various stages of social skills training? Basically there are four phases where clinicians need to conduct thorough analyses of clients' inferences and beliefs. This is best done in conjunction with a behavioural analysis. The three phases are (1) prior to social skills training, (2) during social skills training, (3) the generalization phase of training - where clients strive to put into practice skills that they have learnt in the training situation to everyday situations. In addition, cognitions related to clients' progress should be continually assessed.

Prior to social skills training. Prior to social skills training, clinicians generally conduct thorough-going behavioral analyses to determine deficits in clients' social skills. Clinicians should also use such an opportunity to assess the presence of dysfunctional inferences and irrational beliefs that clients may hold. This may be difficult since clients may typically have evolved a pattern of avoidance and withdrawal from social situations, but clinicians can use creative methods to elicit such data. This can be done by setting up role-play situations in assessment interviews where clients are asked to portray themselves interacting in a social situation with another person who is played by the therapist. After such a role-play which could be tape-recorded the clients could be asked to reflect on what thoughts were going through their minds at the time. The author has found that tape replay aids recall markedly. Another method of assessing cognitions is to ask clients to imagine themselves approaching and not avoiding a particular social

situation and staying in and not withdrawing from
this situation. Particular emphasis should be placed
on the inferences that are elicited. Such inferences
could then form the first stage for inference chaining. It is recommended that clinicians identify
specific social situations that clients would like to
approach and stay in rather than general social
situations which are employed as a diagnostic tool
for all clients.

A particularly useful situation to employ as a
stimulus for assessing dysfunctional cognitions and
irrational beliefs concerns the recommendation that
clients join a social skills group. It is important
to remember that such a group is in fact a social
situation and as such is likely to activate clients'
cognitions about entering social situations. In particular, clinicians should pay attention to the
clients' anticipations of other people's reactions to
them and also their anticipated responses to such
reactions. Secondly, it is important for clinicians
to remember that clients have expectations about
their ability to benefit from such treatment procedures. Common thoughts that clients express at
this stage are: "What you suggest to me won't work";
"I'll never be able to do the things which you have
explained to me". At this stage it is important for
clinicians to move into the intervention phase of
treatment to help clients modify such dysfucntional
cognitions. If such cognitions are not modified then
they may interfere with skill learning.

<u>During social skills training.</u> In order to assess
what thoughts clients have during the process of
social skills training it is important to help
clients report their thoughts. Clients should have
been helped to understand the effect of cognitions on
emotional experiences and behaviours and should be
encouraged to verbalize such thoughts when appropriate. Making such a recommendation to clients in
fact serves as a stimulus for further negative cognitions in that quite often clients experience shame
that they have negative thoughts about themselves and
social situations. This should be addressed as a
common experience and all members of a group should
be encouraged to verbalize such thoughts if they have
them.

As mentioned before, the training procedures
used in social skills training are excellent stimuli
for eliciting negative inferences and irrational
beliefs. Such exercises as behavioural rehearsal,
video-taped role-play, and simulated social

situations, such as group wine and cheese parties can be usefully employed by clinicians not only as intervention procedures to enable clients to practise and shape up social skills, but also as part of the assessment of dysfunctional cognitions.

Lastly, clinicians should pay particular attention to clients' thoughts about the skills they are being asked to learn. Because such clients have not typically enacted such skills, the learning of thoughts such as: "This is silly"; "This is not me"; "I'll never be able to put this into practice", may interfere with skill learning.

Generalizing from a Social Skills Group to Everyday life situations. At this stage it is assumed that clients have been helped to identify and correct their negative inferences and irrational beliefs which give rise to dysfunctional emotional experiences such as anxiety, anger, shame, depression, and guilt, and furthermore have made progress in acquiring social skills as a result of practising them in the group situation. It is now time for them to put their learnings derived from the group situation into practice in their everyday life experience. It is at this stage that clinicians had better be aware of the existence of beliefs derived from discomfort anxiety or low frustration tolerance. Such beliefs are implicit in clients' actions. For example, consider John, a social skills group member who made a lot of progress in both learning social skills in a group and disputing his irrational beliefs concerning the need for approval. He was given the homework assignment of going to a discotheque and asking a girl to dance. He returned to the group a week later in a discouraged mood. He related an incident where he saw a girl at the other side of the hall, made his mind up that he was going to ask for a dance, but as he began to approach her to ask her for a dance was overcome with panic and avoided the situation. The group members helped him to see that he was demanding that he feel comfortable in making such an approach and when he began to experience some anxiety, viewed such anxiety as too much to bear. As a result of his failure to ask her to dance, he then concluded that he was a miserable failure and that he would never be able to develop relationships with members of the opposite sex.

The generalization stage is the most important stage in determining the degree of therapeutic gain to be achieved by social skills group members. At this stage, clients have developed social skills but are awkward in executing them and have not yet learnt the skill of correct timing in the enactment of such skills - a skill which is only learned through social intercourse. As a result, clients may still be rejected because they come across awkwardly to other people. It is discomfort-related beliefs that will interfere with clients persisting in the face of adversity. Such cognitions as: "This is too hard for me, I'll never get what I want"; "The fact that I'm still getting rejected means that I'm no good" may be expressed.

A somewhat different form of discomfort anxiety is manifested in what Maultsby (1976) has called "the neurotic fear of feeling a phony". Maultsby notes that often clients do not persist in practising skills which would improve their chances in gaining what they want in life, precisely because at some point in the skill acquisition process they claim that "they don't feel like themselves". Such clients might express such statements as: "I feel as if I'm not being me"; "I feel strange and different and I don't like it"; "what sort of a person am I turning into?", etc. Therapists need to be aware of such cognitions if they are to help clients persist at this crucial stage of therapy.

Progress related cognitions. The final area in which continued assessment of negative inferences and irrational beliefs is necessary concerns clients' views of their own progress. Close observation is needed to determine how group members view their own progress. Progress in acquiring social skills, putting them into practice in a persistent way so that some degree of expertise in their application is acheived can be a notoriously slow process. Clients with high achievement needs often become discouraged and disappointed. Thus, for example, Bob, a socially withdrawn university student who had responded well to social skills training in the initial stages, became discouraged because he thought: "I'm not making as much progress as I hoped for". Through further exploration the group leader ascertained that Bob was feeling depressed because he wasn't progressing as fast as he should be. In this case, this thought related to Bob's ego anxiety based on perfectionism. However, a similar thought expressed by Ron, another group member, was more closely related to low frustration tolerance. Ron believed that he had to improve quickly because he found the practice exercises "too boring to put into practice". Again on further exploration, the group helped Ron to see that he was r8e.

ts.h

yh

hhhhhhhh

Social Skills Assessment and RET

defining the practice exercises as "too boring" to put up with and that this was the source of his discouragement concerning his rate of progress.

CONCLUSION

The major thesis of this chapter has been that assessment of clients' negative inferences and irrational beliefs is a crucial component of a comprehensive assessment of clients' social problems. Clinicians had better assess cognitions at virtually every stage of treatment ranging from initial assessment to termination. Furthermore, clinicians need to be creative in devising novel assessment strategies to help clients become aware of inferences and beliefs which are not in their immediate awareness. The purpose of such a thoroughgoing assessment of such cognitions is to facilitate the development of a multi-modal approach to social skills training.

REFERENCES

Beck, A.T., Rush, A.J., Shaw, B.F., and Emery, G. Cognitive therapy of depression. New York: Guilford Press, 1979

Ellis, A., & Harper, R.A. A new guide to rational living. Hollywood, Calif.: Wilshire, 1975

Grieger, R.M. An existential component of anger. Rational Living, 1977, 12, 3-8

Jones, R.G. A factored measure of Ellis' irrational belief system with personality and maladjustment correlates. Unpublished doctoral dissertation, Texas Technological College, 1968

Lazarus, A.A. Multi-modal behavior therapy. New York: Springer, 1976

Maultsby, M.C. Jr. Help yourself to happiness: Through rational self-counseling. New York: Institute for Rational Living, 1976

Sacco, W.P. Cognitive therapy in vivo. In G. Emery, S.D. Hollon & R.C. Bedrosian (Eds.), New directions in cognitive therapy. New York: Guilford Press, 1981

Wessler, R. So you are angry - what's your problem? Rational Living, 1981, 16, 29-31

Wessler, R.A., & Wessler, R.L. Principles and practice of rational-emotive therapy. San Fransisco: Jossey-Bass, 1980

Young, H.S. Teaching rational self-value concepts to tough customers. Paper presented at Third National Conference on R.E.T., New York, 1980

Chapter Eleven

SOCIAL SKILLS TRAINING FROM A RATIONAL-EMOTIVE
PERSPECTIVE

W. Dryden

INTRODUCTION

In the preceding chapter I outlined a comprehensive
approach to the cognitive assessment of social problems from a rational-emotive perspective. The aim of
the present chapter is to describe a treatment
approach to social problems within the same perspective. The goals of the present chapter are as
follows:

(1) To show how rational-emotive therapists develop
     an effective working alliance with their
     clients.

(2) To outline treatment strategies that rational-
     emotive therapists employ in helping clients
     overcome their social problems.

(3) To describe the treatment techniques that
     rational-emotive therapists use in the service
     of treatment strategies.

DEVELOPING AN EFFECTIVE THERAPEUTIC ALLIANCE

Bordin (1975, 1976) has argued that effective therapy
is characterized by the formation and maintenance of
a strong therapeutic alliance between therapist and
client. He suggests that there are three major components of the therapeutic alliance. These are
bonds, goals, and tasks. The goals represent the
"ends" of the therapeutic journey, the tasks are the
"means" for achieving such ends, while the bonds
refer to the quality of the relationship of the two
travellers. I have argued elsewhere (Dryden 1984),
that "disruption to the journey might occur because
the travellers do not get on (weak bonding), disagree

on journey's end (non-agreement on goals), and/or because they prefer different ways of reaching their destination (non-agreement on tasks)".

Developing Effective Bonds with Clients with Social Problems

Much has been written in psychotherapy on the importance of the therapist being empathic, genuine and respectful towards clients (Trower & Dryden, 1981). Rational-emotive therapists are no exception in endeavouring to offer clients these "core" conditions (Rogers, 1957). However, rational-emotive therapists guard against being unduly warm towards their clients since this may be counter-productive from a long-term treatment perspective in that such warmth tends to reinforce clients' approval and dependency needs – "needs" that rational-emotive therapists, as we shall see, endeavour to help clients relinquish.

There is no single approach in RET for developing effective bonds with clients. An important consideration, however, centres on therapists asking themselves two important questions: (1) which therapeutic interactional style would this particular client best respond to?, and (2) which therapeutic interactional style had better be avoided when relating to this particular client? While there are no clear-cut guidelines to help rational-emotive therapists answer these two questions, the therapist can develop hypotheses concerning the favoured interactional style, both from assessment interviews and initial treatment interactions with the client. It is important for therapists to regard such hypotheses as modifiable and guard against inflexibility. Whichever interactional style a therapist adopts, for the effective practice of RET, a collaborative relationship had better be developed between the two, with the therapist allying himself with the rational part of the client against the irrational part of the client.

Some clients respond better to therapists who stress their expertise; other clients respond better when therapists emphasize their attractiveness. Amongst others, these two variables have been shown by Strong (1978) to be correlated with positive client outcome. However, these variables have not been studied in relation to the practice of rational-emotive therapy in particular.

Agreement on Goals

Treatment goals refer to what clients hope to achieve from therapy. Clients with social problems often request "changes in their personality" when asked about what they hope to achieve in therapy. It is important that therapists help clients operationalize exactly what they mean by "changes in personality" and to try to link these changes in belief and behaviour that they will try to effect. When clients experience <u>both</u> deficits in social skills <u>and</u> dysfunctional inferences and beliefs which affect their social functioning, it is common experience that progress tends to be slow. Thus it is important for therapists and their clients to share a realistic understanding in terms of the rate at which clients' goals will be realized.

One major obstacle to therapists and clients agreeing on clients' goals stems from clients desires for changes to occur in other people or in external circumstances. Some clients deny that they have social problems and say that they would get on fine socially if only other people were friendly towards them. While the therapist may agree that such goals may be possible in that such clients may be helped to work towards influencing other peoples' behaviour, it is important that therapists and clients understand and agree that the primary changes that are to be effected in RET are in the way that the <u>client</u> feels, thinks and acts.

Agreement on Tasks

In rational-emotive therapy, as in all other therapies, both therapist and client have their respective responsibilities in carrying out tasks throughout the therapeutic enterprise. Effective therapy depends very much on the shared agreement of these tasks. The therapists' primary tasks are to help clients understand that: (1) social problems stem both from deficits in social performance and dysfunctional ways of inferring and evaluating information, (2) acquiring "social skills" will aid them in achieving their social goals, (3) changes in belief systems will promote both emotional and behavioural well-being, and (4) they are advised to continually work at practising skill acquisition and belief change.

Client tasks are (1) to observe their social performance, (2) to improve such performance by practising and refining the social skills that they have been taught in the therapeutic situation, (3) to observe their emotional disturbances, (4) to relate these to their cognitive determinants, and (5) to continually work at changing dysfunctional inferences and beliefs by employing cognitive, imaginal and behavioural methods.

Therapist tasks include: (1) helping structure clients' expectations about therapy and correcting any misconceptions that clients may have concerning therapy and the tasks of both participants. (If clients' expectations are at an extreme variance from the treatment approach of the therapist and such expectations are resistant to structuring attempts, then an appropriate referral elsewhere may be the only practical course of action); (2) using language that clients understand and continually checking that clients understand what is being said; (3) fully explaining the rationale for any interventions that they intend making in order to gain clients' understanding and active collaboration; (4) eliciting clients' feelings and reactions to therapy at the end of every session in order to deal with clients' negative reactions as they occur; and lastly (5) effecting a periodic review of clients' reactions to therapy which provides both parties with the opportunity to review progress and to renegotiate goals.

In summary, the strategies and techniques that therapists employ are likely to be more effective when both participants have developed a well-bonded collaborative relationship, when they both agree on the clients' realistic goals and when they agree on each participant's contributions (tasks) to the achievement of such goals. We are now in a position to consider the major treatment strategies that rational-emotive therapists employ to help clients overcome their social problems.

TREATMENT STRATEGIES IN RATIONAL-EMOTIVE THERAPY

In this section it is assumed that therapists have undertaken a thorough assessment of clients' inferences and evaluations which are centrally involved in their social problems (see previous chapter). Goldfried (1980) has argued that between the general theoretical level and specific technique level of therapeutic enterprise lies an intermediate strategy level. Treatment strategies in rational-emotive therapy involve therapists targeting clients' distorted inferences and irrational evaluations for change, the goal here being to help clients make more accurate inferences and rational evaluations. Treatment techniques, in contrast, refer to the specific means by which such changes are effected.

Strategies Designed to Effect Changes in the Inferential Level

Comprehensive RET has been distinguished from classical RET by Walen et al. (1980). Whereas classical RET refers to activities specifically designed to effect changes in clients' irrational evaluations, comprehensive RET involves activities that are designed to effect changes in a wide variety of dysfunctional cognitions. Inferences refer to non-evaluative cognitions whereas irrational beliefs are evaluative in nature. A significant component of comprehensive RET overlaps with the activites of cognitive therapists (Beck et al., 1979; Burns, 1980) who focus a lot of attention on the automatic thoughts that clients have about external events. Such automatic thoughts, since they are first level thoughts, are often non-evaluative and thus inferential in nature. Thus, such treatment strategies at the inferential level are designed to minimize distortion. The purpose of such strategies is to help clients develop realistic thinking, rather than positive thinking, in that clients are helped to form accurate inferences about the events in their lives. Therapists collaborate with their clients in helping them become good empiricists in that they are encouraged to view their automatic thoughts or inferences as hypotheses rather than facts and then to look for data which may corroborate or falsify these hypotheses. Clients are helped to identify their automatic thoughts and to determine whether such thoughts contain distortion. They are then helped to identify the category of distortion made and encouraged to empirically respond to these distortions. Figure 1 describes ten major inferential distortions and corresponding treatment strategies. In Figure 2, examples are provided of each of the major inferential distortions and the client's empirical response to each distortion is provided. Techniques that can be employed to help clients respond to inaccurate inferences will be provided in the section on treatment techniques.

Strategies which Help Clients Respond to their Irrational Evaluations

As noted in the preceding chapter, rational-emotive therapists pay close attention to the irrational evaluations that clients make about events in their lives. Such irrational evaluations are couched

Figure 1: Major Strategy 1 - Helping clients make accurate inferences (general principles)

Category of Inferential Distortion	Description	Treatment Strategy
1. All-or-Nothing Thinking	Client views performances or personal qualities in extremist black-or-white categories	Help client view performances or personal qualities along a continuum. Introduce "grey" area into human experience
2. Overgeneralization	Client concludes that a single negative event will keep recurring	Help client to conclude that a single negative event <u>may</u> recur but is not bound to do so
3. Disqualifying the positive	Client discounts data which conflict with negative self-attitude and pessimistic outlook	Help client to accept data which conflict with negative self-attitude and pessimistic outlook thus introducing dissonance which serves as base to effect changes in underlying attitude and outlook
4. Personalisation	Client relates event - usually negative - to himself when there is no basis for doing so	Help client to think in a less egocentric fashion - to view the event as outside his personal domain
5. Negative Prediction	Client imagines that something bad is about to happen and takes prediction as fact although may be unrealistic	Help client to view prediction as a hypothesis and not fact. Helping him to gather data prior to hypothesis testing

Figure 1 /continued

Category of Infer-ential Distortion	Description	Treatment Strategy
6. Emotional Reasoning	Client takes emotions as evid-ence for the way things really are	Help client understand that emotions are not a guide to reality but stem from inferences and evaluations of reality
7. Mind Reading	Client makes assump-tion that others are looking down on him without validating the assumption	Help client view assumption as a hypothesis and collect further data prior to testing the hypo-thesis
8. Magnification	Client exaggerates situation or mis-takes beyond re-alistic bounds	Help client view situation or mis-takes realistically and to view event in wider context by including all relevant variables
9. Selective Negative Focus	Client picks out and dwells exclusively on negative details concluding that whole situation is negative	Help client collect and focus on all relevant data and to view neg-ative details in context of the Gestalt
10. Minimization	Client views positive situations or talents/efforts as less im-portant than they really are	Help client view positive events in context by helping to collect all relevant data and background material

Figure 2: **Major Strategy 2** – Helping clients make accurate inferences
(specific examples)

Inferential Distortion	Context	Example of Distortion	Empirical Response
1. All-or-Nothing Thinking	Paul faltered in speech twice in 30 minutes while talking to a classmate at lunch	"I ruined the whole conversation."	"I faltered twice in 30 minutes, but for the vast majority of time I spoke clearly. Also the other person is responsible for his contribution to the conversation."
2. Over-generalization	Richard asked a girl for a date but she declined	"I'm never going to get a date. Girl's will always turn me down."	"Just because this girl turned me down doesn't mean I'll never get a date. Since she was only the second girl I've asked, I can't conclude yet that girls will always turn me down."
3. Disqualifying the positive	Ruth went to a discotheque where several men asked her to dance and showed interest in her	"They only asked me to dance as they felt sorry for me."	"I have no evidence that they were pitying me. They seemed to show interest in me and find me attractive."
4. Personalization	David saw his therapist talking to his colleague. He became angry and	"He's talking about my problems and they are both having	"They could be talking about anything. I don't know they are talking about me. I'll ask him about it at my next

Figure 2 / continued

Inferential Distortion	Context	Example of Distortion	Empirical Response
	refused to talk at the beginning of his next session."		session."
5. Negative Prediction	Annie became anxious in case her tutor asked her opinion in class	"If he asks me everyone will laugh no matter what I say."	"I have no evidence that the others will laugh no matter what I say. People do laugh when someone says something dumb but that's rare. When others talk sense the rest just listen."
6. Emotional Reasoning	Roy became depressed after spending the evening on his own afraid to go out dating	"I feel depressed therefore things will never change. I'll never lose my fear of women in dating situations."	"Just because I'm depressed doesn't mean things will never change. My feelings do not predict the future. I can overcome my fear of women in dating situations."
7. Mind Reading	Bill felt hurt after seeing his lecturer in the street	"He ignored me as he doesn't like me. He thinks I'm	"I don't know if he likes or dislikes me. I don't even know if he saw me. He was with someone and they were

	Event	Distorted Thought	Rational Response
		stupid as I never speak up in class."	talking. I'll ask him about the incident the next time I see him."
8. Magnification	Jane met an acquaintance in the street and asked about his father's health only to learn he died a few days earlier.	"He'll never talk to me again. That was the stupidest thing I've ever asked anyone."	"That was an unfortunate thing to ask but I did not know about his father's death. He probably understands and will forgive me."
9. Selective Negative Focus	Sue overheard some of her fellow students criticizing her friend's clothes.	"That's what people are like - hurtful and insensitive."	"People can be hurtful and insensitive but they are often not. These students often say nice things about people including my friend."
10. Minimization	Stan received warm appreciation from fellow social skills group members for asking a girl for a date and being accepted. Stan had not asked a girl for a date in over 4 years and had avoided contact with the opposite sex.	"It's no big deal really."	"Of course it's a big deal. It took a lot of effort to ask her out and it's the first time I've done so for ages. I did very well."

within a <u>demanding</u> philosophy, and the overall
strategy by the therapist at this level is to help
clients acquire a <u>desiring</u> philosophy. Irrational
evaluations occur in either <u>premise</u> or <u>conclusion</u>
form. Figure 3 outlines major strategies to help
clients give up their demanding philosophy and
replace it with a desiring philosophy. The example
employed is stated in the form "I must . . .".
Similar strategies can be used for beliefs commencing
in the form "you must . . .", or "the world (life
conditions) must . . . ".

While therapists do often help clients correct
their inferential distortions, an important strategy
is for therapists and clients to assume that the
inference is true and for therapists to help their
clients identify any irrational beliefs that might be
made about the now (assumed) correct inference.
Figure 4 takes eight of the distorted inferences as
outlined in Figure 2, assumes them to be true, and
provides rational alternatives to the irrational
evaluations made.

Helping Clients move from Intellectual to Emotional Insight

Clients often say that although they can see that
their new more accurate inference and rational evaluation are correct they still <u>feel</u> that the inaccurate inference and irrational evaluation are
<u>really</u> true. Another example of this is where
clients can say "I see what you mean but I just don't
feel it is true". Here clients are encouraged to
view the believability of cognitions (inferences and
evaluations) as lying on a continuum from, on one
end, cognitions that are lightly and infrequently
believed to cognitions that are very intensely more
frequently believed at the other end of the continuum. Such a discussion provides a springboard for
clients to consider what activities could help them
move from the "intellectual" end of the insight continuum to the "emotional" end of the continuum. In
moving from one end of the continuum to the other,
therapists encourage clients to employ a wide variety
of techniques across the three major modalities that
rational-emotive techniques tap, i.e., behavioural,
cognitive (verbal and imaginal) and emotive.

TREATMENT TECHNIQUES IN RET

The major purpose of all treatment techniques is to
effect changes in the cognitive system of clients –
helping clients to make accurate inferences and

Figure 3: Major Strategy 2 – Helping clients make rational evaluations (general principles)

Irrational Evaluation	Reasons why the irrational evaluation is untenable	Rational Evaluation
1. Premise: I must do well in social conversations	– 'Must' implies that there is a law of the universe that states that I must do well. Clearly no such law exists except in my head and I can change that. Therefore there is no evidence to support this belief.	I would like to do well in social conversations but I don't have to
Conclusion 1: I'm less worthwhile if I don't do well in social conversations	– This implies that I equate myself with my performance. It is clearly an over-generalization to say that I'm more worthwhile if I do well and less worthwhile if I do poorly – 'I', as a human, am too complex to be given a global rating which less worthwhile implies – 'I' am an ongoing everchanging process and as such can't be given a global rating which implies that 'I' am static – 'I am less worthwhile' implies that everything about me is less worthwhile since 'I am' is a	I'm neither less or more worthwhile if I perform poorly or well. I'm a fallible human being who can't be given a global rating. I can choose to accept myself as a fallible human and still not like the fact that I don't do well (sometimes) in social conversations

Figure 3 / continued

Irrational Evaluation	Reasons why the irrational evaluation is untenable	Rational Evaluation
	statement about my identity. Clearly this is incorrect	
	- If I have 'worth' as a human this is invariant and thus does not vary with my performances. I can take the position that I am worthwhile no matter what I do since someone could argue that I am worthless no matter what I do. I would be better to adopt the position 'I exist as an unrateable fallible human being and can choose to accept myself as such'	
	- Rating myself will hinder rather than help me achieve my goals	
Conclusion 2: I can't stand not doing well in social conversations	- I have obviously stood not doing well in social conversations many times before. I have stood it as I'm still here. If I really couldn't stand it I would die or disintegrate. This hasn't happened	I can stand not doing well in social conversations although I'll never like it. I can stand what I don't like
	- Telling myself that I can't stand something is not the same as not standing it. I am standing it although I could better tolerate this	

unlikeable event

- I can stand it until I disin-
tegrate then it won't matter. So
I'd better more accurately remind
myself that I can stand it

Conclusion 3:
It's
awful

- 'Awful' means first that my performance is totally 100% bad which
is incorrect since it could have
been much worse

- 'Awful' further means that my
behaviour is more than 100% bad,
i.e., 101% bad or even greater.
Since nothing exists that is 101%
anything my performance is not
awful

- 'Awful' further means that there
is no behaviour in the universe
worse than my performance. Hardly
likely!

If I don't do well in
social conversations
that's bad but hardly
'awful'

Figure 4: Major Strategy 2 - Helping clients make rational evaluations
(specific examples)

Assuming the Inference is Correct	Irrational Evaluation	Rational Evaluation
1. "I ruined the conversation"	"I'm a failure" (evaluative conclusion derived from premise: I must ensure that conversations go well)	"I failed on this conversation but that doesn't make me a failure" (evaluative conclusion derived from premise: I would like to ensure that conversations go well)
2. "I'm never going to get a date. Girls will always turn me down"	"That would be terrible" (evaluative conclusion derived from premise: I must get a date with a girl to be happy)	"That would be very bad, but hardly terrible. I could gain satisfaction in other social activities and in non-social activities" (evaluative conclusion derived from premise: I would like to get a date with a girl although I don't need this for my happiness)
3. "They only asked me to dance as they felt sorry for me"	"I can't stand being pitied. That makes me a pitiful creature" (evaluative conclusion derived from premise: other people must take me seriously and not feel sorry for me)	"I can stand being pitied although I'll never like it. I'm not a pitiful creature. I'm a human being with social difficulties" (evaluative conclusion derived from premise: I'd prefer people to take me seriously and not feel sorry for me)

4. "He's talking about my problems and they are both having a laugh at my expense"

"How dare they make fun of me. They're rotten" (evaluative conclusion derived from premise: other people must act fairly towards me)

"Other people have a right to make fun of me although I strongly dislike this. They are not rotten, just human beings acting in a rotten fashion" (evaluative conclusion derived from premise: I would prefer it if people acted fairly towards me)

5. "If he asks me, everyone will laugh no matter what I say"

"That would be unbearable. I will have made a fool of myself" (evaluative conclusion derived from premises:
(a) I need other people's approval
(b) I must not act foolishly)

"I cannot make a fool of myself. I can accept myself as a fallible human who acts foolishly and I can bear it when I do" (evaluative conclusion derived from premises:
(a) I want other people's approval
(b) I don't like acting foolishly)

6. "I feel depressed, therefore things will never change. I'll never lose my fear of women in dating situations"

"That would be awful" (evaluative conclusion derived from premise: I must overcome my fear of women in dating situations)

"If I never lost my fear of women in dating situations that would be bad but hardly awful. I can still approach women even though I am anxious" (evaluative conclusion derived from premise: I would like to overcome my fear of women in dating situations although I don't have to)

Figure 4 / continued

Assuming the Inference is Correct	Irrational Evaluation	Rational Evaluation
7. "He ignored me because he doesn't like me. He thinks I'm stupid as I never speak up in class"	"I'm not worthy if people don't like me" (evaluative conclusion derived from premise: I need other people to show they like me)	"If people don't like me that's sad but doesn't prove I'm unworthy. I can accept myself as a complex human whether others like me or not" (evaluative conclusion derived from premise: I desire other people to show they like me but don't need them to)
8. "He'll never talk to me again. That was the stupidest thing I've ever asked anyone"	"What a stupid idiot I am" (evaluative conclusion derived from premise: I must not ask people stupid questions)	"I'm not a stupid idiot for asking a stupid, idiotic question. A stupid idiot can always and only do idiotic and stupid things. I don't qualify for that label!" (evaluative conclusion derived from premise: I would greatly prefer it if I don't ask people stupid questions)

rational evaluations. There are two ways of conceptualizing the treatment techniques. First, it is possible to classify techniques according to the treatment modality employed. Here we shall look at the three major modalities used: (1) Cognitive (verbal and imaginal); (2) Emotive, and (3) Behavioural. Secondly, it is possible to consider the techniques employed as to whether the therapist or client has the major responsibility for initiating the technique.

Techniques that Therapists are Responsible for Initiating

Cognitive techniques. One of the more commonly used procedures is that of disputing. Ellis (1977a) considers that there are three components of the disputing process which therapists employ in helping clients make accurate inferences and rational beliefs. These are debating, discriminating and defining (Phadke, 1976).

In debating, therapists ask clients a number of questions which are designed to help clients correct inaccurate inferences and irrational beliefs. Questions such as: "What evidence supports this belief (or inference)?", "In what way does it have truth or falseness?", and "What makes it so?" are frequently employed. Therapists proceed with such questioning until clients acknowledge the inaccuracy of their inferences or the falseness of their irrational beliefs and in addition acknowledge the truth of the more accurate or rational alternatives. In discriminating, therapists help clients clearly distinguish between nonabsolute values (wants, preferences, likes and desires) and absolutist values (needs, demands and imperatives). In defining, therapists help clients make increasingly accurate definitions in the language they employ.

Ideally, the disputing process is initiated by therapists in the context of a Socratic dialogue with clients, or what Beck et al. (1979) call inductive questioning. Therapists ask clients open-ended questions and involve them in the process so that they are encouraged to think in a concerted manner about the irrational evaluations and inaccurate inferences they have made. While the Socratic dialogue is favoured by rational-emotive therapists, such a method is not effective with all clients. When the Socratic method breaks down, therapists do not simply rely on evocative methods of disputing but introduce more explanations. Clients are helped in this dialogue to analyse the validity of their irrational evaluations

and inaccurate inferences by systematically collecting evidence which demonstrates the falseness of
these ideas. Therapists may employ inductive questioning to help clients consider alternative ways of
interpreting and appraising events.

Particularly when helping clients dispute inaccurate inferences about events, therapists should
draw on the work of Beck et al. (1979) who in their
pioneering work on cognitive therapy have developed a
number of methods to help clients correct inaccurate
inferences. Basically these methods involve therapists helping clients see what category of cognitive
distortion (faulty information processing style) they
are employing, and to substitute a more accurate form
of information processing in its place. For example,
a client may indicate that he is making a firm conclusion when the data at his disposal do not warrant
such a conclusion. The therapist might teach the
client the differences between hypotheses and facts
and show him he is making an arbitrary inference. He
would then encourage the client to list alternative
conclusions and to weigh such alternatives against
the original in terms of inferential accuracy.

During the disputing process and at other times,
therapists may employ another major cognitive technique: information-giving. Information is given when
clients reveal ignorance which contributes to inaccurate inferences or irrational evaluations. For
example, a common cognitive distortion that clients
make is to infer that feelings of extreme anxiety
mean that they are going crazy. Therapists may
correct such a misconception by providing clients
with information about the effects of extreme
anxiety. Since a large number of clients seen in
mental health clinics suffer from such a misconception - termed phrenophobia by Raimy (1975) - providing such information often serves to correct such a
misconception.

Another major cognitive technique that therapists use is: interpretation of defences. It is well
known that clients are likely to either deny the
existence of an emotional problem or distort the
extent that the emotional problem exists. When
therapists suspect such defensive behaviour they test
out such hypotheses by searching for hidden self-
condemnation which serves as a motivating force for
clients employing such defensive strategies. By
helping clients to accept themselves for their
emotional problems, rational-emotive therapists are
often able to help them to fully admit the existence
of such problems.

While the above cognitive methods are primarily verbal, therapists also employ <u>imagery</u> methods. A common imagery method that is used in the course of disputing irrational beliefs and inaccurate inferences is: <u>time projection</u>. The purpose of time projection is to help clients move beyond immediate interpretations and evaluations and thereby view events from an increasingly greater time perspective. This is often employed as an indirect disputing method. Clients are helped to see, that events judged as "awful" at the present time are evaluated in a less extreme manner when viewed from a different perspective. For example, the writer often employs time projection techniques with students who evaluate rejection as a "dreadful", "horrible", experience. By helping them move forward in time from the event, clients are able to see that although rejection is a bad experience, it is not the "end of the world" it seems in the present.

<u>Emotive methods</u>. Critics of RET often make the point that it is lacking in its emphasis on the emotive modality. This is in fact a misconception since rational-emotive therapists often employ emotive methods. One major emotive method is: <u>unconditional acceptance</u> of clients. The purpose here is for therapists to demonstrate that no matter how poor clients' social skills are, they accept such clients as fallible human beings who can and often do act poorly. Unconditional acceptance of clients is communicated not only by therapist attitude and behaviour towards clients but also by frank therapist self-disclosure of their position to clients. Unconditional acceptance does not mean that therapists accept everything about clients. The point is that while therapists may not condone or even like certain client behaviours, they can accept clients as human beings who act in undesirable ways.

Another important therapist-initiated emotive method is that of <u>therapist self-disclosure</u>. Rational-emotive therapists are not reluctant to admit their own social failings and fallibilities, but in doing so show that they can fully accept themselves for such aspects. They can frankly admit that they may not like aspects of themselves but refuse to damn themselves for these unlikeable aspects. In doing so therapists often serve as role models for clients in the teaching of rational principles.

Therapists also employ <u>humour</u> in therapy sessions. Such humour is directed either at aspects of clients (never at clients themselves) or at aspects of therapists' own behaviour (but never at therapists themselves). The aim here is to help clients adopt a stance of "not taking themselves and their problems too seriously", and this is often an effective way of loosening up clients in therapy. Another humorous method often employed, particularly by Ellis (1977b), is humorous songs (each of which communicates a rational principle). This method is often employed in groups but can also be employed in individual therapy. There is indeed a tape of rational humorous songs which clients may be encouraged to listen to and perhaps sing at various times to aid the process of self-disputing (Ellis, 1977b).

Therapists also employ <u>analogies</u> and <u>parables</u> in their teaching of rational principles. Thus for example, the case of Nathan Leopold* is often related to clients who condemn themselves as thoroughly rotten individuals for committing some presumed sin and who are afraid that other people might discover this. The purpose here is to help clients see that doing something seriously wrong does not make them bad persons and that by accepting themselves they will become less anxious about other people discovering the "sin".

Other emotive-dramatic methods are used in therapy to teach clients rational concepts and/or aid them in the disputing process. Therapists are only limited by their own imaginations when it comes to devising such methods. However, it is important for therapists to monitor the effects of such dramatic techniques, preferably by asking clients at the end of therapy sessions their reactions to such methods. Perhaps the use of such methods is inadvisable with clients who have enduring negative reactions to them.

The dramatic methods aim to encourage clients to raise their level of frustration tolerance and to accept themselves as fallible humans. Thus therapists might in the course of talking to clients about self-acceptance for acting foolishly, suddenly leap to the floor and start barking like a dog. Startled clients are then asked for their reactions towards therapists for such behaviour. Are clients going to condemn the therapists for acting in such a

---

* "Nathan Leopold along with Richard Leob committed the 'crime of the century' in the 1920's by kidnapping and killing a young boy. Years later, Leopold was pardoned as a changed person, became a social worker, married and spent much of the rest of his life doing good work" (Wessler & Wessler, 1980, p126)

foolish way in the same way as they might condemn themselves? Often such dramatic methods serve to reinforce the more traditional verbal message.

Another emotive method that therapists may initiate is: role-playing - to either aid clients in behaviour rehearsal or to facilitate the disputing process (rational role reversal). In rational role reversal therapists may speak for the rational part of themselves. The purpose here is to help clients improve their skill at answering back and responding to their irrational voice. This is best done with clients who show some prior skill at self-disputing.

Behavioural techniques. While most of the behavioural methods employed are the responsibility of clients to initiate, therapists can initiate a number of skill-training methods to improve clients' social skills, to help clients develop skills at self-assertion, or to help clients become more proficient problem-solvers. While such skills are not specifically designed to help clients change their inferences or beliefs about events, they often have that secondary effect. Thus, clients who are able to assert themselves with their boss, may learn in the process that nothing awful will happen as a result of such assertion. However, therapists generally employ such skills training while reminding clients that negative responses from others, or negative outcomes in the environment may very well follow, and in so doing initiate the disputing of any inaccurate inferences or irrational evaluations that clients might make concerning such responses and outcomes (Ellis, 1977c).

Techniques that Clients are Responsible for Initiating
The techniques that clients are responsible for initiating are all designed to help them put into practise in their everyday life what they have learned during therapy sessions. The purpose here is to help clients become autonomous from their therapists and in a sense become their own therapists. Therapists have an important role to play in helping clients initiate such techniques outside the session. Thus, therapists are advised to fully explain the rationale of any techniques that they suggest clients employ outside therapy. It is best to teach clients these techniques in a clear and concise fashion and get feedback that clients understand and accept the validity and purpose of such techniques. Furthermore, therapists had better determine in advance any

obstacles that clients might anticipate experiencing which might prevent them from carrying out these techniques. In addition it is important to make it a priority to follow up and discuss with clients their experiences in carrying out the techniques or, if clients did not carry them out, to determine the reasons which prevented them from doing so. However, since therapists cannot make clients initiate techniques outside of therapy sessions, it is a major responsibility of clients to initiate such techniques themselves.

Cognitive techniques. Clients are strongly advised to employ the same disputing techniques that therapists employ with them during therapy sessions. Thus, for example, clients can use several homework forms that are available for the purpose of debating. For example, the client takes a disturbing emotion or self-defeating action, writes down the context in which this occurred, and using the instruction - "cherchez le should" (look for the should) - determines for himself what (if any) irrational evaluations he was making in the situation. He can then move on to debate the truth or falseness of such beliefs and if they are found to be false replace them with rational beliefs (see Appendix 1). The more that clients learn to dispute their irrational beliefs, the more likely they are to be believe in the rational alternative. Another technique that clients can employ outside therapy sessions is: DIBS (disputing irrational beliefs, Ellis, 1977d). Clients are provided with a structure in which they can ask themselves six questions and their task is to come up with as many answers to each question as they can:

(1) What irrational beliefs do I want to dispute and surrender?

(2) Can I rationally support this belief?

(3) What evidence exists of the truth of this belief?

(4) What evidence exists of the falseness of my belief that I must. . . . ?

(5) What are the worst possible things that could actually happen to me if I. . . . ?

(6) What good things could happen or could I make

happen if I never. . . . ?

Clients, of course, fill in the blanks with the content of their own particular irrational belief.

Client-initiated discriminating involves first the detection of an irrational belief, then writing the rational alternative to this belief and clearly providing reasons why they are different and what different effects each type of belief would have. Clients might also provide themselves with reasons why they would prefer to adopt the rational belief as opposed to the irrational belief. In addition, other aspects of discrimination include clients showing themselves adaptive as well as maladaptive aspects of their behaviour, observing the distinction between undesirable and "unbearable" results in their lives, clearly showing themselves that hassles do not equal "horrors" and clearly distinguishing between logical conclusions about their lives and those which do not follow.

Using defining techniques, clients learn to write down both their evaluations and inferences and in doing so learn to identify and correct the semantic errors in their thinking, particularly those which are associated with the verb "to be". Thus, when a client writes "I am a fool", he might correct himself by reminding himself that if that were true he would only be able to act foolishly and might correct his semantic error by saying "I am a person who acted foolishly in this instance". The above three methods of debating, discriminating and defining clearly rest on clients' abilities to detect and to record their thoughts, inferences and beliefs. Thus, therapists need to help clients whenever they demonstrate difficulty in the detection process.

While the self-disputing techniques are of great importance in RET, there are other cognitive techniques that clients can initiate to reinforce changes derived from therapy sessions. Thus, for example, they can initiate bibliotherapy. This refers to self-help books or novels with a particular therapeutic purpose for clients to read outside therapy sessions. While therapists try to ensure that the suggested reading material is suitable for the clients' comprehension levels, clients can negotiate with their therapists an appropriate amount of material to read. After the material has been read it is best for clients to discuss with their therapists what they have learnt from the material.

Two cognitive techniques which are designed to help clients practice their new rational philosophies are: (1) <u>employing more accurate and rational self-statements in a written form</u>, and (2) <u>using RET with others</u>. In the first technique, clients take 3" x 5" white cards and write on them new rational self-statements which they then carry around, look at and repeat a number of times daily, particularly at times when they are vulnerable to emotional distress. Such cards serve as helpful therapeutic aide-memoires in situations where clients might not make spontaneous rational responses to their inaccurate inferences and irrational evaluations. Using RET with others provides clients with opportunities to rehearse rational messages for themselves. It also provides them with opportunities to think through rational arguments, for they are likely to meet opposition when they come to debate such ideas as: "It is not necessary to gain the approval of a significant other". If clients are prepared for such opposition and are discouraged from believing that they must convince the other person of the correctness of their own position, then this proselytizing technique has much potential value, particularly if the other person is willing to constructively debate the issue at hand.

Two further cognitive techniques that clients can employ involve them learning to cope with heightened emotional reaction and help them resist self-defeating social responses. These are self-instructional training and distraction techniques. <u>Self instructional training</u> was originated by Meichenbaum (1977) and involves clients talking to themselves in constructive ways in order to cope with extreme emotional reactions. Thus, for example, clients who become very anxious may initiate such rational self-talk as "this is only anxiety, it is not dangerous, it is merely uncomfortable and I can cope with it". In addition self-instructional training may be used to overcome avoidance prior to entering a threatening social situation. Here clients can instruct themselves to keep their emotional reactions within manageable bounds.

<u>Distraction methods</u> serve a similar purpose in controlling clients' emotional reactions but involve them redirecting their attention away from their emotional experiences to specific aspects in the environment. Thus, clients who are particularly anxious in a particular social situation might refocus their attention and describe to themselves in great detail an object that is present in the anxiety-provoking environment. In addition, clients might distract themselves from their own emotional

reactions by instructing themselves to initiate relaxation procedures and then to carry out such procedures in the social situation.

Clients can employ several imagery techniques outside therapy sessions, such as those suggested by Arnold Lazarus (1978). Two such imagery techniques are: rational-emotive imagery and cognitive (memory) rehearsal. Rational-emotive imagery was designed to help clients bridge the gap between "intellectual" and "emotional" insight. The purpose of this technique is to provide clients with practice at holding new rational beliefs and/or getting practice at changing their emotional experiences from dysfunctional to functional ones.

There are two forms of rational-emotive imagery, one devised by Maultsby and one modified by Ellis (Maultsby & Ellis, 1974). In the Maultsby version clients are encouraged to visualize the activating event which is often the worst that they can realistically imagine. Whilst keeping such an image clearly in mind, clients are encouraged to practise the new rational beliefs that had previously been identified through disputing. Clients are encouraged to go over the rational belief in their minds' eye and are then asked to observe changes in their emotional reactions. Clients are then encouraged to practise this technique several times a day usually over a 30-day period.

In the Ellis version of rational-emotive imagery, clients are again encouraged to imagine the activating event and are further encouraged to experience the same dysfunctional emotions that they would normally experience when exposed to such an event. They are then encouraged to change such negative dysfunctional feelings to negative functional feelings (for example, changing from depression to sadness, from anger to annoyance, from anxiety to concern). Clients are asked to signal when they are able to do this and then are asked how they managed to change their feelings from dysfunctional to functional. Clients invariably say that they achieved such change by altering their beliefs about the activating event. Clients are then encouraged to carry out this technique on their own several times a day, again for a 30-day period.

In cognitive rehearsal, clients prepare themselves, for example, to enter an avoided social situation and mentally rehearse approaching that particular situation while covertly repeating such rational self-statements that have been developed during the disputing process. Raimy (1975) has written that it is the repeated review of such events in imagery that is important. Thus, clients are encouraged to repeatedly rehearse such new cognitive and behavioural responses before actually doing this in real life. This procedure is particularly valuable for clients who claim that they cannot "see" themselves putting into practise these new responses (Lazarus, 1978).

Emotive techniques. The emotive techniques that clients can initiate often involve dramatic force and vigour. For example, clients may be encouraged to rehearse rational self-statements in a passionate and vigorous manner, where they adopt both the rational and irrational standpoints. They ensure that when they adopt the rational standpoint they are more passionate and vigorous in their arguments than when they adopt the irrational standpoint. This method which Burns (1980) has called externalization of voices, can also be conducted by clients using a tape recorder.

Other emotive techniques that clients can employ themselves involve an additional behavioural element. Thus, for example, clients can undertake various shame-attacking exercises for which RET is well known. The purpose of shame-attacking exercises is for clients to gain practice at doing something which they would ordinarily experience as "shameful". In doing so they are provided with an opportunity to accept themselves for the "shameful" act. Shame-attacking exercises also provide information concerning other people's reactions to the clients' "shameful" behaviours and thus provide them with information which may correct any inaccurate inferences that they have made. Shame-attacking exercises have traditionally involved such tasks as standing in the lift facing other passengers, taking a banana for a walk and selling yesterday's newspapers. Therapists had better ensure before clients initiate this technique that they will not get themselves into trouble at work or with the police and that the planned exercise will not unnecessarily alarm or inconvenience other people in their environment.

A similar but perhaps less dramatic, technique is the risk-taking exercise. Here clients are encouraged to take risks that they might ordinarily avoid. Clients are prepared in advance by their therapists who help them identify and correct inaccurate inferences and self-defeating beliefs before they initiate such risk-taking exercises. Examples of risk-taking exercises are: returning slightly damaged goods, or asking a waiter to provide a new set of clean cutlery. Risk-taking exercises, in general, involve clients correcting inaccurate inferences about others' reactions and disputing beliefs concerning dire needs for approval. Another newly developed emotive technique is the "step out of character" exercise. Clients are asked to identify ways of behaving or relating that they would ideally like to adopt but which involve a step out of character for them. Again clients are prepared cognitively before embarking on such an exercise.

These three exercises often involve clients confronting their discomfort anxiety in which irrational evaluations such as "I have to be comfortable in doing something and I can't stand being uncomfortable" are made. Since these exercises involve clients confronting their discomfort anxiety, they can additionally be viewed as exercises in raising clients' level of frustration tolerance.

Behavioural techniques. There are some proponents of RET who claim that one of the best ways clients can change beliefs is by behaviourally contradicting them. However, when clients initiate acting in a new way or when they confront social situations that they have previously avoided, they also practice in vivo cognitive disputing since they are encouraged to enter the social situation while rehearsing rational self-statements. Since the purpose of such behavioural techniques is to effect cognitive changes, rational-emotive therapists prefer to suggest to clients that they confront situations that they wish to avoid, such as their own anxiety or social rejection, as well as suggesting that they expose themselves to situations that they would like, for example, acceptance. Thus, common behavioural homework exercises that clients often initiate are ones that expose them to potential rejection, a situation which will provide them with a golden opportunity for showing themselves (1) that they can stand rejection, (2) that such rejection does not mean that they are less worthwhile, and (3) that rejection is not an "awful" experience. Needless to say therapists can prepare clients for this somewhat unorthodox type of homework assignment. In other words, therapists need to clarify the rationale behind such an assignment. Such behavioural techniques are either designed to help clients raise their level of frustration tolerance or to help them to dispute ego-anxiety ideas.

Behavioural techniques that clients can initiate to raise their level of frustration tolerance include in vivo desensitization whereby they actually go out and confront situations that they would ordinarily avoid such as talking to other people, going to parties, or asking a woman to dance. When used as a technique to raise clients' levels of frustration tolerance, in vivo desensitization is used in its "flooding" rather than "gradual" form. However, quite often clients simply refuse to directly and implosively confront such feared situations and prefer a more graduated desensitization approach. While rational-emotive therapists regard the flooding paradigm as more "elegant" (i.e., promoting greater attitude change), it is more expedient not to allow their own preferences to disregard clients' own desires. In other words, therapists would do well not to threaten the therapeutic alliance.

Grieger and Boyd (1980) have written about a group of techniques which they call "stay in there" activities. These techniques are designed to help clients put up with chronic rather than acute discomfort, and as such, these activities are liable to be better accepted and completed by clients. Clients can also initiate anti-procrastination exercises which are designed to help them, for example, initiate social contacts earlier rather than later, thus behaviourally disputing dire needs for comfort.

A major behavioural technique, used extensively by cognitive therapists (Beck et al., 1979), is: behavioural experiments. The purpose of the behavioural experiment is to help clients collect data to test a hypothesis. First, the therapist helps the client identify an inaccurate inference and to view this inference as a hypothesis and not a fact. Then the therapist and client design an experiment to test the hypothesis. Frequently the data contradict the client's hypothesis and enable him to correct his inaccurate inference. Clients with social problems often make negative predictions concerning the responses of other people. For example, Bill predicted that if he asked girls to dance they would not only refuse but laugh at him. The therapist asked Bill if he would consider his prediction as a hypothesis and gained his agreement to test his hypothesis. He would ask five girls to dance and observe and then record their reactions (data collection stage). Three girls accepted his invitation, two declined and none laughed. This procedure helped Bill to correct his distorted inference. Often clients will carry out tasks they would ordinarily avoid if the "hypothesis-testing" rationale is fully explained.

To encourage clients who wish to initiate such

behavioural techniques but are doubtful as to whether they are able to go through with it, therapists can employ <u>operant conditioning techniques</u>. For example, clients say that they wish to do an anti-procrastination exercise but doubt whether they will in practice; therapists might help them identify some everyday rewarding experience which they are willing to forgo until they complete the exercise. Furthermore, therapists help clients identify particularly unpleasant tasks that they would endeavour to avoid and gain their clients' agreement to do these tasks if they have not completed the anti-procrastination exercise by an appointed time. Clients may fail to do an anti-procrastination exercise <u>and</u> refuse to initiate operant conditioning techniques. However, in such cases therapists need do no more than to remind clients of their responsibilities for that choice and can help them tolerate better the consequences of that choice.

CONCLUSION

The purpose of this chapter has been to show that for RET to be effective in the treatment of social problems, both therapist and client need to discharge their responsibilities. RET is a non-mystical therapy where therapists openly talk about techniques, their rationale and purpose. It is the responsibility of therapists to form an effective working alliance with their clients, to present the structure of the therapy in such a way that clients can understand and agree with the major tasks of each participant. Furthermore therapists are well advised to employ as many techniques as is deemed appropriate to help clients to achieve their goals. However, no matter how competent therapists may be, they can only help clients achieve their goals if they (the clients) also understand and are prepared to discharge their responsibilities. These responsibilities lie mainly in the area of putting into practice the insights that they have gained from therapy sessions and to develop the outlook that ongoing improvement requires ongoing work to consolidate change. When both parties are willing and able to discharge their responsibilities, then rational-emotive therapy is a powerful adjunct to skills-based social skills training in the comprehensive approach to helping clients overcome their social problems.

REFERENCES

Beck, A.T., Rush, A.J., Shaw, B.F., & Emery, G.
   Cognitive therapy of depression. Chichester:
   Wiley, 1979
Bordin, E.S. The generalizability of the psycho-
   analytic concept of the working alliance. Paper
   presented at the meeting of the Society for Psy-
   chotherapy Research, Boston, June, 1975
Bordin, E.S. The working alliance: Basis for a
   general theory of psychotherapy. Paper presen-
   ted at the meeting of the American Psychological
   Association, Washington, D.C., September, 1976
Burns, D.D. Feeling good: The new mood therapy. New
   York: William Morrow, 1980
Dryden, W. Rational-emotive therapy: Fundamentals
   and innovations. London: Croom Helm, 1984
Ellis, A. The basic clinical theory of rational-
   emotive therapy. In A. Ellis & R. Grieger
   (Eds.), The handbook of rational-emotive
   therapy. New York: Springer, 1977 (a)
Ellis, A. A garland of rational songs. Songbook and
   tape cassette recording. New York: Institute for
   Rational Living, 1977 (b)
Ellis, A. Skill training in counselling and psycho-
   therapy. Canadian Counsellor, 1977, 12, 30-35
   (c)
Ellis, A. How to live with - and without - anger. New
   York: Reader's Digest Press, 1977 (d)
Goldfried, M.R. On the search for effective inter-
   vention strategies. In C.E. Thoresen (Ed.), The
   behaviour therapist. Monterey, California:
   Brooks/Cole, 1980
Grieger, R., & Boyd, J. Rational-emotive therapy:
   A skills-based approach. New York: Van Nostrand
   Reinhold, 1980
Lazarus, A.A. In the mind's eye. New York: Rawson
   Associates, 1978
Maultsby, M.C. Jr., & Ellis, A. Techniques for using
   rational-emotive imagery. New York: Institute
   for Rational Living, 1974
Meichenbaum, D. Cognitive-behavior modification: An
   integrative approach. New York: Plenum Press,
   1977
Phadke, K.M. Bull-fighting. A royal road to health
   and happiness. Unpublished manuscript, Bombay,
   1976
Raimy, V. Misunderstandings of the self: Cognitive
   psychotherapy and the misconception hypothesis.
   San Francisco: Jossey-Bass, 1975
Rogers, C.R. The necessary and sufficient conditions

of therapeutic personality change. Journal of Consulting Psychology, 21, 95-103, 1957

Strong, S.R. Social psychological approach to psychotherapy research. In S.L. Garfield & A.E. Bergin (Eds.), Handbook of psychotherapy and behavior change, Second edition, New York: Wiley, 1978

Trower, P., & Dryden, W. Psychotherapy. In M. Argyle (Ed.), Social skills and health. London: Methuen, 1981

Walen, S.R., DiGiuseppe, R., & Wessler, R.L. A practitioner's guide to rational-emotive therapy. New York: Oxford University Press, 1980

Wessler, R.A., & Wessler, R.L. Principles and practice of rational-emotive therapy. San Francisco: Jossey-Bass, 1980

Appendix 1 A guide for solving emotional and behavioural problems by re-examining self-defeating thoughts and attitudes

A

DESCRIBE THE SITUATION THAT CONTRIBUTED TO YOUR UPSET

IF YOU EXPERIENCED ANY OF THE FOLLOWING EMOTIONS GO TO B:

ANXIETY, DEPRESSION, ANGER, GUILT, SHAME EMBARRASSMENT

GO TO B IF YOU ACTED IN A SELF-DEFEATING MANNER.

C

DESCRIBE HOW YOU FELT AND ACTED

B

LIST ANY DEMANDS YOU MADE OR MIGHT MAKE OF YOURSELF, OTHER(S) OR ON THE SITUATION, LOOK FOR SHOULDS, OUGHTS, MUSTS, HAVE TO'S, GOT TO'S.

SELF: 1
2
3

OTHER(S): 1
2
3

SITUATION: 1
2
3

LIST ANY RATINGS THAT YOU MADE OR MIGHT MAKE OF YOURSELF, OTHER(S) OR THE SITUATION IF THE WORST HAPPENS.

SELF: 1
2
3

OTHER(S): 1
2
3

SITUATION: 1
2
3

D

QUESTION YOUR DEMANDS

SELF: 1
2
3

OTHER(S): 1
2
3

SITUATION: 1
2
3

QUESTION YOUR RATINGS

SELF: 1
2
3

OTHER(S): 1
2
3

SITUATION: 1
2
3

RATIONAL ANSWER

SELF: 1
2
3

OTHER(S): 1
2
3

SITUATION: 1
2
3

RATIONAL ANSWER

SELF: 1
2
3

OTHER(S): 1
2
3

SITUATION: 1
2
3

NEW FEELING AND ACTION

INDEX

Index

Index

Index

Index

personalization 292,297
Personal Questionnaire
   260, 270-8
person/situation contin-
   uum 21, 28-33
person variables 18-19,
   28-9, 34-5, 42, 120,
   122
phrenophobia 332
physical skills 183
physical versus social
   skills 183-6
Piaget, J. 67
pitch of voice 223-4
Plato 93, 101
positivism 7, 67
Powers, William 151-2, 166
prediction-making 292
pregnanz 67
Presentation of Self in
   Everyday Life
   (Goffman) 73
principles 152-3
privacy 94
probabilities 63
problems about problems
   299-300
process orientation 191-8
problem-simulation 304-5
problem-solving 167, 244-
   5; interpersonal 243;
   social 243
programme control 153-4
progress 312-13
prominence 218-220
psychometric instruments
   306, 309
public discourse 96, 98-9

questionnaires 36, 263-
   76; construction 263;
   individual-centred
   methods 265-6; grids
   266-70; self-report
   36; sympton statements
   271
Quine, W. 63

raters of recordings 22-
   3, 26
rational beliefs 293-4,

296
rational-emotive im-
   agery 339
rational-emotive the-
   rapy (RET) 9, 89,
   284-343; applica-
   tions to social
   skills training
   286-300; assess-
   ment strategies
   300-13; bonds with
   clients 315; clas-
   sical 318; com-
   prehensive 318;
   overview 286-7;
   training 286-300;
   treatment strat-
   egies 317-24;
   treatment tech-
   niques 324-43
rationality 99, 101-
   2, 104
rational role rever-
   sal 335
reality 57, 112
reasoning 94
recording 15-17, 21-
   7; intermediate
   level 42; judges
   22-3, 26; molar
   level 21-5, 27,
   41; molecular
   level 19, 25-7, 41
reductionistic be-
   havioural approach
   17; objections 19-
   21
reductionistic be-
   havioural model 22
reification 72-3
reinforcers 113-15
Repertory Grid 266,
   276
response acquisition
   groups 38
retention 116
Retreat to Commitment
   (Bartley) 58
rewards 136
right hemisphere of
   brain 97

351

Index

Index

TOTE principle 142
Toulmin, S. 75
trait attribution app-
    roach 17-19
trait attribution mod-
    el 22, 25
trainers 51, 53-4, 66,
    126
triad, symbiotic 104
Trower, P. 33, 135
turn-taking 214-16
two-chair dialogue
    304

unconditional acceptance
    of clients 333
uni-directional determin-
    ism 4

vetoing 119
Vigotsky, L.S. 96

Wallander, J.L. 28
warm/cold dimension 193
Weiner, B. 123
Wessler, R.A. 289-90, 293
Wessler, R.L. 289-90, 293
Wittgenstein, L. 63, 67,
    94
Wolpe, J. 10, 11
women 99-100